(IN)FERTILITY

SECRETS, STRUGGLES, & SUCCESSES

WISE WOMEN BOOK COLLECTIVE

IBSN:978-1-7372657-1-9

CONTENTS

INTRODUCTION

I had a vision for this book. I dreamed of bringing together holistic practitioners who promote fertility together with women who have struggled to bring a baby into the world. The women authors in this book were called here together by a larger presence that knew all of their stories and knowledge were the perfect combination to help other women.

We make no promises of quick fixes or universal cure-alls. We share stories of miracles but recognize that it doesn't always work out that way for everyone. The one thing we will promise is to hold a space for anyone who is coming to this book at a rough time in their life.

I had two miscarriages before I conceived my first child, and it was a devastating experience both times. I had been interested in fertility and exploring different avenues to be the healthiest I could be before trying to have children. But I never thought I would be on the other side; the scary side, the hard side, and the "I never thought this would be me" side.

No matter how long or how hard your journey has been, a universal experience of those who have experienced pregnancy loss, infant loss, or infertility is the pain, the loneliness, and the emptiness. Even if your journey was on the shorter side, the mark of those feelings and the experience is always there. There is strength and hope in coming together with others who understand those feelings, and that is why I needed to bring this book to life.

The authors in this book are opening their hearts, stories, and wisdom to you. They have included ways to reach them if you feel so moved as to contact them. They have also shared their social media accounts so you can follow more of their journeys.

(In)Fertility: Secrets, Struggles, & Successes contains many personal stories, and some might be triggering. I want to let you know this now so you can read each chapter when you are in a space to feel your full spectrum of emotions. Each author represents themselves in their chapter and is not speaking on behalf of any of the other authors. I would also encourage you to talk with your medical team about any information you read about here that is of interest to you to see if that approach is right for you and your situation.

Join us on Facebook in our private group: (In)Fertility Book Community

Colleen Reagan Noon

1

HOLISTIC APPROACH TO FERTILITY

DR. AUMATMA, ND

HAVE you been trying to get pregnant for quite some time but not managed? Have you sought medical help that proved unfruitful? Do you feel like you are at your wit's end on your fertility journey? If so, you are not alone. In the U.S., one in eight couples between the ages of 18 and 35 has difficulty getting pregnant. That number increases after 35, as fertility is considered to decline considerably after 35. This journey is often trumped by confusion, grief, frustration and anxiety. What does it mean to be infertile? What can you do to get pregnant?

If you are like most of my clients, you have tried and tried – you've been to Dr. Google frantically searching for the answer, the key to unlock the mystery, and frustrated with your doctor that only has a few very reserved answers for you. Usually, the first answer from your OBGYN is to try clomid and intrauterine insemination. And if that doesn't work, it's onwards to in vitro fertilization (IVF). If you have a progressive team, they might propose that you get acupuncture along with the cycles of IUI or IVF. But the truth is "infertility" is an umbrella label and doesn't tell you much about how you can treat it or support yourself in increasing your fertility.

Hi, I'm Aumatma. I'm a trained naturopathic doctor and board certified naturopathic endocrinologist. I have been helping women with their health, vitality, and fertility for close to 15 years. For the last 10 years, my practice has focused solely on fertility and having healthy babies, because I have seen the lack of options available for women and couples struggling with infertility. I have dedicated a lot of time to create a program that truly supports women **and** their partners to bring their health into an optimal state. In turn, following the program and improving their health and vitality, while addressing the root causes of their fertility struggles, helps them to conceive easily and carry the child to term.

I'm passionate about this work because I have had my own journey and questions about fertility. I woke up on my 32nd birthday, married to a guy that I *knew* I couldn't have a child with. I had married the wrong person and was quickly realizing that I didn't have many years left till the "fertility cliff at 35." Luckily, I picked up *"Women's Bodies, Women's Wisdom"* by Christiane Northrup which inspired me to think about age-related infertility in a different way. Dr. Northrup suggests that there are (were) women in other, more remote parts of the world who could healthily conceive children at 60 years old- so then, what were 'we' (in Western Society) doing wrong? I went on a rampant search for "the answer" and I came to the conclusion that surely, age does impact our fertility—but it likely has more to do with stress and the impact it has on our physiological age, along with lifestyle factors and the underlying factors that were causing the reproductive system to shut down.

My research has revealed that a lot of what we say about age-related fertility decline comes out of research studies from the 1800s. In fact, more recent studies have demonstrated only a 3% decline between the 25-29 age group compared to the 35-39 age group. I have also seen in my clinic, 45 year olds who have gone on to have amazing results and 30 year olds that needed egg donors. In fact, I have seen a deeper correlation between hormone levels and fertility than I have purely with age. I have also seen couples who have triumphed over all odds that were predicted by their reproductive endocrinologist, and they went on to have a baby naturally, some even went on to have two babies after being told there was nothing available to them outside of getting an egg donor.

On a personal level, I decided that having a child with the wrong man was not what I wanted to do with my life. My now ex-husband and I ended up parting ways, and I went on to have a baby many years later. Yes, I went on to get pregnant on our first "try!" But, I spent a year prior to conceiving, healing and preparing my body-mind-spirit to have a child. A lot of women feel like I'm "different" but I'm not. I literally did all the steps that I'm going to share below, and these are the same steps I guide our clients through. These steps are what I call the Fertile Foundations™ that I guide my clients through every day. There are also many Fertile Foundations™ practitioners that I have trained around the world so that they can support women/ couples who cannot physically travel to us and want someone local. Our clients have an average of 50-85% success rate when they follow the steps, with the success rates being connected to age and other factors that we find impacting fertility. Most of our couples get pregnant within a few cycles of completing the process.

Many women believe that with IVF, they will get pregnant the very first month they decide to go through a cycle. Unfortunately, IVF success range between 2.5-35% success, based on age. With my clients, the focus isn't conception. Our focus is fertility optimization and healthy babies. We are not just looking for that big fat positive, but rather we want to ensure a healthy baby. Of course, we can't guarantee it, but we've only had 2 pregnancy losses experienced by clients over the almost 10 years that I have specialized in supporting couples on the fertility journey.

"Infertility" is just a label for a condition that can have many root causes. As a naturopathic doctor, I integrate the best of east and west. The truth is Western medicine is quite brilliant! It has many tools and ways of understanding the physiology and chemistry of the body, which, when used with curiosity, can give us some great information. The success in my clinic is based on whether or not we're able to clear the body of the blocks to pregnancy, rebalance the body and hormones, and heal the mind–body state so that conception can happen.

Fertile Foundations™ is a four step process that is systematized and *bio-individualized*, at the same time. The four steps are as follows: Discover, Detox, Rebalance, Receive.

Step 1. Discover the root cause. This is by far the most important step. So many women write to me daily asking me how to support their fertility, often with lab results. But, conventional lab results (even with a comprehensive panel of tests, which is more rare than you would want to believe!) are honestly not enough to truly get to the root of the problem. This is the part where a skilled practitioner begins with asking you questions to more fully understand what might be standing in the way of your fertility. As Fertile Foundations™ Practitioners, we aim to find the possible blocks, and then will often suggest getting tested to verify with quantifiable results to understand what might be happening. The questioning process may range somewhere between 2 to 4 hours. From what clients have told me, this is the most intensive questioning and listening they have experienced on their fertility journey. After the questions, I know I usually have a sense of what I think is happening. Then, we are ready to test the 'hypothesis' of what might be happening via in-depth functional testing. Functional testing is essentially designed to help clarify root causes on how the body is *functioning* or doing its job. Once we get results back, we'll start putting the pieces together to create an action plan to restore, rebalance, and optimize your fertility.

Here is a preliminary list of tests to request from your doctor. And, once you have the results, you can use this same guide *Cheatsheet to Understanding Your Lab Results* to better understand if your results are optimal for fertility success. Since many doctors don't spend the time with clients to review their results and help you better understand what the results mean, I created this Cheatsheet (holisticfertilityinstitute.com/cheatsheet) so that you can be empowered to understand your own results.

One woman who came to me at age 34 had been told by her doctor to keep trying because everything looked normal. However, she had been trying for more than a year, and she hadn't conceived. She had been to acupuncture for over six months, her periods were regular, and there was no "reason" that she was not getting pregnant. Western medicine said she was fine; Eastern medicine was addressing her "spleen qi deficiency," but she was not feeling any different, so she proceeded to look for other help. First she went to the nutritionist who put her on a gluten-free diet. Then she went to the energy healer who she decided to work with regularly. Lastly, she checked in with a psychic to see if she would get pregnant soon. No one thus far understood what was happening. Did she have nutritional deficiencies? Were her hormones out of balance? Has the stress she has experienced in her life damaged her ovaries (reversibly)? When we started working together, I knew that the first step was helping her discover and identify the cause of her "unexplained infertility." In our discovery, we identified estrogen dominance through a more comprehensive hormonal analysis. I truly believe that was the game-changer in helping her achieve fertility success.

Step 2. Detoxification. Often, women come to me having done a lot of different detoxes on their own. Detoxification can be great but also can be harmful if done incorrectly. Within the context of fertility, it is suggested that couples DO NOT detox within 3-4 months of trying to conceive. If you have just completed a detox, we suggest waiting for a few months before trying to conceive. Matter of fact, actively prevent pregnancy after a detox. This is because an effective detox will possibly activate the movement of toxins out of cells (i.e a cellular detox) but your liver will need time to process them and get them out of your body. A hormonal detox is extremely specialized based on what we're trying to detox. But, there are several detoxification steps that every couple on the fertility journey should take. I will highlight them here:

1. Remove the potential toxins in your environment and those going into your body. There are many modern toxins that are sneaking into our bodies that have been researched to cause infertility in women *and* men. I've created a book called the *Diva's Detox Guide* (holisticfertilityinstitute.com/detox)

2. that you can download here that will guide you through detoxing your home and environment, reducing the chances that you're being exposed to reproductive toxins.

3. Eliminate major toxins like cigarettes, alcohol, and recreational drugs. These are non-negotiables when on the journey to conception.

4. Reduce caffeine intake, and eliminate it completely if you cannot function without it. Often, reliance on caffeine is a sign of adrenal dysfunction, and it's important to get support quickly if you feel depleted or exhausted on days that you don't have caffeine. If you function normally **without** caffeine, feel free to consume it on occasion and enjoy it guilt free!

5. Try to go organic as much as possible. Sometimes, it can be challenging to only eat and live organic, but organic doesn't only mean the exemption of toxins. Often, organic soil is more nutrient-rich so it's giving you 'bang for your buck!"

Step 3. Rebalance. This is the point in the process where we take everything we 'discovered' in phase 1 of the journey and create a bio-individualized action plan. Often, this process is highly customized, and is never a cookie-cutter approach to giving you a protocol. I find a lot of couples are often misguided in taking a lot of supplements, but those supplements are frequently the wrong types of supplements. They range from extremely poor quality nutrients, to the wrong supplements for you. Unfortunately, too many charlatans claim to know just which supplements you need to help support your fertility. So many women are seeking the "magic bullet" supplement or food that's going to help them become mothers. Let's make sure not to get fooled by the "shiny objects" in front of us, promising miraculous results but rather recognize that we need to do *our* work. I have found that the only consistently accurate way to determine which supplements you might need is through appropriate testing. Spending a couple hundred dollars on testing can save you thousands of dollars of the wrong supplements, or unnecessary supplements. So, when you think about how to rebalance (or you are working with a practitioner who's supporting you) your body for fertility, make sure you and your practitioner fully understand the goals of the supplements and herbs you are taking. Just knowing that it is researched to help with "fertility" or that someone you know got pregnant because of it, is not reason enough. If you're not deficient in commonly suggested nutrients fertility, don't take them. I've seen many couples overdosing on supplements they don't need. And although it's not always harmful, sometimes it is harmful, and often it is unnecessary.

One client who came to me was a 38-year-old woman with high FSH (follicle stimulating hormone), low AMH (anti-mullerian hormone), and low progesterone. She had been trying to conceive for three years. She had tried several rounds of IVF, done acupuncture, and taken the herbs and followed the diets. Nothing was working. Her reproductive endocrinologist could just suggest another round of IVF —maybe the next one would be more successful. She was frustrated and didn't know what to do. When she came to me, she was very upset about all the money and, even more importantly, the time she had spent. She and her husband had started having challenges both in the bedroom and outside of it. She felt worn out, and her partner was tired of having to time sex rather than letting it be the spontaneous fun it used to be. She was tired of having to work on herself. On a deeper level, she felt like her body had failed her and something was wrong with her. In the discovery phase, we identified that we would need to lower her FSH and support her egg quality, which in turn would support increasing her progesterone naturally. In the rebalance phase, we supplemented nutrients she was deficient in, and used herbs to reduce her FSH. She also very much needed increased stress resilience which was supported through easy tools she could integrate into her busy life with 2-5 minutes per day. Her hormones rebalanced quickly. Her partner needed to release some of his emotional blocks around the frustration and neglect he had been experiencing. They went on to getting pregnant after 6 months and now have a healthy baby.

Similar to the "shiny objects" or quick-fixes that are marketed to women, there are similar products frequently marketed to men- and unfortunately those products don't always work. As you know, our Fertile Foundations™ programs are for men and women, because men need support too! What I have found to be truly surprising is that when men have a little guidance and support to apply fertility-focused lifestyle and nutritional changes, the sperm respond quickly for the better. We've created the *Super Sperm Quick Guide* (holisticfertilityinstitute.com/supersperm) just for your partner! Have your partner download this gift so that he too can be on his way to creating Super Sperm. Remember, unless you're a solo-mom-by-choice, this journey is equally shared between you and your partner. And, if you're a same-sex couple, the journey is equally shared between you and your partner, plus the sperm donor (if you know who that will be). In order to create a healthy baby, it's important that there is a healthy egg fertilized by healthy sperm. When both those factors are not considered, there is more left up to chance, and often may not create the family of your dreams. So, get your partner involved. You may think he's uninterested, but based on what I hear from the men in our programs the results are spectacular. Most men report feeling healthier, more vibrant, having more energy, improved sex drives which leads to better sex, and improvements in sleep-- in addition to super sperm. Who doesn't want that, right?

Step 4: Receive. This is the mind-body phase of the Fertile Foundations™ program. This is where we want to check our mindset, and heal the relationship we have with stress. Stress has such a big negative impact on fertility, yet I am sure you don't want to hear yet another person tell you not to stress. Instead, for this journey, we want to increase your stress *resilience*. Stress resilience has to do with being able to experience stress (which we all have plenty of!) without it not creating lasting imprints on your body, your hormones, and your fertility. In the Fertile Foundations™ course, we give you tools that you can increase your stress resilience, as well as give you some possible mindset shifts you can adopt to support your fertility.

Additionally, for those that are working with us directly, there are also personalized sessions to release emotional-mental-spiritual blocks that might be blocking a couples' fertility. Allow me to share a few examples.

One of the women I worked with many years ago had an intense fear of dying in childbirth. It was something she was aware of and shared with me pretty early on in her journey, but what she didn't know is that it was a likely component of why she wasn't getting pregnant. When we got to the Receive phase of her program, I started doing mind-body sessions with her. One of her sessions was all about how she had died during childbirth in a previous life. Whether or not you believe in past lives (she was a Christian woman and wasn't sure she even believed in this idea of a previous life), almost everyone can wrap their head around the possibility that our spirit is aware of certain possible outcomes. So, as I was in session with her, she started shaking violently on the table. I kept working through the steps in healing what her spirit was telling me, and by the end of the session she had stopped shaking. She got off of the table feeling a little lighter but didn't notice anything else that was different. A few weeks later, she reported that she no longer felt the intense fear of death that she had been experiencing. Very soon after that, they also called me delighted that they were pregnant with their first child!

Another example is one of a couple that came to me because they already had a special needs first child, and could not bear the thought of it happening again. They had also experienced a few losses after child #1. So, I started working with them through all the steps. I was intuitively getting a message that the male partner actually needed more support than he was letting on. So, I asked his wife, what's happening? Everything okay with him? And she said, yes, he's fine fertility-wise but he has really intense back pain that needs weekly appointments with three different practitioners, which he had been doing for almost three years already. I suggested he schedule some time with me. In my appointment with him, he conveyed that he could not sit down— he went from laying down to standing all day. He also couldn't lift or play with his three year old. We started working through his mind-body blocks, and over the course of six sessions with him, we needed to release many fears he had around being an "older" dad, given his childhood was one in which his father never played with him because of his age. We also needed to release doom-and-gloom thoughts about the end of the world, which were all being facilitated by the books and TV shows he paid attention to. As we released his blocks over the course of six sessions, his back pain released. By the end he was able to sit, play with his child, and reported feeling more optimistic for the future. Not two weeks later, his wife surprised me at the office to share the good news- they were pregnant! They went on to have a healthy baby.

A third client who sought my help was a 35-year-old woman who had had two miscarriages around weeks six to seven. She felt a lot of grief from losing the first two pregnancies and blamed herself because she couldn't figure out why this would happen. Her husband wanted to be supportive, but she felt all alone and scared. Her doctor didn't have any suggestions for her—only told her that her next pregnancy might be different. This client likely had a progesterone deficiency that couldn't be addressed by taking extra progesterone (she had already tried that in her second pregnancy). I am not a proponent of blind progesterone usage (plus she had already tried that after her first two pregnancy losses). Especially in younger women, I have frequently found that low progesterone levels are a result of poor egg quality, so our approach was a little different. First and foremost, she and her husband were to take a break from baby-making. They needed *not* to get pregnant while we were addressing some of the root cause imbalances. Then we started with increasing her egg quality, improving the positioning of her uterus and ovaries through gyno-visceral manipulation, and flooding her body with the right nutrients. We also found that she had a heterozygous genetic anomaly (MTHFR) that caused mal-absorption and mal-utilization of folic acid. With a deeper look, we found many defects in her genetic pathways that needed to be addressed. Also, her husband lived and worked in a high-stress environment and needed some holistic support to bring more vitality into his body and increase the nutrient levels in his body, while simultaneously increasing stress resilience.

They wanted to fast-track their program, so they completed it in three months. Two weeks after finishing the program, they got pregnant. She had a freak-out as soon as she got the positive pregnancy test because she hadn't planned to get pregnant that quickly. So we continued with mind & body support through the first trimester of her pregnancy and a couple of check-ins and rebalancing appointments in the second and third trimester. She was able to carry to term and gave birth to a healthy baby girl. She actually went on to have another baby many years later.

There are many healing approaches that work with the body-mind-spirit. But, the tools we use in my practice are ones that I have found to be truly magical in helping to identify and release blocks from the cellular levels in the body, increasing stress resilience, and helping couples to conceive successfully.

So many couples that I have worked with over the years were struggling with having the one thing they wanted more than anything else—a baby. This is a unique kind of want; it's a deep desire for procreation, for manifestation, for something deep within them that cannot be equal to anything else. It's a calling to be a mother, father, parent. These couples come to me with very different underlying problems, but with the holistic approach of Fertile Foundations™ the focus is on getting to the root of the problem and addressing it in a way that is truly healing, rather than a band-aid solution.

Each of these clients and couples are unique. Their stories are unique. And so is yours. One of the women or couples I mentioned in this chapter might resonate with you. However, there is no magic formula or pill that I can suggest for everyone across the board. Everyone needs different things, and no one remedy or special fertility diet can fit all. Also, there is no super food that is magically going to help you get pregnant.

There is, nevertheless, a template for learning about the body and understanding that blueprint *can* help with conception and healthy birth. More than magic pills and bullets, what I hope this chapter has demonstrated is that it is a path, a journey, and a perspective you can carry with you. What I hope that you will carry with you is the vision that becoming a parent is possible for you too with following a step by step approach to conception. I wish you success on your journey, and please reach out if you want support beyond the free resources I have given you access to throughout the chapter.

With love, Aumatma

DR. AUMATMA, ND

Dr. Aumatma is a double board-certified Naturopathic Doctor & Endocrinologist, in practice for close to 15 years. She specializes in fertility and is the best-selling author of "Fertility Secrets: What Your Doctor Didn't Tell You About Baby-Making." Dr. Aumatma was awarded the "Best Naturopathic Medicine Doctor" award locally in 2015 & 2020, and recognized as a top "Women In Medicine" Doctor in 2020. In addition to supporting couples through individualized care all around the world, she also trains practitioners who want to specialize in fertility. Dr Aumatma has been featured on ABC, FOX, CBS, KTLA, MindBodyGreen, The Bump, etc., along with being interviewed for countless podcasts on topics of fertility, pregnancy, and postpartum health.

Website: www.holisticfertilityinstitute.com
Connect with her directly at:
www.instagram.com/holistic_fertility_expert

2

IVF NEVER GIVEN UP

UNEXPLAINED INFERTILITY, IVF, AND A MIRACLE BABY 12
YEARS IN THE MAKING

AYALA GROSS

IF YOU HAD TOLD me when I was 22 years old that I would have undergone nine years of infertility, I would have probably been ok with it. Being the control freak that I am, I would have mentally prepared and back pocketed the longing and yearning to be a mother. It would not have been easy, but at least I would have been prepared for what lay ahead. But infertility pulled the rug from under my feet. It didn't let me prepare for longer than 30 days at a time. The unknown, the inability to do anything about it, the depression, the thoughts that I may never become pregnant or a mother were the bricks that sank me in my years of trying.

It's the unknown, the fear, the shame, the bloody monthly reminder, the false hope. And If you have heard of "Unexplained Infertility", you will know that it adds an extra layer of confusion to the mix. It is a diagnosis that 1 out of 4 couples who struggle with infertility suffer from. There is no strong indication that there is a male or female factor, only that the doctors cannot see from the charts and tests that there is any major underlying cause to the infertility and why the couple are not able to conceive.

And that was our diagnosis—unexplained infertility. I remember the first time I heard it; we were living in Queens New York and hear it from a doctor in Brooklyn, with whom we had done our 6th IUI. I had just received the news the cycle had failed, and I ran past the receptionist's desk to yell at him—I felt I was his fault. I needed someone or something to blame. Crying, I met him in the hallway—I said, "WHY ISN'T THIS WORKING," and he told me we had Unexplained Infertility. I was so angry, defeated—it sounded like a bad excuse as to why HE was failing US!

I told him that I would have been OK if he would have told us that there was some major issue and begged him to look into it further— but he said we had done all the tests we could do and this was our reality. Unexplained infertility was terrifying to me because it meant I had no control; there was nothing I could fix. I had to sit in a proverbial "waiting room" with no indication of how long I would be there and wait indefinitely for my turn to be a mother. I was absolutely terrified and unsure of what to do next. That's when we stopped doing more IUI's. I couldn't take another failed cycle, and I knew IVF was the next solution.

At this point, my husband and I could not afford to do IVF. The costs were astronomical, and I thought that if IUI was this stressful, IVF must be worse. We took a six month break and started with a new IVF clinic, this time in Manhattan.

When we went to the new clinic, they did all the same tests and ran us through the same protocols. I asked the doctor what our next course of action would be, and I begged him to give us a "real" diagnosis, not this unexplained one. To my dismay, he agreed with our previous doctor and told us that we, in fact, did have Unexplained Infertility & the only way we could get pregnant was to do an IVF.

Defeated, I went home and cried to my husband. I had no idea what we were going to do. My husband also felt defeated, and we realized we could not do anything at that current time, only hope that we miraculously would get pregnant on our own, naturally.

Cue the boxes of negative pregnancy tests, the hope and the let down, the darkest years of my life.

With every period from that point on, I would fall into a deep depression that I again could not get pregnant. I took it very hard, and for days before and after I got my period, I would be a total mess. I shut myself off from the world, and I distanced myself from my friends, especially the ones that had children. I felt a deep jealousy and hatred towards those who got pregnant easily. I couldn't look at a pregnant woman without feeling such sadness. I hated the way I was feeling, and I knew this was not me. I knew these feelings were not who I was deep down inside. They were surface wounds that were not representing who I truly was on the inside.

After some time, we decided that we were going to move down to Florida. My husband is originally from Florida, and we wanted a different pace of life. Being I am originally from Australia, the warm weather beaconed me, and we found jobs and moved down to Florida within three months of making our decision. I had this hope in the back of my head that I would still be a mother, and maybe Florida, a change of scenery, change of doctors would be the answer and help us in our journey.

The year following our move, year 6 of trying to conceive, we decided we were ready for IVF. IVF for me was exciting! Yes, there was a lot on the line, and there was a lot of money as well as emotions, and the slim 35% chance it would work, but I was incredibly excited to finally be doing something toward my goal of being a mother. At this point, I had done six IUIs and was about to start my first round of IVF. I wish, looking back, that I did not waste all that time on IUIs. Yes, IVF was a hill we could not have climbed in our first five years of trying, but at the same time, I look back and feel that maybe we wasted a little bit of time and put our selves through more stress than we could have otherwise.

IVF costs were astronomical, so I started a little side business making baby blankets to help with the costs. We reached out to every organization, borrowed left, right, and center, until we scraped enough together to amass a small fortune to cover the costs of one round of IVF.

We made seven embryos, and only two of them made it to day five blastocysts. The doctor's office called us, and he told us that neither was very good on a grading scale, and their suggestion was to implant both, hoping that one would make it, with little hope either would.

Sadly, neither took, and that spun my husband and me on a very dark, sad path. I tried to stay positive by making more baby gifts— somehow, it calmed me, and gave me a release for my longing to be a mother. It was extremely therapeutic to bring other babies handmade gifts I made, which took me outside of my pain. Literally after the phone call that the cycle didn't work, I needed a distraction so I pulled out my sewing machine and made a blanket that I still have today. My business grew from my hobby into a full-time job, and today, I employ two amazing ladies. Together, we make baby gifts and donate a portion of proceeds to organizations that assist couples struggling with infertility.

Back to my journey, after our failed IVF, we felt lost. At that point, we had no other way to pay for IVF, no idea of what to do, and we felt that we would never be parents. I was extremely depressed and felt like nobody would understand me. Everyone around me had children. No one had time to hang out with me. I needed friends who were like me, but no one was in the same boat as I was. It was around that time when my husband found an advertisement for an infertility support group at my local synagogue. I scoffed and told him I would never go. I was certain that those women would not understand me or know my pain and I didn't want to hear everybody else's sad stories.

But then life started getting darker, I felt more alone, and I decided that maybe there is somebody who goes to that support group like me, and I could offer some of my strength to her, the very little of what I had left. So I went, and I met an amazing group of women, all of which had already had their first child and were struggling with secondary infertility after primary infertility or were just there to offer support. I didn't feel like I belonged. I wanted to run out. No one had primary infertility like I did, and I felt none of these women got me. They all already had kids. I was mad. Again, I was alone. I felt nobody knew how hard primary infertility was. They already had experienced having a baby in their arms. Why are they complaining, why are they here? Why am I here?

Reluctantly, I sat through the meeting, and by the end, I started feeling fellowship and connection to the women. It made a tiny fracture in the barricade I had around my heart. Through a wall of tears, I decided to open up and share my story, which I had never done before. I was very closed about it. I didn't want anybody to know my secret. I felt shame, and I felt like my body had failed me. I left feeling exposed, like my heart was being held outside of my body, but also relieved.

Thank God that I went to this group because through there, I got more information on what I should be looking for when it came to doctor's offices. I heard of a new treatment called intralipid treatments, which I tried along with a few more rounds of IUI. Although they didn't work, they gave me new hope in my battle again infertility and I was happy that I was able to try something else.

One of the hardest things, when you're struggling with infertility, is not doing anything. It's the stress of the pause. What do we do? Where do we go? Do we do nothing? Is it going to happen naturally? So many unanswered questions and no real answers.

In year 8 of trying to conceive, about a year after my 11th failed IUI, a family friend of mine who I had known for many years had spoken to my husband and heard of our predicament. He called me and told me that he wanted to help us get our baby. The details I won't share as I would like to protect the privacy of his family, but in essence, he took care of everything we needed for IVF. This was a miracle that I had prayed for, and I didn't even know that I had prayed for it! I couldn't believe it. We had another chance! Our friend was very sick and didn't live to see our son, but we got to see him one last time not long before he passed and were able to celebrate the news of our pregnancy together in person. We named our son after him, hoping he will embody his amazing characteristic and merit to be the man he was. His positivity, generosity, and love permeated my world and brought our miracle baby earthside. I pray one day, we will be able to reciprocate the same kindness to a couple struggling with infertility.

From here, the doors opened once again. We were able to go to one of the top clinics in America, RMANJ. It's not so much the doctors that are important, but more so the lab. In fact their lab is so good that other fertility clinics around the country send their specimens and embryos to RMANJ to be tested. We flew back and forth a few times to the clinic, one time for our initial visit/blood tests, the second time for egg retrieval, and the third time for frozen embryo transfer.

We did all our testing in Florida, and they sent our blood and transvaginal ultrasound results to New Jersey. I felt so good and so positive about this cycle. I was so lucky and so blessed. I had someone in my corner. I had also decided to tell my family that we were going to do the treatment. Something I didn't do the first time, but this time I felt that I needed people behind me. I needed their prayers. I needed them to be excited if it worked. I needed them to be sad with me if it didn't. I needed support. Infertility is so isolating and so lonely at times, but I decided that this time after years, I was not going to go through it alone.

We made ten embryos, and again, only two were viable. Those two were strong enough to be genetically tested and frozen (snowflake babies). When the results came back that both were genetically perfect, I was so excited. I had more hope. But I tried to manage my expectations because I didn't want to get ahead of myself. At that point, I realized, you know what, if I'm going to get ahead of myself, I'm going to go all in; I'm either going to be pregnant, or this is going to fail. And I'm not going to try to manage and control my feelings before they happen. I'm going to go into this with positivity, happiness, and hope.

At the time of embryo transfer, I had my mother, aunts, and sister on FaceTime with me for extra support and for them to experience this with me. As I was lying on the table in the room, I saw out the corner of my eye a huge incubator being rolled into the room with a TV screen attached to it. I asked what it was, and they said "that's your baby". My heart skipped a beat. I instantly felt connected, like I wanted to jump out of my seat and grab the incubator and take it home with me. I wanted to hold my baby in my hands. Then they said, "look over here, ma'am," and zoomed in on the TV screen on this tiny dot which got bigger and bigger. That was the first time I saw my son. A little glob of cells moving and jiggling around. They handed me a print out with a photo they had just taken of the embryo in the lab. I saw them remove the embryo into a tube and then watch that tube come over to me. My heart was pounding—I felt my husbands hand squeeze mine. I heard the excitement in my mother, sister, and aunts voices. And then it happened. In one moment they transferred my son, and I knew instantly that he was mine and he was alive— deep down, I knew it worked. I made a promise to God in that very room after all the doctors and my husband left. I spent five minutes talking to my stomach and talking to my baby. It was a secret promise between God and me that I've only shared with my husband and that I have kept to this day.

Nine months later, my beautiful son Sammy was born via C-section. I fell in love with him from the moment I saw his embryo, and when I saw his face, I knew he was mine. The fear of never being a mother disappeared. It was like those nine years of infertility were wiped away the moment I saw him. I sometimes have to pinch myself still to believe it, but I am no longer struggling with infertility because, for years, it felt like a life sentence.

Because we knew that we had another frozen IVF embryo waiting for us, my husband and I decided that when my son was weaned, we would go back and try again. When my son was six months old, my husband and I separated. I was alone with my baby, and those ten months that followed were very difficult. But by the grace of God, my husband and I came back together through a lot of therapy and marriage counseling. Thank God we are back together again to this day.

About five months after we got back together, I started feeling hot one evening. My skin felt dry, and I felt flush. The last time I felt this was when I was pregnant. But I had told myself this was impossible. Doctors told me the likelihood of me being pregnant naturally was very slim, if not impossible.

Against my intuition, I went and bought a pregnancy test. I tucked my son into bed, who was then 21 months old, and kissed him. As he was sleeping, I cried, laying with him, whispering that this might be the last time that I will kiss you and hold you, knowing that you are an only child. That night I took the test, and to my shock amazement, it was positive! I was pregnant! Naturally! I had defeated infertility. My body was working! I was in shock. I was still nursing. I knew I had my period, but how could this happen?

Twelve years after we first started trying to have a baby naturally, my baby daughter Bria came into this world - a beautiful unmedicated VBAC birth. I had to pinch myself. I couldn't believe it was actually happening, and then after she was born, I was still in shock for the first few months that I had two children. There was a time three years ago before my son was born that I wondered if I would ever be a mother – today, my arms and heart are full. I still ask God what did I do to deserve these two miracles!

I know my story has a happy ending, but not everyone has the same happy ending. I often feel guilty for feeling happy. I often feel guilt for overcoming infertility when so many others struggle. I have felt guilt for doing IVF when so many cannot afford to. I often feel guilty for having a baby naturally. The scars of infertility run deep. When I hear of somebody that is pregnant, sometimes I feel a pang of jealousy. And I hate that feeling. I want to be cured of it. But yet, the scars of infertility tell me these feelings will take time to heal.

We don't know everyone's story. You might look at me and see two beautiful children, but you will never know that there were 12 years before my story actually got to this picture-perfect point. You wouldn't know the nine years of sleepless nights and tears. You wouldn't know how many pregnancy tests I took during that time period. You wouldn't know how many promises I made to God. You wouldn't know how many times I wanted to run away from my life. But that's why I share my story. I share my story because I know that there is someone else out there who struggled or is struggling and doesn't see any hope. They may not think that there will ever be a day where they will be called mother. That is one of the most painful feelings a woman can ever feel. The negativity, the hurt, and that horrible feeling in your gut that you can't even name.

But there is hope, and there is hope in connecting. There is hope in opening up, and there is hope in reaching out, in finding support, and connecting. There is no shame. Your body is not failing you. You are not a failure if you have kids or you don't have kids. You are perfect, you are loved, you are worthy of being loved, and you are worthy just as you are. You will get your happy ending, and I would love it if you would share your stories with me one day. Don't give up. Don't ever give up until you have your family. It might not be in your timing, it might not look the way you thought it would, but it will be perfect. It will be whole, and your arms and heart will be full.

AYALA GROSS

Ayala Gross lives in Boca Raton Florida with her husband and two children. She is the owner and designer behind Boca Baby Company, creating custom bespoke handmade baby gifts and accessories, with a portion of proceeds benefiting organizations that assist couples struggling with infertility.

Her diverse background spans across the areas of finance, PR, sales, garment construction and design. Ayala's creativity has also lended her a passion for poetry & writing and has written three children's books. As a young adult, she pursued a corporate career in Commercial Real Estate Finance as an Analyst for some of the largest companies in the field.

Her analytical finance background lends her to running her business while her creativity assists her by designing new items for Boca Baby Co.

Although she does not consider herself a blogger, she enjoys sharing her daily life as a mom and business owner on social media stories. Ayala's journey with infertility is a major component of her social media outreach, where she is active in the Infertility world, while sharing her journey with others.

Website: http://bocababycompany.com
Instagram: @bocababycompany
Facebook: @bocababycompany

3

FACILITATING FERTILITY THROUGH CHIROPRACTIC CARE

DR. ANGELICA M. ORTIZ, D.C.

WHEN MOST PEOPLE think of chiropractic, they think of things like back pain, car accident recovery, or sciatica. Although chiropractors often successfully treat those issues, it barely scratches the surface of what chiropractic care can do, for example, balance hormones, increase fertility, and aid in conception. Chiropractic adjustments are effective for almost any condition because the primary focus is the nervous system, and as you know, the nervous system controls everything we do. The very reason you are able to read this book is because your brain is communicating with your eyes to shift from left to right so that you can read and interpret the words.

The communication happens through nerves that travel from your brain to your eyeballs. Nerves travel from the brain to every part of the body. The brain is the hub of it all, the spinal cord is an extension of the brain, and most nerves are an extension of specific parts of the spinal cord. I like to compare this communication pathway to a freeway, but unlike many busy cities, you want this freeway to run smoothly with no traffic or collisions. Sounds impossible, right? It kind of is. We are constantly applying stress to our body which in turn applies stress to the nervous system. I like to classify stress into three different categories: physical stress, chemical stress, and emotional stress. Physical stressors can come from things like posture, intense workouts, trauma, or even pregnancy. Chemical Stress is something we experience from things we consume like medications, unhealthy food, birth control, toxins, things we place on our skin, or even the pollution that you breathe when you walk outside. Lastly, emotional stress, one we all know too well, emotions such as anger, frustration, guilt, embarrassment, the list goes on. All of these stressors create traffic and collisions on our nervous system highway. The stress can be diminished by creating better alignment in the spine to increase the flow of communication and allow your body to work its magic.

We often forget how magical the body actually is. We forget that we are born to perform impeccably. Perform automatically without the use of drugs or other interventions like surgery and unnatural procedures. Chiropractic adjustments facilitate the innate ability for us to perform on our own. By allowing nerves to flow free of interference, we allow for a pristine highway connecting our mind and body, which maximizes the individual's ability to heal and regulate his or her own physiology.

Your Incredible Body

When discussing fertility, hormones are the name of the game. Hormones control ovulation, fertilization, implantation, and maintaining the fetus from that point on. The hormone that gets everything going in the female body is called Luteinizing Hormone or "LH," Luteinizing Hormone is in charge of triggering ovulation. Ovulation needs to occur for a woman to release an egg that will potentially be fertilized by a male sperm. Hormones are made in the brain, a specific region called the Hypothalamus creates a hormone called Luteinizing Hormone-Releasing Hormone or "LHRH," this release causes a nearby brain structure called

The Pituitary Gland to release Luteinizing Hormone and boom an egg, if available, can now be released. A case study[1] on a 31 year old woman states that 70% of women who experience infertility have hormone imbalances on regulatory hormones like Luteinizing Hormone described above.

In practice, I have found that regular adjustments to the cranium and C1 vertebral segment can encourage hormone balance. My patients have seen success in all perinatal phases, including fertility, pregnancy, and postpartum. C1 is an upper cervical segment, or better yet, it is the highest vertebra in our spinal column and supports the brainstem. Although more research needs to be conducted to prove this hypothesis, it is believed that through creating alignment in upper cervical segments, the uninterrupted brain-body connection allows for better functioning of our core hormone-releasing structures, the hypothalamus, and the pituitary gland.

One patient that comes to mind when thinking of hormone balance is a woman I treated early in my career. She came in when pregnant with her 1st child at 34 years old and late in her third trimester. I assisted her in having a comfortable pregnancy and getting her hips and pelvis ready for birth. She was able to deliver vaginally. However, this mama had a history of depression and endured symptoms of postpartum anxiety. She continued to get adjusted postpartum and always left the office in a visibly better mood. After three weeks of adjustments, she felt emotionally stable again and credited that in large part to her chiropractic treatment and nutritional supplements. Two years later, that same mama returned for regular, weekly treatments to help with fertility. She and her husband had been trying to conceive for six months with no success. After two months of being adjusted, regulating nervous system flow, and focusing on sacral analysis, she was pregnant. She got adjusted throughout her pregnancy and had no postpartum difficulties.

In addition to hormone balance, a chiropractic adjustment also structurally makes a change. Let's take the female pelvis into consideration. There is a triangular bone called the sacrum located at the back of the pelvis. This is where most of our weight is distributed but also where a growing uterus will push up against when developing a fetus. As a prenatal chiropractor, sacral analysis and adjustment are my primary focus when treating a pregnant woman or when preparing a woman to become pregnant. Routine adjustments to the pelvis, along with ensuring that surrounding muscles, tendons, and ligaments are not hypertonic, meaning tight and shortened, is a prime strategy of most perinatal chiropractors. Proper alignment in pelvic and upper cervical structures can encourage reproductive success and sustainability of the pregnancy.

Yes, muscles matter too! After all, muscles move bone, so I can adjust the pelvis all day, but if someone has tight and rigid muscles, that adjustment does not have a good chance of holding for a long period of time. The piriformis is a muscle that attaches to the sacrum bone that we mentioned earlier, but even more impactful are the hip flexors, specifically one called the Iliopsoas. When seated, the hip flexors are in a shortened position. Because many of us sit for long periods of the day, our hip flexors tend to be pretty tight. Hip flexor tension and spasm are only encouraged by things like crossing your legs while sitting or not stretching after a workout. The anatomic location of the hip flexor is directly above important structures like the fallopian tubes and ovaries.

Re-Training Old Habits

One of the most frequent questions I get asked is "How often do I need to get adjusted?" or "How long will it take?" I wish I had a systematic answer to these questions, but unfortunately, I do not.

Everybody is vastly different. The reasons for infertility are different as well, some women may conceive after one month of regular adjustments, while others may take five months of regular adjustments. One study[2] surveyed 11 women with an average age of 31 years old, who had been considered infertile for a mean of three years. The study found that pregnancy occurred, on average, after five months of regular chiropractic treatment.

In neuroscience, this is referred to as "neuroplasticity," neuroplasticity is defined as the ability of neural networks in the brain to change through growth and reorganization. New pathways are formed, and old or improper neural connections can be changed. This process can most easily be compared to potty training a toddler. You can not just show the toddler where the restroom is once and expect them to forever correlate the cues of peeing with going to the restroom. The toddler will learn with repetition through his or her parents repetitively showing the toddler to relate excretion cues with the porcelain bowl. The toddler, when officially potty trained, has created a new neural connection. As adults, our nervous system acts exactly the same. One adjustment after a lifetime of microtraumas will not make too much of a difference. By microtrauma, I am implying years of birth control, toxins, stress, bad posture, etc. We have to retrain alignment to allow for better nervous system flow and improved neural connections to be made.

Our nervous system has two autonomic states, better understood as "automatic" states. These states are known as the sympathetic state and the parasympathetic state. Without any effort, our body will choose which state to be in. This happens based upon our environmental surroundings and external cues given to our nervous system. Our sympathetic nervous system is, unfortunately, where most of us spend too much time. This system is active when we are in a stressful situation, better referred to as our "fight or flight mechanism." In this state, we are in survival mode. Our physiological actions are comparable to when you are running from danger. For

Example, imagine being on a camping trip then spotting a bear approaching your camp, immediately blood vessels are constricted, cortisol levels rise, pupils are dilated, heart rate increases, muscles are contracted, and you are on high alert. Although not as severe as a camping trip gone wrong, sympathetic states can be encouraged by things like work deadlines, an argument with a partner, infertility struggles, bills, and so much more. Being in the sympathetic, stressed state can decrease the probability of conception because your body is focusing on survival.

The parasympathetic state is the opposite. It is referred to as our "rest and digest" mechanism. When picturing parasympathetic states, envision your most relaxed beach day. You are lying in a cabana, enjoying the waves crashing in front of you, and have just finished a delicious lunch. The physiological actions were taken by the body administer complete decompression: blood vessels are dilated, pupils are constricted, heartbeat slows down, digestive juices are secreted, muscles are relaxed, and because the uterus is a muscle, you are giving your reproductive organs go-time cues.

Our body chooses when to act in a sympathetic or parasympathetic state. However, we can influence those autonomic systems by managing our surroundings, learning to channel stress, and by physically facilitating parasympathetic regulation. The parasympathetic nervous system lies in the areas of the cranium and sacrum, so creating balance and alignment in these areas can help even the most stressed person naturally unwind. The sympathetic nervous system lies in the vertebral levels of T1-L3, more easily described as the mid back and higher segments of your low back. Utilizing a lighter chiropractic technique to these areas can gently create better flow and can also help minimize arousal of the sympathetic state. The sympathetic state is not extremely welcoming for implantation or reproductive sustainability because if the body is under stress, it is harder to create and maintain life.

Our Greatest Wealth is Health

Age is another topic that is marginalized and creates stress for many women. As a chiropractor, you can actually feel age when palpating a body before an adjustment. However, the "age" palpated does not always correspond with the numerical age we associate negative connotations with. As a chiropractor, before an adjustment, we analyze things like posture, imbalance, joint motion, muscle tone, and overall function. Let's start by discussing joint motion, or "joint play" as many in the field describe it. A healthy joint can be depicted by a smooth glide along each vertebral segment or extremity joint. This means that it is painless, the joint is well lubricated and moves easily. When this is felt, a chiropractor will move on and leave that segment alone. A subluxated or misaligned joint is often tender or even painful to palpation, stiff, and has almost no glide. This can imply many things, such as a simple subluxation or more severe implications like inflammation, arthritis, or intervertebral disc desiccation. When these signs are displayed, a chiropractor will analyze what they have felt, feel for the motion that joint is lacking, and make that joint his or her primary target.

Of course, before ever touching a patient, I have a full understanding of their history, age, and symptoms. However, there have been many times where their age has no correlation to the way their body feels. I have had a twenty-two year old patient whose body presented as if she was in her early fifties. Tense and rigid everywhere, locked up joints galore, and exhibiting numerous symptoms. In retrospect, I have had a patient in their fifties present as if she were in her twenties, functioning well, lots of joint play, great muscle tonicity, and nearly no symptoms. The reason for bringing this up is that health is supposed to be correlated with young age, which is often not the case. Young women who have been under lots of stress, practiced bad nutritional choices, and who have been exposed to many toxins can be unhealthy and infertile. Whereas older women who have taken care of their bodies, detoxed, and put in effort towards a healthy lifestyle can be extremely fertile.

I practiced as a doula before and during grad school and witnessed moms of all ages give birth. One of the most empowering births I ever experienced was a natural, vaginal birth of twins from a 45 year old woman. During our interview process, I was curious about conception and asked many questions. Her answers simply pointed to one truth...preparation. She created a "fertility bootcamp" as she called it with her holistic practitioners, detoxed, and nutritionally and physically prepared her body before attempting to conceive. Although trying for children later in life, she had complete trust in her body and never thought of herself as "old," she naturally conceived after one year of trying and was able to carry and deliver twins.

In the chiropractic profession, health is the ultimate objective. We aim for our patients to wake up on a daily basis and actually feel healthy. Wake up with energy, feeling fired up for the day ahead of them, rather than fighting through morning aches and pains. The day ahead of them most likely includes healthy eating choices, movement, supplements if necessary, rehabilitative exercises, postural awareness, and adequate hours of sleep. The best part of the chiropractic approach is that it is drug-free, which means there are no drug side effects and associated financial challenges. This approach is achieved by utilizing the nervous system as a tool to facilitate health.

If you have ever seen more than one chiropractor, you have probably realized that everyone has their own technique. There are many techniques that are proven to enhance nervous system flow. However, some chiropractors have specialties in areas like fertility, pregnancy, and postpartum care. If you are going to the chiropractor for fertility, finding a Perinatal Chiropractor in your area is a great way to start. Chiropractic is a way to maximize an individual's ability to heal and regulate his or her own physiology, a woman's incredible ability to create life is without a doubt a physiological process. The remarkable transformation is inspired by cues from the nervous system and hormones, as discussed in this chapter. Chiropractic is a powerful mechanism for those wanting to establish fertility, other holistic modalities in conjunction with chiropractic can enhance the probability of fertility as well. The potential of holistic care comes from its strategy of looking to the body to find the root cause of the issue and restore it.

---

1. https://www.princetonchiropractic.com/wp-content/uploads/2019/01/publishedinfertilitystudy.pdf
2. https://www.ncbi.nlm.nih.gov/pmc/articles/PMC6173223/

DR. ANGELICA M. ORTIZ, D.C.

Dr. Angelica is a Perinatal and Pediatric Chiropractor in San Diego, California. She attended Southern California University of Health Sciences for her Doctorate in Chiropractic and has a Bachelor's degree in Neuroscience from the University of California Riverside. Angelica has undergone extensive training to fuel her passion for helping moms and children, including Certifications in the Webster Technique, the International Chiropractic Pediatric Association, and serving as a birth doula for four years. Her passion for birth began at a young age when witnessing her mother naturally deliver her youngest sibling, that birth empowered her as a woman and intrigued her to learn more about the incredible female body. After attaining her graduate degree, Angelica let her passion lead the way and Co-Founded Life Adjusted Wellness, where she works to educate and empower women, and establish wellness lifestyles for moms and families in her community.

Website: www.lifeadjustedwellness.com
Email: hello@lifeadjustedwellness.com
Facebook: www.facebook.com/angelica.ortiz.75491
Instagram: @lifeadjustedwellness
TikTok: @lifeadjustedwellness

4

JOURNEYING FROM INCOMPETENCE TO ABUNDANCE

HOW HEALING AFTER PREGNANCY LOSS RESULTS IN A RAINBOW BABY AND DREAMS COME TRUE

DOCTOR OF PHYSICAL THERAPY, DR. CHRISTINA HARRIS, PT, DPT

Birth of Purpose

June 9, 2017. As the alarm sounded, I rolled over our extra-large air mattress and stretched my arm out to dismiss the notification on my phone. Another day had dawned, and it was time to get ready for work. My husband, Dave, and I were 3,000 miles away from home and temporarily in Modesto, California, on a travel work assignment for Dave, a Registered Nurse (RN), and I, a Doctor of Physical Therapy (DPT). Every day was an inward struggle as I was anxious to return home to Atlanta, Georgia. I missed my family and the comfort of familiarity.

That day was a little different. A nudge in my spirit led me to reach under the vanity to take a pregnancy test. In February, I stopped taking oral contraceptive pills as we decided we were ready to start trying to get pregnant. Historically my cycle was irregular, so the fact that I had not seen it in a couple of months didn't necessarily surprise me. That morning, still blurry-eyed, I re-read the instruction pamphlet and followed the directions. I set a timer on my phone for the obligatory 2 minutes and placed it on the tub next to me as I completed my devotional reading for the day.

The timer went off. I dismissed it and finished my reading. Nonchalantly, I looked over, with no expectations, and to my surprise, two lines! I swiftly retrieved the instruction sheet from the trash and read it again. I probably checked the picture nearly five times before it truly registered what I was looking at. A line in the circle and in the square equaled a positive pregnancy test. My jaw literally dropped. Dave was still sound asleep; it was his day off, and my stirrings did not phase him. I eeked out a near silent exclamation and mouthed the words 'OMG'.

Musing over the perfect way to share the news, I took my secret with me to work. Dave's birthday and Father's Day was a week and a half away, and I considered waiting until then. However, every hour that passed, my excitement grew; I could hardly contain myself. As soon as I clocked out of work, I rushed to buy a Father's Day card, printed off the picture I took of the test and wrote a little note. When I arrived home, eyes wide with excitement, I did my best to keep my cool. Dave was busy blasting his favorite tunes as he cleaned up, so my strange behavior went unnoticed as I slunk into the bedroom. Finally, I called Dave to the room and announced that I had something for him. Cautiously, he opened the envelope, sliding out the card. The picture fell out face down. A puzzled look came across his face as if to say, 'why are you giving me this? You got the wrong card' or 'does she know she's a week early for my birthday?'

Expectantly, I stood across the room, cell phone perfectly positioned to record his reaction to my big reveal. If you know anything about Dave, there are two reactions possible for a situation like this. He would either try to keep it cool, or there would be an outburst of yelling, laughing, or running. Honestly, I was hoping to catch the latter on video. Instead, he opted for the cool, calm, collected version--not very exciting for the camera. We embraced, talked, and dreamed the rest of the evening until we fell asleep, snuggly wrapped in each other's arms in a state of peaceful joy. I bought books and researched everything over the next few months. The passion for Birthwork previously instilled within me began to intensify as I embarked on my Motherhood journey.

On September 11, 2017, Dave and I finished packing the last of our belongings into a rental van and began our cross-country road trip back to Atlanta. We took our time, making multiple stops for me to stretch my legs and pay homage to my bladder. One week later, we arrived home in Atlanta and settled in with my parents. By this time, I was 20 weeks gestation, and the much anticipated anatomy scan[1] was coming up; we would find out the biological sex of our growing baby. Overall, I was feeling great and ecstatic to be back home. My nagging early pregnancy symptoms had declined, I started to show a little bump, and I even felt tiny little flutters across my belly from time to time. I made an appointment to establish care with a midwifery[2] group and began my search for a Doula[3].

As I started a new contract job, my pregnancy was no secret, and my new coworkers were excited and helpful. By the end of the week, I was tired and grateful for the upcoming weekend. On Thursday, I felt mild cramps in my back but figured it was due to fatigue. It continued as I got home, and I told my family. Dave asked if I wanted to get checked out, but I read that Braxton Hicks[4] contractions were normal in the second trimester, so I chose to rest, which seemed to help stop the pain.

The next morning I made my usual trek to the bathroom, and to my surprise, I started losing my mucus plug[5]. I gently called out to Dave, again sound asleep. He hurried into the bathroom, dizzy from getting up too fast. He immediately sensed something happened before I said anything. I told him what happened, saying, "I've never been pregnant before, but I don't think that's supposed to happen." We called the Midwifery group I was slated to see the following week, and they advised me to go to my local hospital for assessment in the Emergency Department (ED).

On our way to the hospital, I called my mom and asked her to join us. Upon assessment by a doctor, I was told my symptoms were due to dehydration[6] and round ligament pain[7]. While those may have been true, I knew in my Spirit that wasn't the full story. I advocated for myself and re-emphasized my symptoms; the doctor agreed to do a full workup. Following my cervix assessment, she noted dilation[8] and a bulging sac[9]. I was diagnosed with Incompetent Cervix (IC)[10]. In a whirlwind, I was admitted, placed on bed rest in Trendelenburg Position[11] to decrease the bulge, and given IV medications to stop labor.

Later that evening, a team came to do an ultrasound and anatomy scan. First things first, "It's a boy!" and he was perfect. Every bone, joint, and organ function was perfect. I was only 21 weeks pregnant at that point, so the main focus was to maintain pregnancy for as long as possible. By 24 weeks gestation, a baby is considered viable[12] outside the womb, and life-saving measures can be employed. If all went well that night, I could expect to spend at least three weeks upside-down on strict hospital bed rest. My only thought was, 'I will stay here forever to save my baby.'

Throughout the day, there was a barrage of doctors and specialists in and out of the room. They spoke of performing a Cerclage[13] the next day if the membrane sac was no longer bulging. That night, Dave and I held each other and brainstormed boy names. While dating, Dave mentioned if he had a son, he loved the name Gamaliel, and envisioned calling him 'Game'. We agreed on the name Gamaliel, a biblical name that means *God is my reward.*

Despite the medications and hydration efforts, I continued to have contractions throughout the night; some so intense they disturbed me from my sleep. I finally woke up at 5:55 am and had a deep-seated intuitive feeling that I would not receive good news. Still, I prayed fervently for a good outcome and peace regardless of what happened. Another doctor did the cervix assessment that morning; he noted more bulging and confirmed IC. After the assessment, there was a pool of blood due to progressing labor, and he could no longer recommend a Cerclage. We were presented with options: do the Cerclage with the risk of sepsis[14], wait for labor to continue on its own and the waters to break with the risk of hemorrhage and/or infection, or induce labor[15] and Birth Game at 21 weeks gestation - knowing he would not survive. Devastation.

Dave and I discussed the options, none of which we preferred; we opted to induce. Before the induction process began, our nurse reviewed a bereavement packet with us, and we agreed to get complimentary pictures following Birth. Then, she hit us with the hard stuff; handling Game's body after Birth. That was when everything became real. Our son was not going home with us. I never imagined being in this place, to decide how and where to bury my child, my son. It was heartbreaking for both Dave and me, and our nurse gave us time to process.

Eventually, induction medications were given, and labor proceeded, and boy was it a doozy. I did my best to recall the information I gained regarding labor: breathing, positions, hydration, nourishment, but it was not as effective as I had expected. In a room full of people, I felt like I was laboring alone.

Dave, my mom, and mother-in-law hovered near me with fear and uncertainty. My nurse was glued to her computer screen. The doctors were nowhere to be found, despite my repeated requests and announcements of feeling imminent sensations of Birth. Nobody in the room was on the same page as me nor understood the support I most needed. I desperately needed someone to be in my corner. Someone who understood my labor-related emotional, mental, physical, and spiritual needs. I needed someone to help navigate the decisions that come with preterm labor[16] and pregnancy loss. I needed someone to guide me with proper breathing, help me get into pain-relieving positions, set a calm and reassuring atmosphere, coach my family, affirm and validate my thoughts, feelings, and choices, and so much more.

All of these things could have been provided by a Doula. However, due to our recent relocation and preterm labor, we hadn't hired our Doula yet, and the support I yearned for was unfortunately out of reach. Physically, I did everything I could, but the emotional, spiritual, and mindset pieces of the puzzle were missing. Occasionally a thought surfaced, "I'm going through all this pain in this experience, and I won't even have a baby at the end." I quickly dismissed it and instead embraced the miracle of birth and the love and support that was present.

After 1.5 hours of active labor, at 12:00 pm on September 30, 2017, our son, Gamaliel, was born. The intensity of the physical, mental, and emotional anguish halted, and all I could exclaim was, "My baby, my sweet baby boy!" He was so small, 15 oz. His skin was so thin, I could see all of his blood vessels. He didn't make a sound. His eyes never opened. It seemed as if he had no idea his entire world changed; and so did mine. His movements continued to mimic those in the womb. He was at peace. The medical team wrapped him up in a blanket and placed him on my body as Dave cut the umbilical cord. I held my sweet baby boy. My firstborn. Gamaliel. He made me a Mother; pure joy and love enveloped me. I admired and examined every body part. His hands, his perfectly formed fingers, even his fingernails. His feet and nose that looked like his Daddy's. His little ears like mine. He was beautiful. He was perfect.

After this moment of bliss, my blood pressure dropped as my body struggled to Birth the placenta[17]. I was in and out of consciousness, and the amount of blood I lost nearly required a blood transfusion[18]. At one point, I came back to consciousness and heard the doctor urge me to push to assist with placenta delivery. I was exhausted. I barely understood how to coordinate my muscles. Eventually, the placenta was delivered. However, the doctor had to manually scrape my uterus to ensure no pieces were left behind that could lead to sepsis; I lost consciousness again. Hours later, I regained consciousness and saw Game had been cleaned and dressed in a cute cloth diaper. I was told he maintained a heartbeat for 1.5 hours, most of which I missed during my struggle with consciousness.

The next day, once I was medically stable, we were released to go home. The hospital provided us with ample resources regarding Pregnancy And Infant Loss (PAIL) and gave us a donated memory box from a local organization called Rachel's Gift[19]. The days, weeks, and months that followed were some of the lowest and darkest in my experience. I retreated. I was consumed with thoughts and feelings of guilt and shame as I grieved. I felt guilty that I could not save my child. The diagnosis of Incompetent Cervix made me feel incompetent. The thing my body was created to do—conceive and carry children—it could not do. "I was supposed to be his protector, but I could not carry my son long enough for him to be born healthy and viable; I failed him."

The only person I truly opened up to was Dave because he too lost Game as a son. We had a beautiful village of support around us, and many women in my life opened up to me about their previous experiences with loss; for many, sharing their story for the first time. Hearing story after story began to strike a chord in me. I wondered how many people were silently suffering from the pain of pregnancy and infant loss? How common was loss? Why don't we hear more about it? Statistics show that 1 in 4 women experience Pregnancy And Infant Loss (PAIL). Prior to Game, I had no idea the PAIL community was so extensive, but now I knew I wanted to do something to break the silence; provide an avenue for people to talk, share and receive support.

Inspired and Aligned

My healing journey has taken many turns and continues as grief has no time limit. It first took me inward into a Spiritual awakening in which I grew closer to God and developed an intimate relationship and understanding of Spirit. I explored holistic healing modalities such as acupressure and yoga for physical healing, Reiki[20] and Chakra[21] balancing for energy healing, and positivity for mindset, self-development, and alignment.

The majority of my comfort came from the stories and promises in the Bible. A story that resonated deeply with me is Peter walking on water in Matthew 14:22-32. A portion of the story described Peter believing and trusting in Jesus as He beckoned him to walk on the water. Peter took action according to his faith, but when the winds blew, he took his eyes off of Jesus, got distracted, and started to doubt. This caused him to sink. Jesus, in His mercy, took Peter by the hand and pulled him back into the boat. This passage mirrored my early grief journey. As long as I stayed connected to God and the Word, I did okay. However, when negative thoughts distracted me, and I started to doubt and worry, I found myself in a downward spiral of depression and anxiety. Mercifully, God's Spirit reached out and took hold of me and my thoughts and bathed me with the warmth of peace that passes all understanding. Although the loss of Game is not made easier or fully understood, I am reminded I am not alone, I can get through another day, and there is something larger at work.

Another great outlet for me has been journaling. In a letter to Game, I retold his birth story, shared my thoughts and feelings as I processed. I wrote: "I will hold you in my heart. You are and will always be alive in my heart." "Alive In My Heart" has become my mantra surrounding Game's life. It is inscribed on the marker where he rests and shirts that were made in his honor.

Occasionally, Dave and I walked on a nearby trail as I listened to podcasts. One day I listened to a podcast called "Pregnancy Loss Journey" in which the special guest shared her story and profoundly expressed she did not want her story of her child's loss to end in brokenness. She did not want others to have the impression that her child was the source of her depression. Instead, she opted to do something positive and shift her child's legacy into supporting other families enduring pregnancy and infant loss. This woman's story and perspective deeply resonated with me and kindled a spark in my Spirit. I, too, affirmed that Game's life would not be of brokenness but of legacy.

Rainbows and Promises

Six months after Game's birth, we were surprised with a rainbow baby[22] pregnancy. This time, we quickly established care with a medical provider. We advocated to work with a Perinatologist/Maternal-Fetal Medicine (MFM) doctor[23] to help navigate the intricacies of Incompetent Cervix and Pre-term Labor. In addition, we interviewed and selected a Doula, knowing that Pregnancy After Loss (PAL) can be incredibly mentally, emotionally, and spiritually challenging. We learned we were expecting another boy and named him Caleb. Amidst the excitement, there was an undercurrent of fear and anxiety. I was in a state of constant worry that the same thing would happen with this pregnancy. Every trip to the restroom was fraught with anxiety, and I was exhausted from being super vigilant about every sensation in my body.

Every week I went to the doctor's office for an injection of progesterone hormone to prevent preterm labor. Every other week I had an appointment with the MFM for a transvaginal ultrasound[24], and they performed cervix length checks to determine if we needed to proceed with the Cerclage procedure. Fortunately, my cervix continued to measure really long until 24 weeks, when things began to change. Instead of my cervix measuring at 4 cm, at 24 weeks, it measured 2 cm. Anything below 2.5 cm is considered short and, from my understanding, was an indication for reassessment and possible Cerclage procedure. However, the specialist discharged me from care with no explanation and no further communication. I advocated for myself and spoke with the Obstetrician (OB)[25] at my next appointment two weeks later and requested another ultrasound. At that point, my cervix measured 1.8 cm; concern arose, and I sought out a second opinion from another MFM. By this time, I was 27 weeks pregnant, and my cervix measured 1.0 cm. The Cerclage was not able to be completed because I was now "too far along". It was suggested I stop work, go on modified bed rest at home, and I increased my monitoring and awareness for signs of preterm labor.

In theory, bed rest sounds like the working person's dream. No work, no cleaning, no cooking! In reality, after the first week, it gets old. I was granted bathroom privileges, allowed one trip up and down the stairs a day, and could keep my weekly field trip to the doctor's office for my progesterone injection. Dave continued to work as normal, so sitting at home alone, all day, every day, allowed me a lot of time with inner thoughts. I was intentional about keeping my thoughts positive for both me and Caleb, as I knew my emotions and stress levels could impact him and potentially initiate labor. I used this time to ponder ways in which I could utilize my skills, knowledge, and experience to support families on a similar path. With my Physical Therapist hat on, I brainstormed programs and put myself through bedrest safe exercises. I envisioned how I wanted to structure my support services. Every day Game's legacy rested on my heart, and although I could not do much physically, my imagination was hard at work.

At my 34 week appointment with my OB, I shared I was having mild cramps and noticed some discharge. The doctor did a cervix check and discovered that I was 3-4 cm dilated and sent me straight to the hospital. "Here we go again," I thought. I called Dave at work, and we went to the hospital together. That evening I dilated to 6 cm, so I called my Doula and mom for support. After several hours, labor stopped on its own as I was experiencing prodromal labor[26]. Since I was 6 cm dilated with a high-risk pregnancy due to IC, I was admitted to the High-Risk Perinatal Unit of the hospital. I spent the next two weeks; endured another round of prodromal labor and celebrated my birthday.

When labor actually began, Dave, my mom, and my Doula were all present, and it was a beautiful experience. I felt well supported, free to move, vocalize, and enter the coveted "labor land". A near trance-like state, where time did not matter, and I was completely unaware of people entering and leaving my room. I was in the zone. While labor with Game was short, it was definitely painful. Overall, I did not perceive my labor with Caleb as painful. The one instance I felt pain was when the providers urged me to lie on my back to push - which I did not want to do. I knew the impact that could have on my body, and unfortunately, it did result in a grade 2 perineal tear[27]. On November 8, 2018, I birthed my beautiful son, Caleb, at 35 weeks and six days gestation[28]; a success in terms of IC. Caleb was immediately placed on my chest as the staff performed their duties. He was perfect and, to my surprise, looked nothing like his big brother. Although born preterm, he did not need any special accommodations or time in the NICU (Neonatal Intensive Care Unit)[29].

Our rainbow baby was here; healthy and thriving. I committed to staying home with Caleb for one year prior to him starting daycare. The bond we developed was strong as I was able to witness and document every 'first' milestone from the comfort of our home. I felt fulfilled and secure as I witnessed my heart's desires manifest right before my eyes. I spoke to Caleb about his big brother, showed him pictures, and took trips to visit Game.

Healing to Manifesting Dreams

Early in my postpartum recovery after Caleb's birth, I started having some common symptoms that I knew indicated abnormal function of my Pelvic Floor muscles. I experienced urinary incontinence[30], as well as continuous pain at the site of my perineal tear and repair. Although I had not gone for my six-week check-up yet, I was my own advocate and found a local Pelvic Floor Physical Therapist (PFPT) to address my concerns. I received treatment for Pelvic Floor Dysfunction[31], and the spark of inspiration kindled a little hotter as I sensed a shift in my career.

This spark grew, and I contemplated various avenues I could provide support, knowledge, and empowerment to help individuals and families as they navigated Pregnancy, Birth, Postpartum, and Loss. My minimally supported Birth story with Game inspired me to incorporate my skills as a Physical Therapist, my passion for Birthwork, and the lessons I learned during my Spiritual awakening. As a result, I specialized as a Perinatal and Pelvic Floor Physical Therapist (PFPT), certified Birth and Bereavement Doula, Naturopathic Reiki Practitioner, and slated to receive certification as an acupressure comfort measures instructor, Yoga Teacher, and have visions to incorporate more holistic modalities into my skill set.

As Caleb transitioned to daycare, I began working as a Physical Therapist in a local Pelvic Floor Physical Therapy Clinic, and I also provide virtual Doula services. Every day I live my dream. Both in and out of the clinic, my personal mission is to support individuals and families as they flow from awareness into alignment, healing, and manifesting their positive pregnancy, birth, and postpartum seasons. I incorporate self-discovery, PT expertise, and evidence-based care to encourage individuals and families to actively participate, advocate for themselves, and shift their mindset in order to witness the unfolding of their heart's desires of a positive childbearing experience.

Hidden Gems Revealed

As I serve my patients and clients in this space, I notice trends that expose a gap in care and education of Birth and our bodies.

"I didn't even know this was a thing...I wish I knew about Pelvic Floor Physical Therapy before."
At this time in the United States, PFPT is not widely known, and we are working diligently to increase education and awareness. Some people express feelings of abandonment and deceit by their medical team for not referring them to a PFPT at the onset of issues.

"My OB said I was fine at my six-week check-up. Why didn't they tell me about PFPT?"
Please know this may not be an intentional omission on their part. Your OB or Midwife is assessing you at the six-week mark from a different perspective. They are assessing how your healing process is progressing, the presence of infection, the need for contraceptives, etc. There may be some functional healing that needs assistance, or you may not feel "fine", and that is where PFPT is appropriate. After all, your body endured nearly one year of transformation and literally brought forth new life.

"I thought it was just something I had to deal with after having a baby."
Sometimes individuals endure years of pain, discomfort, and embarrassing symptoms that seem to have no end or may resort to the use of "band-aids" such as pads or medications to survive.
If you, a friend, or a family member are having these thoughts or feelings, please be assured you are not alone. You are not crazy. Yes, there is help available with Pelvic Floor Physical Therapy.

"What is a Physical Therapist, exactly?"
A Physical Therapist (PT) is a medical health professional holding a

Doctorate level degree in Physical Therapy with specialized training and education in order to address normal versus abnormal movement and function. In a nutshell, PTs evaluate, diagnose, and treat conditions that impact an individual's ability to fully participate in their daily activities throughout the lifespan; ranging from holding up their head to Olympic levels sports. The fundamental goal of a PT is to provide individuals with education, tools, and empowerment to live and move their bodies freely. PTs love seeing patients thrive and return to or even discovering new adventures and abilities. Ultimately falling in love with their body and the things they can do.

"What is the Pelvic Floor? Where is it?"

The Pelvic Floor includes a group of muscles at the base of your trunk that forms a hammock or bowl shape. They have several roles such as mobility, postural support, organ support, sexual function, and reproduction, as well as appropriate control of bladder and bowel contents. Due to its location, the Pelvic Floor/Bowl doesn't get much shine. In our Western society, talking about things "below the waist" is deemed taboo, shameful, and private - leading many people to silently endure dysfunction, pain, and challenges alone because speaking about them is not generally accepted. For example, a common misconception is to expect urinary leakage after pregnancy or reaching a certain milestone age. This, in fact, is a huge myth. It is never normal to leak urine, ever. It does not matter if someone has Birthed two dozen children or is 107 years old. It is simply not a normal function of your body. Common? Yes, but not normal.

"What does a Pelvic Floor Physical Therapist do?"

A Pelvic Floor Physical Therapist (PFPT) receives general Physical Therapy education and chooses to further extend their knowledge and expertise to address Pelvic Health conditions. It is important to note that a PFPT is for anyone with a pelvis, regardless of gender identification or expression. A PFPT uses their skills to evaluate and treat a multitude of conditions.

What A Pelvic Floor Physical Therapist Treats

Pain
LOWER BACK PAIN OR PAIN IN THE AREA OF THE PELVIC BONES, ABDOMEN, GENITALS, BUTTOCKS, OR WITH FUNCTION SUCH AS AROUSAL, MOVEMENT, INTERCOURSE, OR RELATED TO MENSTRUAL CYCLES

Function and Support
ANY ABNORMAL OR LESS THAN OPTIMAL FUNCTION OR POSITIONING OF THE ABDOMINAL OR PELVIC REGION ORGANS OR GENITALS

Bladder and Bowel
ISSUES MAINTAINING APPROPRIATE CONTROL AND EMPTYING OF THE CONTENTS OF THE BLADDER OR BOWELS

Childbearing
CONDITIONS THAT MAY ARISE DURING ALL STAGES AND PHASES OF CHILDBEARING INCLUDING FERTILITY, PRE-CONCEPTION, PREGNANCY, LABOR, BIRTH, AND POSTPARTUM

Surgical
PRIOR TO OR FOLLOWING SURGICAL PROCEDURE OF THE ABDOMEN OR GENITALS

Prevention and Education
PHYSICAL THERAPISTS THRIVE ON PREVENTION AND EDUCATION SURROUNDING ALL OF THESE AREAS

DR. CHRISTINA HARRIS, PT, DPT

"How Can a PFPT help during the Childbearing Seasons?"

It is not all about Kegels. PFPT can focus on serving individuals throughout the many seasons of fertility, preconception, pregnancy, labor, birth, and throughout postpartum recovery. These specific seasons are crucial points in time when some may discover limitations, fear, and unknown variables in regards to their growing bodies and baby. Having a PFPT on your team can provide an avenue of permission, possibility, and resources to experience the journey of fertility, childbearing, and postpartum as desired; allowing you to be an active participant.

Dr. Oluwayeni Abraham PT, DPT states, "Pelvic Physical Therapy puts the joy back into the reproductive process." Further explaining that, Physical Therapists are able to address female mechanical infertility[32], utilizing techniques to influence changes in the body to optimize the ability to conceive and carry to term. In 2012, Dr. Mary Ellen Kramp, DPT, CLT-LANA, conducted a study following ten women experiencing infertility to investigate the impact of a physical therapy protocol. The study revealed that after receiving an average of three treatment sessions, six of the ten women became pregnant within three months. With further research, this powerful physical therapy protocol can prove to be an affordable and viable option for individuals facing infertility[33].

In addition, PFPTs have the expertise to address underlying conditions related to pelvic floor dysfunction, pain management, flexibility, strength, coordination, alignment, and prevention education to promote a healthy, active lifestyle and prepare the body for conception. During the numerous bodily transformations of pregnancy, a PFPT provides education regarding posture, pelvic floor function, labor, and birth positions, as well as preparing for postpartum. Similar to the work of a Doula, a PFPT has the skills to support during labor by encouraging mobility, in addition to guiding optimal positioning to avoid injury and progress labor. PFPTs are also able to support Cesarean births with education and preparation for the procedure, postpartum recovery, and safe return to activity.

"How do I find a PFPT?"

It is never too early or too late to receive treatment from a PFPT, and everyone can benefit from an evaluation. If you notice any issues arising, it may be in your best interest to advocate for yourself and mention PFPT to your primary health provider and request a referral.

In the United States (US), most insurance plans cover Physical Therapy, which includes Pelvic Floor Physical Therapy. However, all PT clinics may not accept your insurance plan, and some clinics are cash-based and do not accept insurance. It is best to locate your local PFPT provider and discuss how they handle fiscal responsibilities. Financials aside, bear in mind that due to direct access[34] in the US, you are able to at least receive a Physical Therapy evaluation without a doctors referral.

Legacy of Abundance

Although my journey to this point in life has not been an easy one, I am grateful that I am able to find purpose from my experiences. The Birth of Game opened my eyes and heart to serve with a level of compassion that may be challenging for others to embody. The shift in my career to focus on Pelvic Health and Birth is one of the best choices I have made, and every day I bask in knowing I am living my dreams and empowering others along the way. Pelvises and Birth are a bit taboo in our society. However, I enjoy talking about the things no one else will because there are people that need to be seen, heard, and helped. Knowledge is power, and with support, individuals have the opportunity to reclaim control over their bodies and experiences to truly embrace the life they desire.

My heart continues to yearn for closing the gaps in health care and its impacts during the childbearing seasons, especially in regards to Black perinatal and infant mortality rates[35]. I am privileged to have Birthed two children and still be alive today. As a Black Woman in the US, regardless of my level of education or socioeconomic status, the chances of my child or me dying are astronomically high. Research shows that individuals receiving continuous support and education, such as Doula support, are at a decreased risk of perinatal complications, medical interventions, and mortality. It is becoming increasingly evident that possessing a robust team of Birth professionals dedicated and aligned to supporting the family in their choices is literally saving lives. There are many Birth professionals doing amazing work in a variety of avenues to provide comprehensive support, education, and advocacy. I am humbled by the opportunity to be part of such high-caliber professionals in both the Doula and Physical Therapy spaces to help bring about a shift in the Birth culture to progress towards optimal experiences, outcomes, and justice for all Birthing people and babies to thrive.

The life and legacy of Game and the abundance of joy Caleb brings
every day are the driving forces in my work and founding Competent
Heart Perinatal Specialist, LLC. The name holds a special meaning.
The diagnosis of Incompetent Cervix led me to feel "less than". To
combat that negative connotation, I boldly proclaim and instill in my
clients they are competent, adequate, and worthy. While 'Heart'
signifies the deepest, truest aspects of us as humans. It signifies
compassion, connection, and warmth; all of which I bring in my
service to my clients and community. Competent Heart Perinatal
Specialist, LLC exists because of the enormous love my heart holds
for my two boys and showing me I am worthy of being their mom.

1. *Anatomy Scan:* Typically an abdominal ultrasound during pregnancy to assess how the baby is developing. Usually done between 18 to 22 weeks gestation.
2. *Midwifery:* Primary health care profession involved in the care of individuals during pregnancy, labor, birth, and the postpartum period, as well as care of the newborn
3. *Doula:* A professional support person who provides continuous physical, emotional, educational, and familial support and advocacy during the childbearing seasons
4. *Braxton Hicks:* Sometimes known as "false labor", are contractions of the uterus that do no result in changes in the cervix, nor indicate initiation of labor
5. *Mucus plug:* Thick jelly-like substance the body creates as a barrier to keep bacteria and infection from entering the uterus during pregnancy.
6. *Dehydration:* When your body loses water faster than consuming and can lead to serious pregnancy complications and even premature labor.
7. *Round Ligament Pain:* The Round Ligament is a supportive structure in the body. As it stretches during pregnancy, can cause sharp pain usually felt in the abdomen or hip area, especially during change of positions
8. *Dilation:* Opening of the cervix to allow baby to be born
9. *Bulging Sac:* When the amniotic sac the baby is enclosed in during pregnancy is exiting the uterus prior to initiation of labor.
10. *Incompetent Cervix* (IC): *Early* opening of the cervix due to weakness or other risk factors leading to preterm birth or pregnancy loss
11. *Trendelenburg position:* A position technique where the feet are elevated above the head
12. *Viable:* Typically the 24th gestational week in which the baby has a chance for survival outside of the womb with extensive medical support
13. *Cerclage:* Cervical stitch to support and treat Incompetent Cervix
14. *Sepsis:* Widespread immune response of the body due to infection that can lead to organ damage

15. *Induce labor:* Use of synthetic hormones or medications to stimulate the body to begin the process of labor and uterine contractions

16. *Preterm labor:* Uterine contractions resulting in cervix changes before 37 weeks gestation; may lead to preterm birth and/or pregnancy and infant loss

17. *Placenta:* Temporary body organ created during pregnancy to support the fetus as it grows

18. *Blood transfusion:* Procedure in which blood is given via IV setup after extensive blood loss due to an injury or illness

19. Rachel's Gift - https://www.rachelsgift.org/

20. *Reiki:* A non-invasive, Japanese healing technique utilizing hand placements to facilitate movement of energy to facilitate balance of physical and emotional well-being

21. *Chakra:* Refers to energy centers throughout the body that can become unbalanced or blocked leading to physical, emotional, mental, or spiritual disease

22. *Rainbow baby:* Refers to a pregnancy and baby conceived following a previous loss

23. *Perinatalogist/Maternal Fetal Medicine (MFM):* A subspecialty branch of medicine and obstetrics that handle high-risk cases and manages the health of the pregnant person and fetus

24. *Transvaginal Ultrasound:* Ultrasound imaging scan of the pelvic organs. Usually utilized during early gestational weeks

25. *Obstetrician:* A physician specializing in pregnancy, childbirth, and female reproductive system

26. *Prodromal Labor:* Labor that starts and stops before active phase of labor begins

27. *Perineal Tear:* Most common form of vaginal childbirth injury resulting from stretching and straining of the perineum tissue between the vagina and anus

28. *Gestation:* Refers to the number of weeks of fetal development following conception

29. *NICU (Neonatal Intensive Care Unit):* Where newborns needing specialized attention and medical interventions receive treatment and care

30. *Urinary Incontinence:* Uncontrolled urine leakage

31. *Pelvic Floor Dysfunction:* Difficulty recruiting, relaxing, and coordinating pelvic floor muscles that result in a variety of symptoms

32. *Infertility:* According to the Center of Disease Control (CDC) is the inability to conceive after 1 year or unprotected sexual intercourse

33. Kramp, M. E. (2012). Combined Manual Therapy Techniques for the Treatment of Women With Infertility: A Case Series. *The Journal of the American Osteopathic Association,* 112(10), 680-684. http://www.joao.org

34. *Direct Access:* Every US state, the District of Columbia, and the US Virgin Islands is no longer mandated to have a physician referral prior to receiving Physical Therapy evaluation and treatment. There do remain some state specific limitation

35. *Perinatal and Infant Mortality Rates:* Death of a pregnant person, fetus, or newborn during pregnancy, Birth, or within 1 year postpartum

DR. CHRISTINA HARRIS, PT, DPT

Dr. Christina Harris, PT, DPT, is a licensed Physical Therapist specializing in Perinatal Pelvic Health, certified Doula, and International Best Selling Author. She was born and raised in South Florida until her move to Atlanta, GA, in 2003. Dr. Harris received her Bachelor's Degree in Exercise and Sports Science with a minor in Child and Family Development from the University of Georgia and her Doctorate in Physical Therapy from the former Medical College of Georgia in Augusta, GA.

In 2020, Dr. Harris founded Competent Heart Perinatal Specialist, LLC in order to embrace her passion for comprehensively supporting individuals during the childbearing seasons or enduring pelvic dysfunction with education and tools to be active participants along their journeys. She values community and holistic approaches which promote healing by bringing the body and mind into awareness and alignment.

When not working with patients, clients, or engaged in her latest educational course, Dr. Harris enjoys expressing her creativity through handcrafted customized items, spending time with her husband and son, or enjoying a good laugh with friends.

Website: www.chperinatal.com
Email: competentmama@gmail.com
Facebook: www.facebook.com/chperinatal
Instagram: www.instagram.com/chperinatal

5

INTEGRATIVE AND CHINESE MEDICINE IN SUPPORTING FERTILITY NATURALLY

AN ACUPUNCTURISTS ACCOUNT OF HELPING FAMILIES ALONG THEIR FERTILITY JOURNEYS

DR. DEB DAVIES, DACM, L.AC.

I was SO excited when my friend Colleen decided she wanted to write a book on fertility. I knew I HAD to contribute as I believe Chinese medicine has somewhat magic qualities in helping women conceive who otherwise could not. I have tons of colleagues that also specialize in conception, so my goal for this chapter is to share options and hope for those families trying to conceive.

Most women and families who encounter difficulties trying to conceive go directly to IUI/IVF treatments. This often is extremely costly, plus can wreck havoc on your body due to the daily injections of hormones and therapies involved in the process. Many families mistakenly think medical interventions are the ONLY option. I want to shout from the rooftops to help spread awareness of all the helpful natural options families needs to help with conception.

My Inspiration

I became inspired to work with pregnancy clinically and become a birth doula after having my first birth. Sadly, I had a stillborn baby at full term after an uncomplicated, low-risk pregnancy. I found out the baby died when I was in early labor. I begged for my doctor to give me a C-Section, but she refused by saying that we had already lost one patient (the baby), and she didn't want to risk losing me in surgery. She told me she wanted me to have another baby, and it would be easier for me if I gave birth vaginally. It was the strangest car ride ever, for it was rush hour as we drove to the hospital. Everyone was going about their business as usual, and here I am about to give birth to a dead baby. WTF! I remember calling my chiropractor on the way to canceling my appointment that day and letting them know why. It was the worst thing that ever happened to me!

My mom, who lived 3,000 miles away, had intended to join me for labor & birth. She got on the first plane once she heard the news to attempt to be there for the birth. I had my husband, his two brothers, my father-in-law, my dad, stepmom all in the hospital trying to support and comfort me in my labor. I was sad and troubled as this baby was so very much wanted. I succumbed to all the medications and was completely drugged up as I gave birth to my first daughter, Mia Belle Davies. My mom arrived minutes before the birth, and I was so grateful to have her by my side for one of the hardest days of my life. I gave birth vaginally with the help of forceps after 16 hours of labor to my beautiful baby girl, Mia. She had dark curly hair and blue eyes, just like me. They asked me if I wanted to hold her, and of course, I said yes. The nurse put her in my arms, all wrapped up in a blanket, and the first thing I noticed was her jaw drop open as she was not alive. It was my first time seeing and holding a dead person. It was filled with so much emotion. My husband at the time could not even touch nor kiss her, and that was so sad for me. I had no idea what was going on, and they said they were going to take her away, so I got a whole five minutes with my baby. Enough time to kiss her hello and kiss her goodbye. Her image is forever burned into my memory.

This event was truly the worst thing that ever happened to me and is my why. Everything I do is to honor Mia's memory. I am SO incredibly passionate about helping women during pregnancy, birth, and postpartum. This loss has lead me to help many moms over the years have the healthiest possible pregnancies, births, and postpartum healing. I did go on to have another healthy baby girl a year later, and she is currently thriving as a freshman at college.

My mission statement at my private practice, PUSH San Diego, which is my acupuncture clinic specializing in infertility, pregnancy, birth, and postpartum, is to educate and empower expectant couples to have safe and healthy pregnancies, births, and recoveries by offering natural options in health care. After 20 years of working with this population, there is SO much we can do to help. I want to yell it for all to hear to let all the mamas know we have more options!!

In the clinic, I will see a fertility patient or pregnant woman many times along her journey. I can offer acupuncture support with anything from getting and staying pregnant to hold this baby in, to nausea and vomiting support, to pelvic and back pain to labor preparation and promotion, even the high risk and weird things like skin rashes, itching from PUPPS, or cholestasis, and more.

First of all, I would make sure to help her gather her health care team. As we women know, it takes a village, which is no time to skimp on finding your people. I think it is imperative women have diverse medical support professionals to give them a rounded view of health.

Each time she visits my office, I would ask questions about what is bothering her physically and mentally and best support her. We tend to discuss stress a lot and ways for her to feel supported and empowered. I would also strongly advocate for her to get additional education on her health, especially things she can do at home to optimize her health, such as getting enough sleep, water, nutrition, and exercise.

During the fertility acupuncture treatments, I like to offer acupressure education and support. Often I will see the fertility women once to twice a week, in the beginning, depending on their state of health and age. I talk about how it takes 120 days to rebuild a blood cell and that we need this time to adjust and improve her reproductive health; we would see her weekly for acupuncture, moxibustion, and lifestyle discussions. Often she will see positive changes in her menstrual cycle during this time. If she has PMS pain, it will often diminish. If there are clots, they will shrink and dissolve. If her periods are all over the place, she will get more towards the 28-30 day cycles.

With pregnancy, I can treat anything from hold the baby in, exhaustion and nausea, and vomiting in the beginning to placenta previa, breech baby, back and pelvic pains, and preparing for labor. I would see pregnant women more frequently as the birth gets closer. Typically, I will see moms once a week starting around 34 weeks for labor preparation to help get their body and mind ready to give birth again. This is especially important for they need to go into labor on their own accord prior to being induced because of concerning conditions. In each session, I will do acupoints for calming her mind, stimulating the hormones for birth, and reducing any existing pains or discomfort.

Integrative Medicine

I'm a big believer in integrative medicine for any and all health-related conditions: the more support, the better. Integrative medicine is the combination of various and diverse medical practices of both eastern and western medicine. It is talking to more than a primary care physician to receive different views & support on the condition you seek help for. I am all about helping women find natural options in health care. Integrative medicine focuses on a relationship between patient and practitioner, with respect and communication, with the patient's thoughts and preferences in mind. There is often a lot of trust with this person, and the provider shares evidence-based research to back up their abilities to help. Integrative medicine combines the patient's culture and values with the practitioner's evidence and beliefs to co-create a treatment plan. This kind of care often improves patients' satisfaction, and it can reduce medical expenses overall.

In the world of fertility, there are SO MANY different practitioners women and men can improve their fertility chances. This includes and is not limited to acupuncture & Chinese medicine, nutrition, naturopathy, Ayurveda, homeopathic medicine, energy healing, massage, chiropractic, and more.

As a doctor of acupuncture and expert in women's health, I regularly rely on my colleagues in various professions to help support my patients. I humbly admit I do not know everything there is to on the topic of health and healing. It takes a team of committed people to make this work. Utilizing integrative medicine, I do not have to be the end-all for each of my patients, but instead use other doctors' and healers' strengths and expertise to have the most optimal patient support.

What is integrative medicine, and why should I care about it?

I first started learning about integrative medicine after I lost my firstborn child. In addition to seeing my doctor for all my follow-up visits after giving birth, I saw a psychologist and an acupuncturist. This was helpful to balance my body and my mind. I was determined to conceive again and have a healthy baby, and I eventually did after only three months of trying to conceive, after a full-term loss. I was blessed to have a healthy baby girl who is now a young woman in college at SDSU.

My experience with integrative medicine.

I began my master's program shortly after my pregnancy loss. I attended school at Pacific College of Oriental Medicine to become an acupuncturist and went to several meetings and events with UCSD. They had a group called HI-Med. It stood for the Holistic-Integrative Medial Discussion Group. After attending several Hi-Med groups and inviting my colleagues one month, 40 acupuncturists showed up to the HI-Med meeting, and the med students told me I needed to start my own group. In 2006, I founded the Integrative Medical Discussion Group at Pacific College of Oriental Medicine to bring Eastern and Western medical students & professionals together. We had monthly meetings where we would discuss a topic such as integrative women's health. We would choose four professionals: an OBGYN, an acupuncturist, a chiropractor, and a nutritionist. Each professional would have 15 minutes to talk on the topic. Afterward, the audience would have an opportunity to ask questions and then network once the event was over. After ten years of hosting regularly, I had met tons of doctors and healers of various modalities, and our last meeting at UCSD had over 150 participants. During that time, I also served as the director of Alumni Services and Community Education at Pacific College of Oriental Medicine in San Diego and as the Community Partnership Committee co-director of the Center for Integrative Medicine at the University of California, San Diego. I would also often coordinate continuing education events for licensed acupuncturists. I had met hundreds if not thousands of doctors and allied health professionals from all over San Diego to cross-reference with. I was recognized as a Leader in Chinese Medicine and Integrative Medicine from Pacific College of Health & Sciences twice in the last decade. I continue to collaborate with various professionals, learning what I can do to help my patients further. I think it is essential for people to create a team of professionals surrounding them whenever they have a health crisis, and I would consider infertility.

When I refer any patient to another provider, I want it to be someone of high quality. I feel this referral is somehow a reflection of me. I would never willy-nilly send a patient to another provider I do not know or have a respectful reputation. I want to send the right professional to help my patient and be someone they can relate to. Making sure any doctor or health practitioner I refer to has an exceptional bedside manner is extremely important to me! These experiences gave me connections to various healthcare modalities to learn about and share with my patients.

Traditional Chinese Medicine

As a doctor of acupuncture and Chinese medicine, it is my goal to inspire future mamas to feel empowered about conception by sharing natural healthcare options that many women are unaware of. I have been called "magical" and "full of superpowers" repeatedly as it relates to fertility, pregnancy, birth, and postpartum. The examples of stories where I supported fertility moms with acupuncture and acupressure are vast. I see many women early on while they are trying to conceive consciously. I witness women at all stages of fertility, pregnancy, and postpartum, and I am happy to offer natural options for these women's health care. There are SO many ways a licensed acupuncturist can help!

Acupuncture originates from China over 3000 years ago. It is a system of specific diagnosis and treatment of a person through a holistic lens of traditional Chinese medicine. Most people first go to acupuncture to relieve pain or reduce stress. Countless evidence-based research articles are proving the effectiveness of acupuncture and Chinese medicine. Acupuncture is all about balance in the body. If you have pain or disease, then something will be out of balance. It doesn't matter if you have a diagnosis from the doctor. Acupuncturists diagnose by looking at your tongue and feeling your pulse.

The tongue is the only muscle we can see outside of our body, and it gives us a glimpse into our internal state of health. We diagnose by looking at a person's tongue color, shape, coating, wetness or dryness, and anything that stands out at the various geographical locations. With the pulse, we feel subtle qualities more than if it is fast or slow. There are three positions on each side of the wrist, with two superficial or deep levels within each one. Each of these positions correlates to the organs in our bodies. We look for which position is the weakest and which is the strongest. In TCM (Traditional Chinese Medicine), there are 28 specific pulse qualities, such as slippery, choppy, wiry, or flooding. Each one feels different, and it takes years to master this difficult skill. An acupuncture treatment goal would be to strengthen you where you are weak and sedate where you are excess. Acupuncturists train to feel where these areas are in the pulse. An acupuncture treatment causes the body to go back into balance. We determine which acupoints to use based upon what your pulse is telling us.

Not all acupuncturists are all the same. There are many different specialties and styles of acupuncture. I believe an acupuncture session should not be painful, and I use tiny thin stainless steel needles. I like to tout I am a gentle acupuncturist because I believe in the Golden Rule of "Do onto others as you would do to yourself." I hate pain and try my best to make the sessions with my patients as pain-free as possible. Many people are terrified when they think of needles, but acupuncture needles are nothing to fear. You could fit about 20 of my acupuncture needles inside of a shot needle, just to give you an idea of how thin they are, pretty much as thin as one of your strands of hair.

Chinese medicine consists of more than just acupuncture & acupressure. We use additional modalities such as cupping, moxibustion, and Tui Na medical massage. We are also qualified to discuss nutritional and lifestyle therapies, Chinese herbs, and more! During a one-hour acupuncture session in my clinic, I'd do talk therapy, acupuncture, moxibustion, heat therapy, aromatherapy, and possibly herbs. The acupuncture helps move energy or Qi, putting the body into balance, causing a decrease in pain—resolving their complaints.

Using Chinese Medicine, acupuncture, and acupressure, I can help moms surrounding all stages of fertility, pregnancy, and postpartum. Ideally, I'd see a mom within the first week of the baby's birth to help her postpartum healing. These healing include whether the birth was cesarean or vaginal. Often, I travel to the new mom's home to help care for her. One of the things I closely examine is their cesarean scar if she has one. I would look at the scar's size and shape and see if it is raised or not. Ideally, after several weeks the redness will dissipate. Concerns are with keloid scar, scar tissue that extends beyond the original boundaries of the incision, or hypertrophic scars, where the scar is thicker and higher than a typical scar but stays within the original cut's borders. I work on scars by massaging them with Tui Na, a unique Chinese medical massage technique used to help reduce pain and improve blood flow to the area. Additionally, I would use the needles to surround the scar at least once, optimally several 6-10 sessions postpartum to help with postpartum healing and before the subsequent pregnancy.

The benefits of having TCM scar work done after a cesarean include increased mobility, including the ability to sit and stand straighter, decrease in adhesions making less pain in the scar area, and more blood flow to the reproductive organs, improved sexual functions, and more.

Here are a couple of my stories of infertility I'd love to share with you:

Lifestyle Changes
I had this overachiever woman come to see me desperate to have a

baby a few years ago. She was 31 and had gotten married two years prior, and had begun trying to conceive unsuccessfully eight months ago. She was working full time in a busy career and working out six days a week doing CrossFit. She appeared healthy, was fit, and was without any know diseases or disorders. She had a large group of friends and family and was always on the go.

In addition to doing acupuncture and Chinese herbs with her, we discussed her lifestyle. She did CrossFit with her husband and was exhausted at the end of her workouts. I asked her if she was willing to make a change to help her conceive. She was ready to do ANYTHING, she stated. I went on to share that we only get so much energy in our bodies. When we work out to the point of exhaustion, it does not leave room to conceive and grow a baby. We discussed other possible workout options, such as yoga, walking, or swimming. I advised doing yoga three days a week and CrossFit twice a week. Within a few weeks of weekly acupuncture visits, she reported feeling so much more energized with an overall sense of wellbeing. On her 8th week visit, I noticed a sparkle in her pulse that is indicative of pregnancy. Sure enough, she came up pregnant a few weeks later, naturally with twins! I continued to see her throughout her pregnancy, and she successfully gave birth to two babies at term.

Cesarean Scar

One patient came in years ago for infertility after her cesarean birth with her first baby. I always ask to see the woman's cesarean scar to inspect and make sure it doesn't look inflamed or infected. She wanted to have another child and was struggling with infertility. She and her husband had been trying for baby #2 for over one year. I took one look at her scar and instantly knew this was why she could not conceive. She had a chelated cesarean scar raised about 1 centimeter across her low abdomen. It was puffy and, honestly, the worst cesarean scar I had ever seen. I told her I believe this is why she wasn't getting pregnant, as the scar tissue didn't heal correctly. She told her gynecologist this at their next visit, and he decided to help her get pregnant. He asked her to bring in her husband's sperm the next time she was ovulating, and the doctor inserted his sperm into her body thru a tiny tube with incredible difficulty. He said as he reached the scar area, it was painful for the mom, and he had to "jam it in there" to get past the scar tissue to insert her husband's semen into her uterus. She got pregnant on that visit and was able to have another healthy baby ten months later.

A Bun in the Oven

You know the saying, "a bun in the oven, as it relates to pregnancy, right? Most people understand this. A baby does not grow in the fridge! This saying is an analogy of freezing cold women trying to conceive. Almost every woman who comes to see me who is struggling with trying to conceive complains of cold hands, feet, butt, belly, or all over. I hear how it has been this way forever and their whole family, blah, blah.

That coldness in a woman's body is not ok! One of my top advice for not only getting pregnant but STAYING pregnant, carrying to term, AND giving birth to a healthy baby with you healthy afterward is to get and stay warm. There are many ways we can help achieve this warmth.

The first is to be mindful of what you are putting in your body, food & drinks! I hear this so often it's crazy. Every woman tells me, "I eat so healthy. I had a smoothie for breakfast and a salad for lunch." When I hear this, I cringe and think cold, cold, cold! Our bodies crave and need warmth. Energy flows freely when the body is warm. The cold thickens and contracts. It restricts blood flow. To make a baby, you need excellent blood flow.

My recommendations are to eat warm and soupy foods. Eat at regular intervals and around the same each day. Also, please stop drinking anything iced beverage and stop eating anything right out of the fridge. Better to eat an apple at room temperature versus right out of the refrigerator. You are preferred to have water at room temperature versus from the fridge or with ice. If you are going to eat a salad, consider eating some grilled chicken or a cup of ginger tea to balance the temperatures out.

For goodness sake, keep your feet warm! It's crucial to keep shoes and socks on during the day versus wearing flip-flops, sandals, or shoes without socks. When you stay warm, your energy flows better, which is best for both you and your baby. Always err on the side of being too warm versus the possibility of being caught in the cold.

There are three main channels in TCM responsible for reproduction, and they all begin in the foot. Keeping our feet warm helps to strengthen these organs and improves our reproductive health. Another idea is to heat a hot pack before you go to bed at night and put it in bed with you. Warm your feet and your body up before you go to sleep, and at least (hopefully) 8 hours of your day, you are toasty warm.

One of my favorite modalities within Chinese medicine to utilize is called moxibustion. Moxibustion or moxa for short is an herb called Ai Ye, in Chinese, or Artemisia Vulgaris in Latin is a warming technique to help women who feel so cold all the time. I often teach the women how to use moxa at home. I have a link to my YouTube channel if you would like to naturally check out the several moxa videos I have to help at home. Moxa is used for pain (often menstrual cramps in the world of fertility), boosting your energy and immunity, helping increase circulation and warming. Moxa comes in many forms. The one I use the most is a smokeless pole that looks like a cigar and has a hold down the middle. I will use a cup or Bell canning jar (the lid helps make sure it's extinguished) of uncooked rice as an ashtray. I light the moxa with a candle then wave about an inch above my body, typically on the feet, inner legs, and low back &

belly. To extinguish, I will just put the stick out in the rice, and it will extinguish. The whole process can take anywhere from 5-20 minutes, and most women love the feeling during and afterward. Moxa would be something we would use in conjunction with acupuncture, Chinese herbs, and lifestyle suggestions when working with infertility. Moxa is my "magic" that I get to use which helps with most fertility, pregnancy, and postpartum complaints.

PCOS Story
There was this patient, Kate that came in several years ago as a 38-year-old female trying to conceive. She had thyroid issues, PCOS and was always running cold. Kate came to me after suffering a miscarriage at 12 weeks that she & her husband were devastated about. She told me she was willing to do anything and everything to have a baby naturally.

She began with weekly acupuncture visits and got on Chinese herbs to help balance her system out. We recommended supplements like magnesium to help with muscle cramps and digestive enzymes to help with acid reflux. Next, when discussing her diet, we realized there were several things she needed to eliminate. After a couple of months, she stopped drinking coffee and eating gluten and sugar. She began a keto diet and started to lose her extra weight.

One of the modalities we did to help pull the cold out of her body is called naval cupping. It is where we place a large coin wrapped in a tissue on the woman's belly button, light the tissue, then place a large glass cup over the extinguish the flame and pull the skin up into the cup. The coin serves as a barrier to keep the good energy inside. The naval cupping with the coin barrier over the naval only removes the bad, typically coldness from the body. We would leave this cup on for anywhere from 20-40 minutes. Most women love this technique! Patients report feeling warmer, having less painful periods, and better digestive health.

After one year of regular acupuncture sessions, naval cupping, moxibustion, Chinese herbs, lifestyle, and dietary changes, Kate became pregnant. We were able to continue regular treatments throughout her pregnancy, and nine months later, she gave birth to a healthy baby girl. J

Important Take Away's

1. Find a team of health providers to support you & your partner's fertility; consider including a fertility acupuncturist. Work with several providers to help you get all the answers and support you need along your journey.

2. Lifestyle changes including getting enough sleep, doing the proper exercise and not over-exercising, drinking half your body weight in ounces per day of water, getting eight servings of fruits and vegetables daily.

3. Find balance in your life. Be mindful if you are working too much or too stressed out

4. Slow down and think of self-care. Find and make the time to take extra good care of yourself and give your body what it needs.

5. Think about preheating your "oven" or reproductive system. This includes wearing warmer clothes, eating warmer food, utilizing warming herbs, naval cupping, and moxibustion.

DR. DEB DAVIES, DACM, L.AC.

Dr. Deb Davies, DACM, L.Ac., is a licensed acupuncturist, childbirth educator, faculty at two Chinese medical universities, and is the founder of PUSH San Diego. She's spent over 20 years passionately following her mission of supporting women & their families through fertility, pregnancy, birth, and postpartum care. She empowers expectant couples by educating them about natural and integrative health care options.

Throughout her career, Deb has helped thousands of families in their childbirth journey. She is renowned for her expertise in assisting families to overcome fertility obstacles, maintain a healthy full-term pregnancy, and prepare for an optimal birth experience. Deb also supports mamas during labor and birth with acupuncture, acupressure, and massage therapy. She is highly skilled in postpartum recovery care and optimizing C-section recovery time.

Deb brings a remarkable degree of empathy to her practice at PUSH San Diego. Her first daughter, Mia Belle, was stillborn at term from an umbilical cord accident in March of 2001. Her second daughter, Lauryn, was born a year later. Both daughters instill Deb's work with an unparalleled degree of inspiration and passion that enable her to compassionately support women through the childbirth process, including support for miscarriage and recurring pregnancy losses.

Website: www.PUSHSanDiego.com
Email: debdavieslac@gmail.com

Books: Baby Got VBAC
Facebook: @PUSHSanDiego @MamaHealth&Wellness
Instagram: @PUSH_San_Diego
TikTok: @DebDavies2020
Clubhouse: @PUSHSanDiego

6

FERTILITY, SEXUALITY, AND INTIMACY WITH AN EYE ON EASTERN MEDICINE

DR. DENISE WIESNER, DACM, LAC.

JUST ONE NIGHT of hot and steamy kisses and passionate lovemaking, and voila, a baby is made. We experience this in movies, but what really happens between the sheets when a couple is trying to conceive doesn't always look like how a TV show portrays it. I used to get so mad that movies cut straight to the deed and never showed any foreplay. Don't the writers know it takes about 20-45 minutes of foreplay for a woman to become aroused? In the fertility world, baby-making often resembles the story below from a letter I received.

"I started my fertility journey a few years ago when I had some blood tests. My progesterone in my luteal phase was low, and my AMH was pretty low too. I wanted to "check" and see where my body was. I got my IUD out, but my partner and I didn't start trying right away. He wasn't ready yet.

Last January, my partner agreed we could start having unprotected sex. And from May, we would really start trying. We actually got pregnant in September, but it didn't take, and we had a very early pregnancy loss.

We started seeing a fertility specialist, and he started me on medications. It's been so stressful and hard on us. My partner doesn't feel the intimacy and connection when it's ovulation time which puts a big strain on the entire thing.

Our connection is really struggling.

Our biggest intimacy struggle is probably that we have very different love languages and difficulty being open about our sexuality and sexual/physical needs. We both end up in our heads and out of our bodies. "

Does this sound like something you can relate to?

It's hard enough to connect with our partners with busy schedules, let alone try to make a baby. We aren't given a manual to tell us how it should be done. And what becomes even more confusing are the recommendations that you can find in fertility chat rooms like: Eat the seed diet, no eat paleo, no eat Keto. Or get this procedure, try these herbs, and take these supplements. From my experience, no one likes to talk about the topic of sexuality because there is shame around it. More than often, baby-making becomes a chore that sets the stage for problems in intimacy later on. And suppose you have to do western medicine to conceive because you are in a same sex relationship or for other reasons. In that case, your body can become an experimental instrument, and people forget about intimacy. It is because of this that I decided to become a sex coach and weave it into my Chinese Medicine practice for fertility.

I too struggled to conceive my second child, and it was all I could focus on. I remember sitting on the toilet and seeing my fertile cervical mucus and calling to my husband," hey honey, I am ovulating," - hardly a sexy moment. I realized that becoming your fertile self even if you are doing in vitro fertilization (IVF)[1] requires understanding how to maintain intimacy with your partner. My background in Eastern medicine became the perfect way to draw on Taoist secrets to help a woman become her healthiest fertile self while at the same time enriching her connection to her sexuality

I was drawn to Eastern Medicine when I took a shiatsu massage class at the age of nineteen. The instructor, Dr. Kineko, a wise Japanese man, taught us about energy and how it traveled in the body. Later, I read the book, *The Web That Has No Weaver* by Ted Kaptchuck[2]. The concepts of balance, yin yang, and the circular relationship of the elements made me shake my head, "Yes, the body, mind, and spirit are all connected." I then went to Acupuncture college.

Eastern thinking regarding sexuality, intimacy, and fertility helps us all look at the bigger picture. After all, the Taoist concept of "The Tao" or the way encompasses changing both body and mind to higher levels of functioning in accordance with the natural rhythms of the planet. While it is important to look at specific hormone levels as well as anatomy, this doesn't tell us everything about a woman's fertility story. This chapter hopes to get you acquainted with what you can do to not only make your body more fertile but also to help you strengthen your relationship. We will look at secrets from the east and integrate them with fertility.

First, we have to understand some basic concepts as they relate to western thinking by answering the common questions that patients have around this topic. We will start with the three treasures: qi, jing, and shen. The concept of Qi, or vital energy, is made from the foods we eat and the air we breathe. So many people are tired. They spend a lot of time working and pushing themselves. When it comes time for baby-making, they are exhausted.

Check out your diet and your digestion. It is obvious, but a diet filled with sugar, caffeine, and processed foods is not healthy and doesn't aid good qi. Furthermore, how we process food is of the utmost importance and part of the earth element in Chinese Medicine. Many people are bloated, gassy, and constipated or have loose stool. Conditions such as Small Intestine Bacterial Overgrowth (SIBO)[3], irritable bowel syndrome, and colitis, are common in my practice. If this is you, make sure to get this handled because inflammation in the body doesn't help reproduction.

Next is the concept of jing, which is likened to the quality of your eggs and sperm and has to do with growth, maturation, and aging. It is your genetic blueprint. You inherit jing from your parents, and that is why it is important to be in good health when you conceive a baby. How do you slow down your biological clock? Attend to your lifestyle. This means look at stress, your diet, and activity level to help yourself be healthy physically, emotionally, and spiritually.

The last of the treasures is shen or spirit/mind. We see this manifested in the sparkle of someone's eyes. In the fertility sense, our hearts contain our shen that ultimately connects with the shen of our partner. This energy infuses a developing embryo with love. In an episode of Bridgerton on Netflix, season 1, episode 2, Penelope asks Marena Thompson about her " condition, " meaning her pregnancy. She asks how it happened, and Ms. Thompson answers, "My condition was brought about by love."

DIAGNOSIS OF FERTILITY in Chinese Medicine

When you visit a Chinese medicine doctor, not only will they ask questions about your sleep, digestion, stress, menstrual cycle, but they will also look at your tongue, take your pulse, look at your coloring and give you a diagnosis based on patterns of imbalance. Then they will prescribe herbs, do acupuncture, and give you lifestyle suggestions. The patterns of imbalance are complex and will be touched upon in this chapter. Common fertility ones are Kidney yin and yang deficiency, liver qi stagnation, Qi deficiency, and dampness. These organs are not to be confused with the western ones.

There are many other diagnostic techniques in Chinese Medicine that would require explanation beyond the scope of this chapter. This chapter will briefly introduce you to the 5-Elements: Earth, metal, water, wood, and fire. Each of these elements has a taste, sound, emotion when balanced and unbalanced, and opens to organs and tissues. Each element interacts with all the elements as they form a circle. When one is out of balance, it affects the whole. For example, the metal element opens to the lungs and large intestines. The emotion attached to the metal element is grief and letting go, and the metal element also opens to the skin. Paula, a woman who was sexually abused when she was younger, came to see me for fertility. She hadn't had a period for a couple of years and also had itchy skin on her forearms that no one knew what to do with. With the help of Chinese Medicine and working on releasing her old trauma, as well as eating more fat and exercising less, her menstrual cycle returned. She also began a deep breathing meditation practice. With the help of herbs and omega fatty acids, her skin became less itchy. In her case, not only did we work on the metal element, but we also worked on an 8-extraordinary meridian called the Chong meridian, which connects the heart with the reproductive organs. For Paula, this energy was blocked from trauma. After six months, she fell pregnant.

How can Chinese Medicine help you conceive?

Chinese Medicine is over 3000 years old and includes acupuncture, herbs, lifestyle, diet. As far as fertility goes, we can improve egg quality by increasing blood flow to the reproductive organs and working on both the sympathetic nervous system and the central nervous system. Acupuncture is the insertion of small disposable needles into over 365 acupuncture points on the body that are located on energy pathways called meridians. Most people say they feel calm and balanced after treatment. Sometimes with fertility, we attach electrostimulation to the needles around the reproductive organs Chinese Medicine providers use herbs consisting of twigs, roots, and others that get blended into formulas based on individual presentation. These have been given to many women and men to increase their fertility. Because we look at the body as a whole, special meditations and energy practices (Qi-gong) are used to balance a system.

I HAVE a low sex drive what can I do?

Sex drive is complicated for women because sometimes we need to become aroused to have desire. Back in the time of Masters and Johnson in the '60s, they defined the sexual response cycle by four stages (1) excitement, (2) plateau, (3) orgasm, and (4) resolution. We have now learned that for some women, the sexual response cycle is not linear. With busy schedules and worrying about timing it right, many women disconnect from their sexuality. And whether you are trying naturally or trying with reproductive medicine, feeling your sexy self IS feeling your fertile self - biology made it that way. Just remember, for women, it takes 20-45 minutes of foreplay to become aroused.

Some men have issues as well, for it is not always women that have a low sex drive. If a man has a low sexual urge, he should get some tests done. One is to look at Testosterone and make sure the levels are good. The other is to look at medications, other health conditions, and emotions. Some men put all their energy into work and have none left over for their partners. The truth about sexuality is it is different for everyone. The main factor is that both parties are satisfied with the status quo. Although what is normal for couples can change when trying to conceive.

What can you do to increase your sex drive? First, make sure to look at all aspects of your life and assess how you are doing, i.e., sleep, stress, food, your relationship. Next, use Chinese Medicine, specifically herbs and acupressure, to help increase your kidney energy (the water element) which equates to your sexuality and fertility. In some instances, a lack of sex drive can be because one of the 5-elements is holding all the energy and not sharing its energy with the others - The Liver energy (wood element) is notorious for this. We call this stuck energy. What is the antidote for this? Movement and, of course, sex are included in this. People who have stuck energy usually sigh a lot and feel frustrated. It's hard to drop into passion if you are holding resentment. This often happens when we don't communicate with our partners. A practice to resolve anger and frustration is the qigong shaking exercise, where you shake all your body parts. A favorite Chinese herbal formula for stuck energy is The Relaxed Wanderer or, in Chinese, Xiao Yao Wan. When all else fails, there is nothing like a good old fashion talk where you share your feelings using "I" statements.

Another element that affects sexuality is the heart energy (fire element). This element is all about love, but it can lead to prolonged sadness when out of balance. Feelings of despair can usher in withdrawal from life. This can happen when repeated fertility attempts end in failure. The heart energy also opens to the tongue, so passionate kisses are a must to enrich this element.

Carla was a patient of mine who conceived her first baby easily at 34 years old. Now 42 years old and married to her second husband, she wanted another baby. In the midst of trying, she found out her husband had a very low sperm count. Her only solution, her doctors told her, was to do an IVF. She was worried about her age and fell into a deep depression. She didn't feel like having sex with her husband and didn't feel like doing an IVF but tried to rally to get in the mood. When she came to see me, I diagnosed her with heart qi imbalance and low spleen qi. I gave her a formula that I modified called Gui Pi Tang or Restore the Spleen decoction. I also added kidney energy herbs. She worked on finding joy in the little things, and I gave her and her husband exercises to do. The first was to sit facing her husband and place her left hand on his heart and have him place his left hand on her heart while eye gazing with each other for four minutes. This forced an intimate connection where they could see each other. I had them practice this every night as they carved out time together. Carla thanked me because it was the first time in a while that she felt seen by her partner. Soon, they began to have more connection, and this led to intimate touch and finally to making love. A couple of months later, they were ready to do an IVF.

To keep the theme of connection, I instructed them to create a ritual around the IVF medication. I had them light a candle and bless the medicine before he injected it in her. To her surprise, she made three genetically normal embryos, and when one was transferred, they got pregnant.

Jennifer had met her husband in her forties, and they wanted to have their own biological child. When it wasn't happening naturally, she went to a fertility clinic. Many rounds of IVF led to one viable not genetically tested embryo. All her energy went into praying that this embryo would give them a biological child. When she was preparing for the FET (Frozen embryo transfer)[4], she came to see me. Even though she knew the odds of this embryo becoming a baby were low, Jennifer had a lot of hope. This all came crashing down when her pregnancy test was negative. At this point, she stopped doing anything for fertility and withdrew from her friends and family, and stopped having sex with her partner. Her heart energy experienced enormous sadness, and we worked on healing her heart. I gave her a forgiveness meditation to practice because she blamed herself for waiting too long to conceive.

Forgiveness meditation: I like to use **Hoʻoponopono,** a Hawaiian meditation: I'm sorry, please forgive me, thank you, I love you.

Slowly, she came back into her body and reconnected with her partner.

How can I increase sex drive with herbal medicine?

The kidney energy, as mentioned above, governs reproduction and fertility. Herbs are amazing at increasing egg quality, regulating hormones as well as increasing sex drive. Let's face it, when your body is balanced, you will have more energy to give sexually.

The best approach is to work with a Chinese Medicine doctor who specializes in fertility to get a custom herbal formula written specifically for you and your particular pattern of imbalance. Here, I am going to go over some of the herbs that are used to increase sex drive. Note that herbs are not used alone but in combination with each other in herbal formulas.

Here are some to look at:

Ashwagandha - Protects the body and brain from stress-related elevations in cortisol. It can help low testosterone and supports antioxidant levels. It has been shown to boost the immune system, improve energy and alleviate symptoms of anxiety and depression[5].

Maca - This is an adaptogenic herb grown in the Andes in Peru. It has an effect on libido, sperm count, and motility. There are 13 different phenotypes (colors) of maca, and they have different DNA profiles, different analytical profiles, and have a different physiological effect on the body. Black maca has better effects on sperm production than yellow maca, while red maca reduces prostate size, and yellow maca is geared toward helping the adrenal glands and men's sexual health.

Horny Goat Weed (Yin Yang Huo) - This yang tonic increases libido, improves erectile dysfunction, and regulates hormones in both sexes. Some studies suggest this herb helps with immune function, depression, and bone health. Contains the flavonoid: icariin 500mg 2-3 a day. Not good for people with low blood pressure.

Cynomorium (Suo yang) - An animal study showed that there were dose-dependent effects on sexual function. This herb promotes male fertility by strengthening the spermatogenesis in the golden hamsters[6]. This herb can also adjust the hypothalamic-pituitary-gonadal axis by increasing estrogen and makes related biomedical indexes and hormone receptors normal. It can relieve perimenopausal syndrome and perimenopausal syndrome with depression.

Cordyceps - Enhances cellular energy, normalizes immune function, enhances athletic performance, restores normal energy stores, and increases sexual function. It is good for sperm health and restores libido in men and women. Dosage is about 500-1000 mg once a day.

Tong Kat Ali - This herb from Malaysia is also known as longjack. Rodent studies show improved sexual performance following tongkat ali feeding. This herb is good for lethargy, low libido, depression, and fatigue. It appears to have significant potential for restoring hormone balance (cortisol/testosterone) and improves psychological mood state in humans exposed to various modern stressors, including aging, dieting, and exercise stress[7].

Be sure to consult with an herbalist when using herbs for libido and fertility.

. . .

How do we time intercourse when my partner is stressed and has difficulty performing during my ovulation window?

Most problems that come out of timed intercourse for fertility are because couples don't have a plan. You may want to communicate with your partner on how to time intercourse doing your ovulation window if you are trying naturally. Some men want to be involved, and others don't want to know when their partner is ovulating because they feel pressured to perform. The antidote: have more regular intercourse, and you will hit the ovulation window. A second way is to make sex fun again because many couples complain that baby-making sex does not hit the spot. Try more touch, more togetherness, candles, and touch exercises (see couples intimate video on www.denisewiesner.com)

When men can't get an erection in Chinese Medicine when trying to make a baby, we call it Yang Wilt due to psychogenic issues. In general, there are many causes of erectile dysfunction such as cardiovascular disease, high blood pressure, other medical conditions, certain medications, smoking, low testosterone, relationship issues, stress, trauma, depression, and environmental factors. If your partner is having issues other than when making a baby, be sure to get him checked out by a Urologist.

In Chinese medicine, we look at the below patterns of imbalance and attempt to remedy them with acupuncture, herbs, lifestyle, and supplements:

- **Excessive anxiety and worry damaging the heart (fire) or spleen(earth)**: preoccupied with work, worried about performing in the ovulation window. It might be low libido, fatigue, loose stool, palpitations, weak pulse, insomnia, and flabby tongue.
- **Depression of liver(wood) qi** – anger and

frustration. Fertility taking away from intimacy with a partner, emotional repression, fullness, pain distention on the side of ribs, dark tongue

- **Fear and Fright damaging the heart(fire) and kidney(water)** – due to trauma, soreness of back and knees, traumatic past, fine, weak pulse.

If your partner can get an erection most other times, he might want to get help with either natural products or Viagra or Cialis. He can also take products that will help increase nitric oxide, which helps blood flow to the penis. Products that increase nitric oxide include: L-citrulline, L-arginine, and foods like arugula, walnuts, and watermelon.

I FEEL bad in my body, especially since doing all this western reproductive medicine, and I don't want to be touched. What can I do to feel better and bring intimacy back?

Negative body image is a player when it comes time to having sex. One of the reasons many women don't want to be intimate with their partners is they don't feel good about their bodies. This can be exacerbated by western medical treatments. Women aren't the only ones who have this. Men can also suffer from negative body image.

Sarah, a 36-year-old, came to see me because her menstrual cycle had stopped. She had moved to Los Angeles from the east coast four months earlier. When she came to Los Angeles, the movers she hired lost all her belongings, so she and her husband moved here with nothing. She told me that she had gotten two menstrual cycles after they moved and didn't understand why her period wasn't coming. She also went on a strict diet with a nutritionist and was exercising two hours a day. Besides the stress of losing her belongings, I explained that drastic diets are not good for fertility. We need some fat on our bodies to make a baby. Over exercising also has a negative effect on fertility. I explained that the reason she got her cycle three months after she moved is that it takes 90 days for the follicle to go through the growth cycle.

As I got to know her, I found out that she binged and purged and didn't have a good relationship with her body. Boom - it's the self-love piece. Women have grown up comparing their bodies with models and actresses. The phrase I like to tell my patients is that your body is temporary. What is more important is to practice gratitude for your beautiful self. With a treatment of herbs, acupuncture, better diet, less exercise, and self-love practices, her cycle returned.

Western reproductive medicine can wreak havoc on a couples' love life. There are, after all, restrictions on intercourse, swollen bellies, emotions all over the place, and other symptoms. If you have been trying for a while and are using western reproductive medicine, you are contending with disappointment. Many of my patients tell me they gain at least 10 pounds with each IVF. I remind them to love their beautiful bodies through all of it in addition to eating well and exercising. For couples going through a lot of treatments, I suggest a time out - a sort of vacation if you will - even if it is in your house. My patient's partner planned a birthday party for her with a Cuban theme. He decorated the house, had Cuban food ordered, played Cuban music, and had a pinata (even though it is Mexican and not Cuban). This was during the pandemic. I thought to myself, how creative, how fun - a great way to laugh and reconnect. What if you bought new sheets for the bed, played music, watched erotica, dressed up, put on candles, read each other poetry, sang to each other, used sex toys, essential oils, and placed flower petals on the bed to touch each other with? What if you just made time for a date night? Just remember, intimacy is not all or nothing. If you can't have intercourse, there are other ways to enjoy each other. For more information on the timing of sex during an IVF cycle, check out my book, *Conceiving With love,* and the chapter called Timing is everything[8].

No matter what the changes that your body is going through, we all deserve pleasure. Most people are more self-critical than their partners are. Again, self-love is the work.

MY PARTNER HAS difficulty ejaculating in me. What can be done about this?

Sometimes men have a difficult time ejaculating in their partners. There can be many reasons. Medications such as SSRIs can contribute to this. A solution is to see if you can switch to another kind of medication with low sexual side effects or use natural products for anxiety and depression. Some men also practice not ejaculating in a woman for many years, so when the time comes, they can't come. In addition, masturbation styles can also differ from the friction received with vaginal penetration. One solution is to retrain the masturbation style to mimic a vagina by using less force. In the psychological realm, some men have unresolved issues about becoming a father and therefore can't hit a home run. If this is the case, you may want to talk to a therapist. Chinese Medicine also offers tools for helping the body/mind/spirit become balanced. The most important takeaway is there is help.

HOW DO I try again after miscarriage or loss? It's so hard to get my hopes up and connect with my partner.

Lily felt like her body failed her when she had her two miscarriages. She received many tests after, and her doctor concluded it was bad luck. During the time of her second miscarriage, she learned that her best friend was with child. Although she felt happy for her best friend, she also felt left out. When she came to see me, I felt her pulses to assess her energy and also looked at her tongue. Her kidney pulses were weak, and I told her to wait while we strengthened her blood and energy for at least three months. I assessed some blood stagnation and chose herbs that would move blood, and also put her on proteolytic enzymes to help with inflammation. She was still taking coenzyme q 10, vitamin D, fish oils, and vitamin E. The next bit was to help her reconnect with her partner. I suggested they spend some quality time together and gave them some intimate energy practices to do together. They were excited to try something different. They fell pregnant four months later and had a healthy baby girl.

Loss is hard. Both Chinese and Western medicine look at what might have caused the loss but even genetically tested embryos transferred in an IVF cycle don't guarantee a pregnancy. What can you do to nurture your body, heal, and get back on the fertility journey? From an eastern perspective, we first make sure the uterus is cleared from the pregnancy by utilizing both acupuncture and herbs. There is a special category of herbs that we say move the blood that can be added to herbs that nourish the body. We do this strategy and then start to build the body's qi and blood to improve egg quality, endometrial lining, and receptivity. Of course, one also needs to get checked out by a western doctor.

While couples are healing from the loss, I have them create a letting go ceremony. One you can use is to gather a rock or an item in nature and pour your grief into this object while sitting or walking with it. Then with your own prayer, give that item back to nature. Some people prefer planting a tree, but either way, the idea of setting aside time to honor the loss can help couples move forward.

I HAVE NEVER HAD AN ORGASM, **is that a problem to conceive?**

First of all, an orgasm is not needed to conceive. There is a theory, however, that if you do have an orgasm after your partner ejaculates in you that the contractions of the uterus will propel the sperm upward toward the uterus. I knew a same sex couple that had their friend ejaculate in a cup and run it over to them. They did an Intracervical insemination (ICI), and then one partner gave the other partner an orgasm to help the sperm propel upward. They told me they had a lot of fun trying.

If you are not having orgasms, I highly recommend you explore them. There are many books to read on this subject such as, *Come As You Are* by Emily Nagoski[9], or check out Betty Dodson's website, where she has so much information on female orgasm[10]. I even have information on this in my book, *Conceiving with Love*[11]. Many women only orgasm with clitoral stimulation. So, why not have your partner stimulate your clitoris or do it for yourself while you have intercourse. Another approach might be to use a sex toy for clitoral stimulation during intercourse. It's important to get out of your head and get into your body because when you are worried about having an orgasm, chances are you probably won't have one. Be present in the moment and let go. It also helps if you can communicate to your partner your rhythm. When women are in their groove, your partner can be instructed to keep it going.

SECONDARY INFERTILITY - HOW TO connect with your partner when there are little ones around.

I had secondary infertility, and I understand the challenges of timing intercourse with a little one around. I feel like we played musical beds and had to hurry and get it done. There are challenges to being a mom, changing diapers, making food, and then trying to get your sexy on. It can often feel like you are wearing many different hats. I encourage you to glamour it up for yourself. In other words, dress up, take a bath with essential oils, put on clothes/lingerie that makes YOU feel good. Get creative. And if all else fails, laughter is the best medicine. There are many simple eastern practices that can enhance intimacy—breathing together, sitting in the yab yum position with your partner, which is really sitting in their lap, eye gazing, with full-body hugs. Spending time connecting allows the intimacy to grow. And the cliche that women want to be heard and men want to be appreciated is true. Ultimately, babies grow up and sleep through the night, and cultivating a healthy intimate relationship with your partner in all of life's changes goes a long way.

Conclusion

Chinese Medicine, including eastern medicine, is an incredible tool to help couples conceive and have intimacy. We approach the body as a whole, including mind, body, and spirit. This chapter only touches on the many ways Eastern medicine can help you. It is a great adjunct to western medicine as well as a stand-alone for conception. The most important takeaway on this journey toward parenting is to lead with your heart.

Mooji, a meditation teacher, says, "start by saying thank you." Research around a gratitude practice can go a long way in helping us to be connected. Find the place within where love lies inside of you because it is that love that babies are made with. Love infuses your reproductive centers with energy and merges a couple. Foster love, live love, and create with love, and don't forget to have fun in the process.

---

1. *In vitro fertilization (IVF):* is a process of fertilization where an egg is combined with sperm   outside the body, in vitro.
2. Kaptchuk, T. J., & Kaptchuk, T. J. (2008). *The web that has no weaver:Understanding Chinese medicine.* New York: McGraw-Hill.
3. *Small Intestine Bacterial Overgrowth (SIBO):* occurs when there is an abnormal increase in the overall bacterial population in the small intestine

4. *Frozen Embryo Transfer (FET)*: means thawing one or more embryos (frozen during a previous treatment cycle) and transferring that embryo (or embryos) to the uterus in order to try to establish a pregnancy.

5. Nasimi Doost Azgomi, R., Zomorrodi, A., Nazemyieh, H., Fazljou, S., Sadeghi Bazargani, H., Nejatbakhsh, F., Moini Jazani, A., & Ahmadi AsrBadr, Y. (2018). Effects of *Withaniasomnifera* on Reproductive System: A Systematic Review of the Available Evidence. *BioMed research international*, 2018, 4076430. https://doi.org/10.1155/2018/407643

6. Lee, J. S., Oh, H. A., Kwon, J. Y., Jeong, M. H., Lee, J. S., Kang, D. W., & Choi, D. 2013). The Effects of Cynomorium songaricum on the Reproductive Activity in Male Golden Hamsters. *Development & reproduction*, 17(1), 37–43. https://doi.org/10.12717/DR.2013.17.1.037

7. Talbott, S. M., Talbott, J. A., George, A., & Pugh, M. (2013). Effect of Tongkat Ali on stress hormones and psychological mood state in moderately stressed subjects. *Journal of the International Society of Sports Nutrition*, 10(1), 28. https://doi.org/10.1186/1550-2783-10-282013)

8. Wiesner, D. (2019). *Conceiving with Love: A Whole-Body Approach to Creating Intimacy, Reigniting Passion, and Increasing Fertility*. Shambhala.

9. Nagoski, E. (2015). *Come as You Are*. Simon & Schuster.

10. Homepage. (n.d.). Retrieved February 15, 2021, from https://dodsonandross.com/

11. Wiesner, D. (2019). *Conceiving with Love: A Whole-Body Approach to Creating Intimacy, Reigniting Passion, and Increasing Fertility*. Shambhala.

DR. DENISE WIESNER, DACM, L.AC.

Dr. Denise Wiesner, DACM, LAc., founder of the Natural Healing and Acupuncture Clinic in

West Los Angeles, is an internationally recognized traditional Chinese medicine practitioner specializing in women's health, sexuality, and fertility. Since 1994, Denise has helped thousands of couples navigate the tricky, and often stressful, journey toward fertility without losing their loving connection.

Denise is a certified sex coach. She is board-certified by the State of California and the American Board of Oriental Reproductive Medicine (ABORM). She is the author of the book *Conceiving with Love: A Whole Body Approach to Creating Intimacy, Reigniting Passion and Increasing* Fertility and the has a course called " How To Make a Baby and Have Fun Doing It." It is her mission to help as many women and men conceive and overcome obstacles to intimacy. She is a professor in the doctorate program of women's health at YoSan University. When not working, she enjoys yoga, dancing, and hanging out with her two boys, Noah and Ethan.

Websites: www.denisewiesner.com
www.naturalhealingacupuncture.com
Email: info@denisewiesner.com
Books: *Conceiving with Love: A Whole Body Approach to Creating Intimacy, Reigniting Passion and Increasing* Fertility

Facebook: @Denisewiesnerlac
Instagram: @Denisewiesnerlac

7

HOMEOPATHY FOR FERTILITY

GABRIELLE TRAUB, M.TECH (HOM), CCH, HD (HON)

How I discovered Homeopathy

SIX WEEKS before I was born, while I was still nestled in my mother's womb, my 2-year-old brother died suddenly. It sent shock waves and a flood of emotions through my umbilical cord. While the cause of death was "inconclusive", his doctor prescribed a medicine that he likely had a reaction to. Ten years later, my younger brother had a similar anaphylactic reaction. I will never forget my mother's screaming. She was holding my brother, who was limp and blue. We called the ambulance, and the paramedics were able to resuscitate him. We discovered that he was anaphylactic to medications, including Penicillin and Sulfur drugs. After that, my parents became weary of conventional medication and wanted to find a safer, gentler form of medicine. That's when we discovered homeopathy.

Being raised on homeopathy was the norm for me. I never viewed it as alternative. It was the first thing we turned to if anyone in the family got sick. Unlike other kids in my class, I rarely got sick, and if I did, I recovered quickly. When I first started having my periods, I had terrible PMS. I went to my homeopath, who listened to all of my symptoms and prescribed a homeopathic medicine that best matched both me as well as my individual symptoms. I took just a few doses of the homeopathic medicine, and it gently and permanently balanced my hormones. Growing up, I remember being the only one out of my group of friends who never had any period cramps or problems around my period.

I got married older and was even later to start a family. I'm so glad that I waited. I had the chance to travel the world, spend some wonderful years with just my husband and devote my time to helping others in my practice. I never doubted that homeopathy would help me to conceive. At 39 years old, I was a wise and mature first-time mom. Gray-haired doctors with little faith in my body's ability to have a perfectly healthy pregnancy and labor would annoyingly refer to me as "advanced maternal age". I was doing everything perfectly: my diet was impeccable, I was exercising daily and doing yoga, I was doing meditation and qi gong twice a day. However, at six weeks pregnant, I started bleeding heavily.

I could barely get out of bed as any movement caused more bleeding to occur. My husband was out of town. I was alone and terrified. My doctor wrote in my chart that I was having a threatened miscarriage and tried to reassure me that I could always try again. I tried a number of different alternative therapies, none of which had a significant effect. I was deeply attached to my baby growing inside of me, and the thought of losing him was devastating. The bleeding had begun after having a disagreement with my mother-in-law. Despite having resolved the conflict, the bleeding continued. Under the rubric[1] "bleeding after anger," only one homeopathic remedy was listed, *Chamomilla*. Within 30 minutes after the first dose, my bleeding stopped by fifty percent. By the next day, it had decreased by ninety percent and the following day completely stopped. The homeopathic medicine saved my baby! Homeopathy helped me during every stage of my pregnancy: from morning sickness to heartburn to sciatica that prevented sleep.

Together with my amazing talented doula/acupuncturist, Dr. Deb Davies, DACM, L.Ac.[2], HypnoBirthing, and homeopathy helped me to have a non-eventful 8-hour labor despite having a posterior positioned baby. All the work I did to prepare my body for labor paid off! Homeopathic medicines helped me heal physically and emotionally postpartum. It helped in every stage of newborn, infancy, and raising a child. I'm not saying it was all smooth sailing. Believe me, I have had MORE than my fair share of challenges. However, homeopathy was always there by my side, helping me to navigate even the most difficult situations. My eight-year-old is a rarity in that he has never needed to take antibiotics or any other medication for that matter. Not that I wouldn't give it to him if he needed it, but homeopathy always pulled through. My patients often remark: "How do parents do it without homeopathy?" I feel so lucky, as if I have this special secret, and I want to scream it from the rooftops and share it with the world. In this chapter, I am going to give you just a taste of the power of Homeopathy, pulling from over two decades of clinical experience working with thousands of patients.

Hope In a Bottle

Annie came to see me when she was 39 years old. She had tried everything to get pregnant: two rounds of IVF, fertility specialists, Chinese herbs, acupuncture, network chiropractic, osteopathic treatment, naturopathic treatment—nothing worked! She also had hypothyroidism and polycystic ovarian syndrome (PCOS). Annie shared with me: ***"I have given up on getting pregnant!"*** and was seeking help with her thyroid. Annie's periods were irregular, and the blood was black, clotted, stringy, and membranous. She also suffered from ovarian pain, vaginal dryness, and pain during sex. She had rectal fissures and bleeding after stool. She had hair growing in all the wrong places and falling out in spots. She was having difficulty losing weight.

I spent over an hour and a half taking Annie's case. I wanted to know all about her physical symptoms, but I also asked her a lot of questions about her. I wanted to know about her unique qualities. Annie exclaimed, "It's as if we're trying to unravel a mystery, and you're the detective!" Homeopathic treatment is extremely individualized. The homeopathic medicine needs to match the person, not just their disease. When I saw Annie again, we were walking down the hallway, and we hadn't even reached my office when she couldn't contain her excitement any longer and blurted out: "I'm eight weeks pregnant!" She got pregnant on the very first try after the first dose of the homeopathic medicine. It was nothing short of a miracle. Five years later, Annie got pregnant again easily and naturally at 44 years old. She had a natural home birth with a birthing pool and, of course, Homeopathy. Today she is the proud mom of two beautiful children, ages 12 and 8. Annie's kids have been raised on Homeopathy. As new parents, dealing with childhood complaints can feel overwhelming and out of control. Having an arsenal of little homeopathic vials made her empowered. As Annie likes to say: "There's always hope in the homeopathic remedy bottle."

Please note that such rapid response to treatment is rare. Typically, the process can take between 6 months to one year, depending on the age and health of the patient and any underlying conditions.

Listen to Annie share her fertility experience with homeopathy.[3] Be patient. It takes a few minutes to download, but it's worth the wait!

So What Exactly is Homeopathy?

Homeopathy is a science of medicine that was discovered by a German physician, Dr. Samuel Hahnemann. He was disillusioned by the barbaric medical practices of his time, such as bloodletting[4] or giving patients high doses of mercury. He gave up his practice and turned to translating medical journals, where he came across a treatment for Malaria using Peruvian bark (more commonly known as Quinine). From his experience in chemistry, he knew that Peruvian bark causes Malaria-like symptoms. Dr. Hahnemann was curious by nature, and this led him to conduct hundreds of experiments. His findings led to his theory, "Like cures Like." He proposed that diseases are cured by substances that in high doses produce symptoms similar to the disease. Many of the herbs and substances he used were poisonous if taken in large enough quantities. He discovered a way to make the medicines safe yet effective through a special dilution process we call potentization[5].

Homeopathy has been used for over 250 years. Under the supervision of a professional homeopath, it is safe during pregnancy, breastfeeding, the elderly, and even in infants. Patients using homeopathy report powerful positive changes that continue long after the homeopathic medicine has been discontinued.

It is important to find a homeopath who has experience with fertility. Homeopathy is very precise; it has to be just the right remedy to work. I have many patients that have gone from one homeopath to the next without success, and in just a few months, we found the one that worked. As seen in the double-blind clinical studies listed below, homeopathy is effective in helping both female and male infertility.

Optimizing Genetics

Sarah is a very sweet lady who came to see me for PCOS with irregular, painful periods and infertility. She had hypothyroidism despite taking medication and had high cholesterol and asthma. After taking her homeopathic remedy, her labs were greatly improved, cholesterol and thyroid were normal for the first time in years. However, it didn't help regulate her period. Ovulation strips showed that she was not peaking. I then gave her a homeopathic remedy that specifically targeted ovulation and hormone regulation. Over the next few cycles, her menstrual blood went from being painful, dark, and clotted to becoming significantly less painful, with very few clots, and the blood was bright red. After years of having a period every 3-4 months to having a period every 40 days. She reached peak ovulation when testing with ovulation strips. She lost 15 lbs (she is only 5'3"), and her doctor reduced her thyroid medication. Her libido improved, and she hasn't had any asthma since beginning homeopathic treatment. Not only did the remedy help her physical symptoms, but it also helped her emotionally. She didn't take on stress like she used to. She found the courage to quit her job that she was unhappy with and got another job with better hours and better pay. At that point, there was a change in Sarah's picture: she became more weepy, emotional, needing her husband's affection and not wanting to be alone. She also developed a yeast infection. I matched her new symptoms with the correct homeopathic remedy, and after just a few weeks on the remedy, she got pregnant and had a healthy baby boy. While most couples trying to conceive are primarily focused on fertility, addressing other conditions such as asthma, thyroid health, and resilience to stress are fundamental in optimizing the health of our offspring.

Areas Where Homeopathy Can Help Fertility

The most common reasons for infertility include:
1) Problems with the eggs or ovaries, for example, PCOS, age, or poor egg quality
2) Hormonal imbalances
3) Underlying diseases such as hypothyroidism, yeast infections, or sexually transmitted diseases
4) Structural issues such as fibroids, endometriosis, or scarring
5) Problems with cervical mucus
6) Genetic factors such as clotting tendencies or more common genetic SNP's like MTHFR gene variants

7) Stress or age
8) In men, it may be due to low testosterone, sperm issues such as low count, motility, morphology, or erectile dysfunction

Homeopathy can address all the issues listed above. However, homeopaths take a much deeper dive beneath the surface, beyond disease labels. We examine the kind of processes that occur in every cell in your body. We identify specific miasms[6] that can get in the way of conception. These miasms not only affect your fertility, but they can also affect the ultimate health and makeup of your child. The figwort and luetic miasms are especially problematic if not adequately addressed. The figwort miasm makes you more susceptible to producing excess tissue, which can manifest as cysts, fibroids, polyps, endometriosis, tumors, or adhesions. The luetic miasm can make you more susceptible to miscarriages or birth deformities but can also be linked to other diseases such as severe depression or alcoholism in your offspring. In my experience of working with families for over two decades, I have found that homeopathic treatment can optimize gene expression in the offspring of the parents undergoing homeopathic treatment.

For this reason, it's ideal that both partners receive homeopathic treatment. I dream about a world where doctors recommend classical homeopathic treatment for six months prior to conception. I believe that homeopathic treatment, together with a healthy diet, eliminations of toxins, and stress reduction practices are the key to eliminating chronic disease and a healthier future for all of our children. Having said that, any amount of classical homeopathic treatment is beneficial to mom and baby, even if it's only during the last few months of pregnancy.

The Odds Were Against Her

Joan came to see me for infertility. She couldn't imagine her life without having a child but had been trying for the last six years and was losing hope. She had been to see many naturopathic doctors and had tried everything natural under the sun. Her medical history was complicated. She had a history of polyps and fibroids. She has a blocked right fallopian tube, a bicornuate, and a retroverted uterus. She was allergic to her husband's sperm which would irritate and redden her skin, and her body would fight it off like a foreign invader. She had a genetic variant called MTHFR and is Rh negative blood type (her husband is Rh positive). The odds of conceiving were against her. She had painful periods, low sex drive, and heavy vaginal discharges. She had tried two rounds of Clomid and was also taking progesterone. She wanted to use homeopathy alongside Clomid. Her struggle to conceive made her feel like a failure, and she had been putting her life on hold. After just one month of homeopathic treatment, her menstrual blood was cleaner and significantly less painful. Her confidence was back together with her zest for life. To her surprise and joy, she conceived six weeks after beginning homeopathic treatment, and today she has a beautiful 3-year-old daughter.

How to Tell if Your Homeopathic Medicine is Working

Even before you get pregnant, there are ways we can assess whether the homeopathic treatment is working. These are the signs we look for to know that we are on the right path:
1) Changes in your period: Your period becomes regular, less painful, bleeding is a normal amount
2) The blood becomes bright red, cleaner, with **very few clots**
3) Less premenstrual syndrome (PMS)
4) Improved progesterone in the luteal phase

5) Reach peak ovulation when using ovulation strips
6) Healthier cervical mucus
7) Improved sex drive
8) Most of the semen is retained and doesn't leak out after sex
9) Improvement in mood, attitude, and feelings of wellbeing
10) Improvement in other areas such as sleep, digestion, and energy

Some people believe that painful periods and PMS are normal and part of being a woman. I have helped hundreds of women that have suffered from heavy, painful periods or PMS their entire adult lives and are surprised one day when their period sneaks up on them without any of the pain or emotional turmoil.

I work with men and women who want to be parents so badly. Every period is a disappointment and feelings of failure. She is so happy for her third friend in a row who just announced her pregnancy, but at the same time, it's devastating because she has been trying so hard without success. Women who can barely look at other women pushing a stroller because they feel that they will never have that experience. Women who blame themselves and are riddled with guilt because they put their careers first or simply didn't meet anyone they wanted to settle down with. Women who feel that there is something wrong with her body. Men who are to afraid to go to the doctor to discover that there may be something wrong with their virulence and their wife isn't to blame ... we won't even go there. Couples whose sex life's primary purpose is to make a baby and have lost the spontaneity of sex and the passion that comes with it. The toll that infertility has on relationships is tremendous.

At the end of this chapter, I have referenced a list of robust double-blind clinical trials demonstrating the effectiveness of homeopathy in promoting fertility.

Fertility and virulence are fundamental indicators of health. In many cases, both can be addressed naturally with homeopathy. Being a parent is the greatest joy and the most noble privilege. The love between parent and child is unlike any other. I believe that every person should have access to all of the tools available to experience this sacred gift if they so choose to.

Clinical studies showing effectivity of Homeopathy for Fertility

1. Bergmann J, Luft B, Boehmann S, Runnebaum B, Gerhard I. The efficacy of the complex medication Phyto-Hypophyson L in female, hormone-related sterility. Forsch Komplementarmed Klass Naturheilkd. 2000 Aug;7(4):190-9.

2. I., Keller C., & Monga B. (1995). Homeopathic treatment in female infertility. In: Gerhard I. Experiential healing. [Homöopathische behandlung bei weiblicher unfruchtbarkeit. In: Gerhard I. Erfahrungsheilkunde.] [German] Karl F. Haug Verlag: Heidelberg, Germany.

http://homeopathypure.com/infertility_and_homeopathy.html

3.Gerhard, I, Wallis, E, Individualized homeopathic therapy for male infertility, Homeopathy (2002)91,133-144. PMID: 12322866

4.Aziz D, Enbergs H., Stimulation of bovine sperm mitochondrial activity by homeopathic dilutions of monensin. Homeopathy. 2005 Oct;94(4):229-32

5.Die Wirksamkeit des Komplexmittels Phyto-Hypophyson® L bei weiblicher, hormonell bedingter Sterilität. Eine randomisierte, placebokontrollierte, klinische Doppelblindstudie. Bergmann J.a · Luft B.a · Boehmann S.b · Runnebaum B.a · Gerhard I.a. aAbteilung für Gynäkologische Endokrinologie und Fertilitätsstörungen, Universitäts-Frauenklinik, Heidelberg, bSteierl-Pharma GmbH, Herrsching. Forsch Komplementärmed Klass Naturheilkd 2000;7:190–199. (DOI:10.1159/000021343)

6.Gerhard I, Reimers G, Keller C, Schmück M. Weibliche Fertilitätsstörungen - Vergleich homöopathischer Einzelmittel- mit konventioneller Hormontherapie. Therapeutikon 1993; 7(7/8): 309-315.

7.Gerhard I, Reimers G, Keller C, Schmück M. Weibliche Fertilitätsstörungen - Homöopathie versus Hormontherapie, Therapiewoche 1993; 43(48):2582-2588

8.Gerhard I, Patek A, Monga B, Blank A, Gorkow C. Mastodynon(R) bei weiblicher Sterilität. Forschende Komplementärmedizin 1998; 5(6): 272-278 http://www.ncbi.nlm.nih.gov/pubmed/9973660

9. Kalampokas T, Botis S, Kedikgianni-Antoniou A, Papamethodiou D, Kivellos S, Papadimitriou V, Salvanos G, Paparistidis N, Gavaris I, Sofoudis C, Kalampokas E, Farmakides G, Vithoulkas G. Homeopathy for infertility treatment: a case series. Clin Exp Obstet Gynecol. 2014;41(2):158-9. http://www.ncbi.nlm.nih.gov/pubmed/24779242

10.Lai G. [Homotoxicological treatment of female funcional infertility: clinical trial]. La Medicina Biologica 2000; 4: 81-86

11.Wittmann G, Gerhard I, Runnebaum B. Wirksamkeit eines Arzneimittels auf Basis pflanzlicher Extrakte - Mastodynon-NR bei weiblicher Infertilität. Arch Gynecol Obstet 1993; 254: 158–160.

12.Veal L. Complementary therapy and infertility: an Icelandic perspective. Complement Ther Nurs Midwifery. 1998 Feb;4(1):3-6.

13. Viksveen P. Heggemsnes A. Homeopathy can help up to 60% of couples trying to conceive, Dynamis 2005

1. *Rubric:* is a symptom that is listed in our homeopathic books or repertories. Next to each rubric is listed the homeopathic medicines that are helpful in treating that symptom.
2. https://www.pushsandiego.com/provider/deb-davies-dacm-lac
3. https://www.sandiegohomeopathy.com/sound/InfertilityAnnie.wav

4. *Blood letting:* an ancient medical practice where the doctor would bleed the patient using leeches. They believed that this would cure the patient.

5. *Potentization:* is a process in the manufacturing of a homeopathic medicine. It involves trituration, dilution and succession. This process removes the toxicity of the medicine, while still retaining its healing benefits.

6. *Miasms:* are the susceptibility to disease that can be inherited from your parents or grandparents or acquired in your lifetime via contracting certain diseases.

GABRIELLE TRAUB, M.TECH (HOM), CCH, HD (HON)

Gabrielle is a board-certified classical homeopath and international best-selling author. She has worked in hospitals and rural clinics in South Africa. After moving to California, she worked in an OB/GYN practice for a decade alongside a traditional OB-GYN and a fertility endocrinologist. Gabrielle has assisted in natural birthing, taught childbirth classes, and worked extensively with infertility. Gabrielle has taught homeopathy in England, South Africa, Pakistan, Dubai, Australia and the USA. Her online course Homeopathy for Obstetrics and Gynecology is probably the most extensive homeopathic course on women's health. Her new book *Live Right for Your Remedy Type* will be coming out soon. Gabrielle interviewed the queen's homeopath, Dr. Peter Fischer on her radio show, *Vital Force Radio*. While living in London, she practiced at the Hale Clinic which was opened by the Prince of Wales.

A mother herself, Gabrielle now works in San Diego where she specializes in treating women and children. She offers TeleMedicine consults to patients worldwide.

Website: www.SanDiegoHomeopathy.com
Email: support@sandiegohomeopathy.com
Books: https://homeopathicbook.com
Facebook: https://www.facebook.com/San-Diego-Homeopathy-400747I4234

Instagram: https://www.instagram.com/sdhomeopathy
Online Course: http://www.wholehealthnow.com/courses/
womens-health-conditions.html

8

FAITH THROUGH TRIALS

IVF MAMA DUE TO MALE FACTOR INFERTILITY

HANNAH CARABALLO

In our wedding video, there is a clip of my mother-in-law's speech. She jokes about how she wants Irwin and I to have six kids, and the crowd erupts with laughter and shouting—some making sounds of approval, others yelling, "One! Just have one!". We laugh and sip our champagne, knowing that while kids are in our future dreams, they are nowhere on the radar that night.

Irwin and I met in the fall of his senior year of high school and reconnected at a graduation party of a mutual friend the following summer. We were immediately both smitten and inseparable. The following year, I moved down south for college, and we took our shot at having a long-distance relationship. We were constantly texting and video chatting, looking at houses to buy someday, and even making plans for marriage and the future, all before I even turned eighteen. We discussed having a bigger family of four kids and a couple of dogs on a few acres of land in a house we would someday build. We walked through our dreams of him being the head of safety for a big corporation and me having my own successful wedding planning business that allowed us to travel all over the world. Irwin and I were young, in love, and felt invincible. In the years that have followed and over a decade later, I can say we've been very blessed and have worked really hard to have most of our dreams come true, even before they were "supposed to" on my master life plan. Except for one—the big family.

About halfway into 2015, Irwin and I had both accepted jobs that put us closer to reaching our professional goals, and as we edged into 2016, I started having the itch to try for a baby. I had been on birth control since I was a teenager and was only having four periods a year on the pill, so we discussed coming off the pill, allowing my cycles to regulate, and then starting to officially try that summer. During that time, I got my hands on every fertility book and website I had time to read through. We ate the right things, exercised regularly, stopped setting laptops on our laps, and everything else the professionals tell you to do to be successful in your trying to conceive (TTC) journey. Three months after I stopped taking the pill, I still wasn't having regular periods. But each cycle after the 30th day had passed, I was convincing myself we were pregnant when in reality, I was never even ovulating. Something we would figure out later in the year during my annual gynecologist appointment.

At my annual exam, I had told my doctor we were struggling to get pregnant, and I wasn't having a period every 28 days—my cycles were between 60 and 80 days at this time. This was obviously cause for concern that something was off, so he brought me in for an ultrasound and bloodwork 21 days after my next period started to see if I had ovulated. The tests determined what we had been thinking— my body wasn't doing what it needed to so we could get pregnant. He suggested we try Clomid[1] the next cycle to see if that would jumpstart the ovulatory cycle for me and give us a shot at becoming pregnant. On my way out of the doctor's office, I tried choking back tears—wondering why this wasn't something that could just work, why my body was betraying me, and weighing whether or not we would even want to move forward with a medical intervention.

Even before we started trying, I had these notions that any type of fertility intervention was playing God, up to and including in vitro fertilization (IVF)[2]. I grew up Catholic and went to a private school where you're taught; abstinence is best, and if you do have sex, you'll get pregnant. This is why we actively prevented pregnancy for years before deciding to grow our family. I now realize how crazy this is because using birth control can also be considered "playing God". I knew enough about fertility at this point that unless a literal miracle happened, we probably weren't going to get pregnant without doing anything. I called Irwin first to give him the news. We both felt sad and a little angry about the circumstances and weren't sure we would want to move forward, so we made a call to our pastor's wife, Pam, for some guidance.

"Sometimes the miracle is the medicine"

This was the advice she lovingly gave us while telling us of her own infertility struggles back when she was in her young adult years. She gave the examples that typically, someone wouldn't refuse chemotherapy if they were going through cancer or surgery if they needed a joint replacement. Why should this be any different? God is the almighty creator; he put the stars in the sky and the fish in the ocean and created the human that had the brain to create these drugs that can help couples conceive babies. It's amazing! But it still can feel like a huge defeat, especially when you are young, healthy, and all the articles you read say you shouldn't have an issue getting pregnant.

We gave the doctor a call later that week and let him know we wanted to move forward with Clomid treatment once we hit a year of me being off the pill, which was in February 2017. Clomid is a fairly easy treatment of an oral medication, and then the doctor follows up with bloodwork and an ultrasound on cycle day 21 to confirm ovulation. As planned, we began Clomid treatment in February

2017, but unfortunately found out later that cycle that I still had not ovulated. For the next cycle, he upped the dose of Clomid, but also gave us a referral to a reproductive endocrinologist for further testing and treatment options in the event the higher dose didn't work. Having a referral this early in the game was a huge success as a lot of specialists have long waitlists. We were able to exhaust the Clomid doses and immediately transition to a specialized doctor for more intensive treatments.

Our first appointment with the reproductive endocrinologist (RE)[3] was in the early spring of 2017. We spoke with the doctor, she drew an amazing image of how a woman gets pregnant (I say amazing, but we all laughed at her drawing skills—she's a doctor, not an artist, and for good reason), checked my antral follicle[4] count, and took about fifteen vials of blood. Irwin was also scheduled for a semen analysis to rule out any male factor issues, and I was scheduled for a hysterosalpingogram (HSG)[5]. This sounds like a lot, and it was. Still, it gave us a really great picture of our overall fertility health and even uncovered a minor iron deficiency and higher than normal thyroid levels in myself. After I had undergone all my testing and had the results back, the RE started me on Letrozole[6] as I still hadn't had a successful ovulatory cycle. That was looking like it was the main issue, along with Synthroid to lower my thyroid levels to an acceptable level. I went in on the 21st day of my cycle for bloodwork and an ultrasound which confirmed successful ovulation. I was thrilled and finally saw a light at the end of the tunnel.

Until my husband's test results came in a few weeks later.

The semen analysis[7] threw all of us for a loop when every single number was well under where it needed to be. The doctor was cautiously optimistic in asking us to have him tested again in the event of a bad sample, and maybe there would be enough improvement that trying naturally wouldn't be in vain. He was scheduled to be retested three weeks later. Those results, while better, didn't give us the news we wanted. His total sperm count was under 1,000,000, with low motility[8] and morphology[9] to boot. Once all the numbers were taken into account, we were working with about 200,000 healthy sperm every time we tried. Sperm counts have a very large range across the board, but doctors like to see over 15,000,000 sperm per milliliter or 39,000,000 per ejaculate[10]. There wasn't anything off with his blood work and nothing in his health history that signaled a cause for concern, so the RE sent in a referral for Irwin to see a urologist. They were discussing the possibility of a block or another physical problem that could potentially be fixed and finally allow us to conceive. That appointment was another long wait, as the office didn't have an opening until August.

On top of all the testing and doctor appointments and phone calls, we still had regular life happening outside of our fertility journey. It felt like we were attending monthly baby showers, I had accepted a job that I started the week before our initial RE appointment back in April, and we were in the middle of building a house. Life was busy. And that was before you threw on anything else. August rolled around, and we had a closing date for our house—the same day of Irwin's urologist appointment. We went to sign the paperwork that morning, I went to work, and he went to the doctor. In the middle of dealing with a wedding day "emergency" I got a call from Irwin.

"Hey babe, can you talk?"

I immediately knew something was off. My breath shallowed, and my hands started shaking. I quickly walked to a more secluded location in the event any tears started flowing. Irwin went into detail about how they did a full exam and didn't find any blockages or physical issues. Still, prior to his appointment, they had fully examined his three sperm samples and found an acrosome deficiency[11] within all of the samples, affecting more than 60% of his small amount of healthy sperm. As I held back tears, Irwin explained that the acrosome is what allows the sperm to penetrate the egg. The absence of an acrosome means sperm can meet the egg but just bounces off the outer shell and will never allow for fertilization. And because this specific condition doesn't allow for penetration, and the numbers even without this disorder were not good, the urologist urged us to consider IVF with ICSI. Without that, we had a 0.01% chance of ever having a baby.

Men account for over 30% of infertility cases, yet when in a case study by Resolve, only 41% of OB/GYN physicians consider performing a urological exam while treating infertility cases[12]. This could be why, to date, there is very little research on what causes certain conditions and how to either reverse them entirely or slow down any damage. IVF with ICSI is often recommended for these cases as it gives couples the best chance of sperm meeting the egg.

What is ICSI?

Intracytoplasmic Sperm Injection[13] is the process of joining egg and sperm in an embryology lab by injecting a single sperm into the egg for fertilization[14]. This procedure is pretty commonly used for male factor infertility cases and is becoming more widely used in lieu of standard IVF. Standard IVF combines multiple sperm and one egg in a petri dish where the sperm can naturally penetrate and then fertilize the egg. In a case like ours, even this wouldn't have been possible. And when you are faced with IVF and spending the tens of thousands of dollars, it costs, the ICSI procedure gives you a much higher chance of having success in the creation of your embryos.

We finally had the next steps, but we had literally just put all our money down on our new home, and we just couldn't afford another $20,000. So, we waited. We continued to attend our friends' baby showers and watched as those friends welcomed their babies into the world, all while struggling with wanting so badly to have a baby. We were still having timed intercourse in hopes that maybe we would get one of those miracle stories. We were fighting more than we ever had, even over dumb stuff, because we were just emotionally spent. I was crying myself to sleep, wondering if we would ever get the opportunity to bring a baby of our own home and feeling upset for every new announcement, every diaper commercial, and every getting pregnant plotline in the shows we were watching. We toyed around with the idea of foster to adopt, but it didn't feel right. And we definitely didn't have the money to go through a standard adoption. We focused most of our energy during this time on settling into our house, keeping the door to our someday nursery closed to ward off any sadness.

October rolled around, and as we were heading home from picking pumpkins, Irwin muted the music in his car and said, "I want to have a baby, and I know you do too. So how do we get there?" He asked if we could call the RE to have her walk us through all our options and the percentages of success. On the call with her, she only recommended IVF with ICSI. We asked about IUI[15], even knowing the chances may not have been the best, as that was a less expensive option and something we could've afforded, but the doctor was very clear on that being a waste of money, and to put that $500 into our IVF savings instead. We were back to the proverbial drawing board, trying to figure out ways to save the money, considering picking up second and third jobs even though our schedules were already packed and even looking into financing options to afford the chance of possibly bringing home a little one of our own. After a lot of prayer and soul searching, we decided to finance the procedure. We both knew we wanted to have multiple children, and the thought of waiting potentially years to start this process was the complete opposite of what we wanted. So we said a prayer, applied for a credit card with zero interest for eighteen months, and were approved with a $20,000 limit—just enough to cover our estimated out of pocket expenses with a little wiggle room. I began to read more about the

IVF procedure, what the day to day looked like, and what kind of experience we were in for.

It was around this time that a little twinge of jealousy and anger towards Irwin started coming out. I used to be incredibly afraid of needles, and the thought of not only having to get blood work done daily but then having to administer multiple shots daily too was wreaking havoc on my ability to cope with the procedure. And because this was "Irwin's fault" I started directing a lot of the anger I was feeling towards him. A couple more of our friends announced pregnancies. Some of them, this would be their second child since we started trying. And then, on the way to dinner the evening before Thanksgiving 2017, I was scrolling Instagram and noticed someone who had just gotten married earlier that fall announced their pregnancy. It feels so icky even to say this, but the jealousy I felt in that moment is a feeling I will never forget and also a feeling I never want to experience again in my life. I was so distraught that this was something that came so easily to others, but something that we were going to have to endure this long and pain-filled journey for. I was upset this couldn't be easy, and I was taking out my anger on my husband, who truly had no say in this. There was nothing he could've known or done in his life to have different outcomes. It was unfair to him, and he finally called me out on my behavior that night. I personally felt that I was the one who had to endure the needles, medical procedures, and somewhat giving up things in my lifestyle for this to work, for an issue that wasn't even mine. But that's irrational. This man was my husband and again had no say in any of this happening—it's not like he did drugs, consumed much alcohol, was unhealthy, or dabbled in risky behavior. These are just the cards we were dealt in life. And we needed to have this moment where all the cards were on the table to allow us to start that healing process and move onto the next steps.

On December 7th, 2017, we had our IVF intro appointment with our RE. She went over the whole process of what was going to happen, a tentative schedule of when, gave us the pharmacy information, and then took more blood in preparation for the egg retrieval surgery. We were definitely nervous, but for the most part, this is where we started to look up a bit more and get hopeful for the future. Our clinic shuts down annually in December to maintenance all the equipment, leaving us with a January start date. All we had to do was wait for my period to arrive.

On Tuesday, January 16th, 2018, we had our baseline appointment, which measured the follicle-stimulating hormone (FSH)[16] and my estrogen level. I got the call early afternoon that the numbers were where they needed to be, and we were all clear to start medications that evening. I started off on two injectables–Follistim[17] and low dose HCG[18]. Both of these medications help to overstimulate the ovaries so multiple eggs can be retrieved. About halfway through our stimming journey, I started ganirelix injections[19] taken alongside the other two medications. This particular medication helped slow down the process of the follicles that were getting larger, allowing some of the other follicles to catch up in size. During this phase of our IVF journey, I was getting up at 5am to get ready for work and make it to the fertility clinic by 7am almost every day. They would start with an ultrasound to count and measure how many follicles were growing and then take a blood sample to measure estradiol levels. Towards the end of the stimming stage, ultrasounds were taking close to a half-hour or more as they moved the ultrasound wand around and measured each individual follicle. I was taking mental notes of follicle sizes and researching them once I got to work to tie me over until the clinic called me in the afternoon to give me the next steps. My medication dosages changed pretty drastically during the ten days we were stimming, and this is completely normal. Sometimes it's not enough to get those follicles growing. Other times, as in my experience, it's too much off the bat. I went in for my last monitoring appointment on Tuesday morning, one week after our first night of injections, and got the call that afternoon we were going to be scheduled for our retrieval first thing Thursday morning.

On that phone call, I was alerted that while everything looked good and we were moving forward with a retrieval, I was no longer eligible for a fresh transfer as my estradiol level was too high, and transferring would put me at serious risk for severe ovarian hyperstimulation syndrome (OHSS)[20]. OHSS is fairly common but can become dangerous, especially if a pregnancy occurs. We also had to trigger with Lupron[21], a different medication than we originally were prescribed and picked up. This medication was another $400 on top of what we had already spent, but being this far in, it didn't even phase us. IVF is a time game, so medications have to be given at specific times each day. Because of this, we had almost no social life for two weeks. We knew that if we went out, we needed to be home by 7pm to administer the injections, and neither of us was comfortable transporting them as they had to remain refrigerated. The trigger shot was no different, if even more strict. They gave us an exact time to give the shot that would allow the release of the eggs at the exact time of my surgery.

Thursday morning, we reported to the fertility clinic at 6am, met with the financial counselor to pay for the IVF cycle, and were placed in a prep room to get ready for the operation. They prepped me and Irwin on how the procedure works, what happens after the procedure, and went through all the paperwork. I walked back into the OR, got positioned on the table. They confirmed my name and birthday, and I slipped into a deep sleep.

I awoke to the sound of Chip and Joanna Gaines.

After Irwin gave his sample, he turned on Fixer Upper on HGTV. He said I was wheeled back into the room very shortly after he was done with his part, but I was still asleep from the anesthesia. As I was coming too, I asked how many eggs they were able to get... multiple times. I'm not sure if that was out of shock or because I just wasn't totally there yet, but thirty! I was floored and so excited. We actually had a chance to have the family of our dreams. The same day as this procedure, they combine the eggs and sperm and then call the next day with a number of embryos[22] that are continuing to grow. This is typically where you see the biggest drop-off of number. There are many reasons for this, sometimes the eggs aren't mature enough, and sometimes it's because the chromosomes are abnormal, among others[23]. When we spoke with the embryology lab the following day, our thirty eggs had dropped down to seventeen growing embryos. This was still a great number, and we were very excited that many were growing. We next heard from the lab on day three and then finally on day five with a grand total of eight blastocysts[24] sitting on ice. At that point, there was nothing we could do but wait until we could start with our frozen embryo transfer[25].

There is really no right or wrong answer to when you want to move forward with a frozen embryo transfer, but we opted to go immediately into it the next cycle. It's set up a little differently than a fresh transfer as there are different medications you have to take, but up until the week of the transfer, our medications this round were all oral. The transfer and medication structure are based on your cycle, with the progesterone[26] in oil injections starting based on if you have a day three embryo or day five blastocyst. Since we had the day five blastocyst we were transferring, we had to start our progesterone six days before transfer. During that time, I was also on Estrace[27] (to grow and thicken the uterine lining), Doxycycline[28] (to limit the risk of bacteria being introduced during the transfer), and Medrol[29] (to help my body accept and not reject the growing blastocyst).

I took off work the day of our embryo transfer. Once I was dressed, I picked up two edible arrangements to deliver to both the West campus of the fertility clinic where I had all my monitoring appointments, and the East campus where the retrieval and transfer took place. After delivering the arrangement to the West campus, I went to my acupuncture appointment and left just in time to get over to the east side of town for our transfer. Irwin met me there, and we walked in together hand and hand, excited that this day had finally come. Looking back now, I had so much peace that day. The doctor who we had been seeing since April of the prior year was actually there that day to perform the transfer, and both of us took it as a great sign. I think she felt the excitement and hope we were radiating because she was very quick to remind us this only held a 40% chance of working, but since we had other embryos frozen, we still had additional chances if this transfer didn't work. At 10:25am on Friday, February 23rd, 2018, we were taken back to the OR, all dressed in our scrubs. We got to see our embryo on the giant screen, and they confirmed multiple times my name and birthday to ensure we were getting the correct embryo. They did a test run to make sure there wasn't any blockage in the catheter and then inserted the embryo into my uterus. The whole process took all of five minutes before we were wheeled back to the same room where we had our retrieval prep. I had to stay lying down on the bed for a half-hour, and then we were permitted to leave. As we walked out, we relished in the fact that we could've gotten pregnant just now. It felt like slow motion as I walked past the other rooms, where there was another couple who had just been wheeled back from their transfer. There is not a day that goes by that I don't wonder how their journey turned out.

We mostly rested through the weekend. On Sunday after church, I woke up from a nap, and I remember having three very distinct pings in my lower abdomen. I looked up at Irwin and told him I was pretty sure our embryo had implanted.

Tuesday that week, I had to head to the fertility clinic for them to do a progesterone blood draw. My levels on the day of the transfer were lower than they wanted, so they upped my dosage, and this blood work was to confirm the numbers were where they needed to be. When I first sat down, she looked at my chart and said it was a little early for a beta test[30], but I laughed and said it was just for the progesterone draw. A beta test is the blood draw clinics do to confirm a pregnancy. Not all women will have this test done, as usually an at home pregnancy test is sufficient, but beta tests are commonly used in the infertility community to not only confirm pregnancy but to assure the baby is still growing in those early weeks before an ultrasound would be able to pick up a heartbeat.

It took them forever to get one vial of blood, and the longer the needle was in my arm, the more light-headed I started feeling. The sweet nurse got me an apple juice once she was done and let me sit in the chair until I wasn't pale as a ghost. I drank a bit of the juice once I got in my car as I was starting to feel a bit fuzzy again, and it tasted... off. I needed the sugar, so I kept drinking it until I got to work and felt sick to my stomach. I switched out the juice for water and felt fine the rest of the day. The next morning, I had this crazy urge to take a pregnancy test. I needed prenatal vitamins anyway, and since I didn't have any tests in the house, I figured I would pick up two boxes to get me through the rest of the two-week wait, knowing the test I was going to take that morning would be negative but that I'd definitely want to test again the following day. As soon as I got home, I took the test. It wasn't the first morning urine, or after a four-hour hold, so I put the test to the side, knowing it was going to be negative. After I had washed my hands, I looked at the test, and to my complete surprise, there was a second line. I almost didn't believe it. After two years of staring at single line tests and there was a second line on this one, and it was only five days after my transfer. I was shaking and sent a photo via text to Irwin immediately. We did it. We were pregnant.

Over the course of the next couple of days, I continued testing, and the line kept getting darker. After my third day of darker test lines, I called the clinic to schedule my beta. It was originally scheduled for March 9th, but they made an exception and told me to come in on Monday for the test. First thing Monday morning, I walked into the clinic and got my bloodwork done, then left for work. While I waited for the confirmation call, I kept irrationalizing that maybe our home tests weren't accurate and worrying that maybe this test would come back negative. Just the opposite happened, by HCG levels were at 435 – I was confirmed to be pregnant!

Our pregnancy was pretty textbook. I had a small scare a few weeks after my beta that landed us in the emergency room due to some bleeding, but it turned out to be a subchorionic hematoma[31], which is usually harmless and fairly common[32]. That emergency room trip is where I got to see our baby's heartbeat for the first time, it was the strangest feeling of the deepest love I'd ever felt, and I had so much gratitude that nothing was wrong. We found out at fifteen weeks via a private ultrasound that we were having a little girl, which was confirmed at our anatomy scan four weeks later. Our sweet little girl, Cora Elise, was born on Wednesday, November 14th, 2018, just three days past her due date and perfect in every way.

Happy ending, right?

We are now a bit over two years from our little girls' birth and just over three years since Irwin and I were sitting in bed, watching *How to Get Away with Murder* which is when we found out there was an accident at our clinic that rendered the rest of our seven embryos, along with thousands more that weren't ours, non-viable. We are at a point now where we honestly don't know our next steps. We've considered everything from being a one-child family to going through another IVF round, to even participating in foster to adopt. None of these at this point in time feel right - there is guilt around giving Cora a sibling, there is guilt around NOT giving her a sibling. There are money issues in that we really don't want to go back into debt, especially now having a child. And then moral issues in that there is a huge possibility of us having a bunch of leftover embryos from an IVF cycle that would never be used. And then finally, in emotional issues in both a new IVF treatment or the possibility of fostering.

In a way, even though our journey came to a "happy ending" two years ago, I think I'm still mourning what could've been, and in order to take the next step with confidence, I need to work through all those shoved-down-deep emotions. Currently, all I know is that I don't. But I do know that God himself has me in his hands and will show me the way in His perfect timing, even if it's not mine.

So, for those of you reading this, looking for answers, I could tell you that keeping my feet warm and eating an avocado a day during our IVF journey is what helped us obtain and maintain a successful pregnancy. I could tell you it was the acupuncture sessions, or me giving up all caffeine and alcohol, the McDonald's fries I ate post-transfer, or the prayers that others spoke over us, or even the complete positive attitude we had throughout the journey. But I know first hand that all of those things were just extra. That ultimately, we didn't have much of a say in how and when we had a baby, even though the world will be very quick to tell you that it's all in your control by how you eat, manage stress, and live your life. Sure, none of the things up there are bad, and if you're in the midst of your journey, take a stab at these and see if they work for you, but the miracle of birth is predicated by the miracle of conception first and foremost. And the only one who has any say in this is God himself.

Some days it is so hard to pick yourself up, but I would encourage all of you to find someone, anyone—even me, to walk this journey alongside you. Allow them to be the one to pray for you on days where it's hard to pick up your head from your tear-stained pillow. Give yourself grace to have bad days and angry days. Days where maybe you don't attend a baby shower if it means sacrificing your mental health. Give yourself permission to really love your body and all that it does, even after you've gained weight from fertility medications, and on the days you feel that your body isn't working how it's supposed to. Completely surrender this journey you are walking through to God, and he will see you through it—in a day, in a

year, or ten years from now—he will walk with you through the finish
line.

---

1. *Clomid:* clomiphene (Clomid) is used to induce ovulation, to correct irregular
    ovulation, to help increase egg production, and to correct luteal phase deficiency.
2. *In Vitro Fertilization:* a technique where a woman's eggs and man's sperm are
    combined in a special laboratory in order to create an embryo(s)
3. *Reproductive Endocrinologist (RE):* is a surgical subspecialty of obstetrics and
    gynecology that trains physicians in reproductive medicine addressing hormonal
    functioning as it pertains to reproduction as well as the issue of infertility.
4. *Antral Follicle:* a resting follicle and appears as a small fluid-filled sac which
    contains an immature egg
5. *Hysterosalpingogram (HSG):* a radiologic procedure to investigate the shape of the
    uterine cavity and the shape and patency of the fallopian tubes. This means it is a
    special x-ray using dye to look at the womb (uterus) and Fallopian tubes
6. *Letrazole:* not initially created as a fertility drug, but has been used for ovulation
    induction by fertility doctors since 2001 because it has fewer side-effects than
    clomiphene (Clomid) and less chance of multiple gestation
7. *Semen Analysis:* also called seminogram, or spermiogram evaluates certain
    characteristics of a male's semen and the sperm contained therein
8. *Sperm Motility:* describes the ability of sperm to move properly through the
    female reproductive tract
9. *Sperm Morphology:* the size and shape of the sperm
10. https://www.healthline.com/health/mens-health/normal-sperm-count
11. *Acrosome Deficiency:* The acrosome is a cap-like structure over the anterior half of
    the sperm's head. As the sperm approaches the zona pellucida of the egg, which is
    necessary for initiating the acrosome reaction, the membrane surrounding the
    acrosome fuses with the plasma membrane of the sperm's head, exposing the
    contents of the acrosome. A deficiency means this cap is not present on the sperm.
12. https://resolve.org/infertility-101/medical-conditions/male-factor/
13. *Intracytoplasmic Sperm Injection:* (ICSI) is an in vitro fertilization (IVF)
    procedure in which a single sperm cell is injected directly into the cytoplasm of
    an egg.
14. https://www.reproductivefacts.org/news-and-publications/patient-fact-sheets-
    and-booklets/documents/fact-sheets-and-info-booklets/what-is-intracytoplasmic-
    sperm-injection-icsi/
15. *Intrauterine Insemination (IUI):* is the deliberate introduction of sperm into a
    female's cervix or uterine cavity for the purpose of achieving a pregnancy by
    means other than sexual intercourse
16. *Follicle Stimulating Hormone (FSH):* regulates the development, growth, pubertal
    maturation, and reproductive processes of the body
17. *Follistim:* a lab created FSH drug that acts on the ovaries to produce follicles
    and eggs
18. *Low Dose HCG:* prescribed to mimic the LH surge that occurs in the natural
    menstrual cycle. Physicians can prescribe a single dose of HCG to final grow the

eggs because HCG has the same biological activity as LH. HCG will cause your follicles to rupture, like an LH surge does in a natural menstrual cycle

19. *Ganirelix:* A GnRH antagonist, used in controlled ovarian hyperstimulation cycles for IVF

20. *Ovarian Hyperstimulation Syndrome:* is an excessive response to taking the medicines (especially injectable gonadotropins) used to make eggs grow. Women with OHSS have a large number of growing follicles along with high estradiol levels. This leads to fluid leaking into the abdomen (belly), which can cause bloating, nausea, and swelling of the abdomen. When OHSS is severe, blood clots, shortness of breath, abdominal pain, dehydration, and vomiting are possible

21. *Lupron:* GnRH agonists are synthetic drugs that cause the release of FSH and LH initially but with continued use quickly suppress these hormones, thereby creating a clean slate on which to create a controlled ovarian hyperstimulation cycle

22. *Embryo:* the early stage of development of a multicellular organism

23. https://blog.drmalpani.com/2013/04/why-do-some-embryos-stop-growing-in-ivf.html

24. *Blastocyst:* is a structure formed in the early development of mammals. It possesses an inner cell mass (ICM) which subsequently forms the embryo

25. *Frozen Embryo Transfer:* a technique used in conjunction with IVF, that allows cryopreserved/frozen embryos created in a prior stimulated IVF cycle to be thawed and transferred into a woman's uterus.

26. *Progesterone:* Progesterone production is generated by the corpus luteum, and is essential for helping maintain a pregnancy. The vast majority of physicians will prescribe progesterone shortly after the egg retrieval to prepare the uterine lining for embryo implantation. If it's discovered that the IVF treatment cycle resulted in a successful pregnancy, progesterone is often times continued for the first 6-12 weeks post pregnancy.

27. *Estrace:* helps maintain the endometrial lining of the uterus

28. *Doxycycline:* to control bacteria that may affect implantation in the female

29. *Medrol:* a steroid used for its anti-inflammatory effect after IVF oocyte retrieval

30. *Beta Test:* a blood test for hCG to clinically confirm a pregnancy

31. *Subchorionic Hemotoma:* type of blood clot called a subchorionic hematoma that's formed by the abnormal accumulation of blood between the placenta and the wall of the uterus

32. https://www.babycenter.com/pregnancy/health-and-safety/subchorionic-bleeding-during-pregnancy_40005840

HANNAH CARABALLO

Hannah Caraballo is a wife to her husband, Irwin, and a mother to her toddler daughter, Cora. Hannah and Irwin walked through a few years long journey with infertility in trying to start their family, which is where Hannah's interest in the subject began. After her husband was diagnosed with a condition that made conceiving naturally virtually impossible, she dove into medical journals and peers to help get them through the infertility journey. During that time, she was able to mentor countless friends who were struggling with infertility cases of their own and, to this day, speaks with women and advocates for infertility awareness with hopes to mentor on a national scale someday.

Professionally, Hannah is the owner of Hannah Caraballo Designs— a boutique, full-service wedding design, and floral company. She attended college for Business Administration and is certified in wedding planning and event design fundamentals through The Bridal Society. Hannah is an enneagram four, and she loves her church, boating, spending time with her family, and perfecting cookie recipes.

Website: https://hannahcaraballo.com
Email: hannah@spweddings.co
Facebook: https://www.facebook.com/hannah.caraballo11/
Instagram: @hannahcaraballo

LinkedIn: https://www.linkedin.com/in/hannahcaraballo1101/
TikTok: @hannahcaraballo
Clubhouse: @hannahcaraballo

9

FAITH AND FERTILITY

DREAMING OF BECOMING A MOM BUT PLAGUED WITH PCOS

HOLLY ADAMS

I CONSIDER MYSELF LUCKY. I believe that God knows the desires of our hearts. I believe that if my plan for myself doesn't come true, it's only because God has something greater planned for me, even if the road to get there is excruciating. I feel lucky to have this level of "blind faith" in God. I never lost faith that I would have a baby one day. I wasn't sure that I would be able to conceive, but I hoped and prayed for that ability every day.

I have always wanted to be a mother. I thought that's what everyone wanted. Fall in love and have children one day. All my friends have told me I would be a great mom. I just feel that it is destined to be part of my life to love little humans that belong to me in some way. I have always been fascinated by the processes of pregnancy and labor and delivery. I have been eager to experience it for myself since I witnessed my nephew come into this world during my junior year of college. It's truly such a miracle.

I started my period in 8th grade and did not ever have a regular cycle. I heard of other girls tracking their cycles and something about every 30 days, but I didn't have that same cycle, and I didn't think much of it. I still got to join in all the discussion of pads, tampons, and cramps; what did it matter that mine didn't come every 30 days? It wasn't a topic of discussion, and my doctor never asked me about it beyond the typical "and when was your last period?" to which I usually didn't know the answer.

I knew something had to be very wrong in 2012, during my Sophomore year of college. I bled almost constantly from September to February. I went through a year's worth of tampons in 3 months. I would bleed nonstop for, sometimes, up to 2 weeks straight. The longest stretch I would go without bleeding was five days. I finally decided to go to the doctor because I was tired of bleeding. I was sure I was anemic by this time. They did some blood tests, and they all came back normal. They concluded, "Well, you probably aren't ovulating. Let's put you on birth control, and that will give you a regular cycle." They put me on the pill.

I had made lighthearted jokes in the past about how I'll probably have a lot of trouble getting pregnant, but this was the first confirmation that I got where I truly began to know, in my gut, that I really would have trouble getting pregnant one day. I was already with the man that I knew I would want to marry one day and that I would want to be the father of my children. I wanted answers.

I asked the doctor, "If I am not ovulating, and you are putting me on birth control to regulate my period, how will I ever have kids one day?" She responded, "Well, you don't have to worry about that yet." I told her, "I wanted to know now if I can't have kids so I can prepare myself for the heartbreak." She assured me there is nothing to be done until I want to try.

I was used to listening to "authority" and complying with what they advised of me. I didn't push further for answers with my doctor to find out what was wrong with me. However, this was also at a time in my life where through my college experiences, I was learning the importance of advocating for myself. Because of ADHD (Attention-

Deficit Hyperactivity Disorder) and MDD (Major Depressive Disorder), I had to learn to communicate with authority figures effectively and honestly in order to be successful in college. These skills became critically useful when I needed to advocate for my health down the road.

I married the man of my dreams, and we talked about having a big family one day. We wanted six kids. People would gawk when I said that we wanted six kids, and I would always respond with, "Well, we'll see how I feel after the first one." I quickly realized I was only saying that to make them more comfortable, and I began to own that we really did want six kids if it was possible. We always wanted to conceive at least one child on our own but were also open to adopting one day to continue our growing family. We had an ongoing list of our future kids' names that we had built over the years. Names we loved, and maybe some names I put on the list against his will.

Five years into marriage, in 2017, at 25 years old, we decided to stop birth control and stop preventing getting pregnant. It took us six months before we began to officially claim that we were "trying" to have a baby. I had my first day of spotting about four and a half months after stopping birth control. I was told that it was totally normal to take up to 6 months to have any real period. Every period after that happened every 60 to 75 days. After the second cycle, if you can even call it that, I went to see my OBGYN. She took all my blood levels again, and everything came back normal. I told her I wanted to see a fertility specialist, and she said I should try for a year before I got a referral. I explained to her that I wanted answers to why my body was not working properly and that I needed a referral now. She agreed to write me one.

When trying for a year, most women will have twelve chances to get pregnant, I would have only had about four to five chances at the rate I was going, and I wanted to know if there was a way for me to have more chances. I also wanted to know what was wrong with me that was causing my body not to be working properly. The wait to see the fertility specialist was about three months. I continued to track my lack of having a period so that I could have as much information as possible to give the fertility specialist. Even the app I used on my phone to track my period was confused by my menstrual cycle and came up with "error" messages when it couldn't predict my next period. It was all very discouraging.

When I finally saw the fertility specialist, she was very encouraging. She commended me for standing up for my body and coming to see her before a full year of trying to conceive. She commended me for knowing my body and recognizing that it was obviously not working properly for conception.

After a conversation about my symptoms, the fertility specialist began to think I may have PCOS (Polycystic Ovary Syndrome)[1]. She explained that I needed two of three symptoms to be diagnosed with PCOS, and I already had one of them; very irregular periods. The second symptom that I did not have was excessive hair growth or weight gain. She said she needed an ultrasound of my ovaries to look for the third symptom. She explained that the name of PCOS could be very deceiving as it sounds like you have cysts on your ovaries, when in fact, having cysts on your ovaries can just be a side effect of having PCOS, but not the actual initial symptom. The third symptom is if your ovaries have more follicles[2] than the norm or if your follicles measure larger than the norm. Either of these follicle differences can cause your body not to know when or how often to release an egg, leading to irregular periods and ovulation.

She did a transvaginal ultrasound[3] of my ovaries along with another round of blood tests. With the combination of my irregular period and the follicle count and sizes in my ovaries, she diagnosed me with PCOS. She told me that I could wait until my next period and then take a medication, Letrozole[4], which is supposed to induce ovulation.

Letrozole is taken day one through five of your period. I waited for a while, unknowing of when my next period would come. I got my period, August 2018, and I took the medication as instructed. I was shocked when I got a positive ovulation test two weeks after my period. I was even more shocked when I got another period after exactly 30 days. I remember feeling excited and relieved. The medication caused quite a bit of hair loss, but I didn't care. However, after two months, the medicine stopped working.

In December 2018, I made a follow-up appointment with the fertility specialist three months after our initial visit. She said I could try letrozole again whenever my period decided to show up again. She said the next steps were that I could get my fallopian tubes tested for blockage, his sperm tested, and try for IUI (intrauterine insemination)[5]. I met with their office's onsite billing specialist and estimated that we needed to save for about a year before we could afford something beyond letrozole. None of these services were covered by my insurance. It had been a year-and-a-half since I stopped taking birth control, and I was feeling very resentful at my body not working properly.

At this point in our journey, we waited.

The hardest part was not knowing when. I could have all the faith in the world, but faith didn't tell me when my dreams would come true. I dreamed daily of tiny little fingers and toes. I dreamed of my living room being a complete disaster with toys and spit-up rags everywhere. By dreaming, I mean that I tortured myself.

When someone else would announce they were pregnant, my eyes would fill with tears, and not from jealously. I felt empathetic to the news and would daydream about the day I find out that I am pregnant. If someone else complained about being a mom, I found myself feeling bitter because I wished I had their problems.

This level of pain was all-consuming. I spent many days holding back tears and having a pit in my stomach. Every day without a period was a reminder that my body wasn't functioning properly. This pain that left me completely out of control led me to lean into Jesus more than ever. I prayed daily to trust in God's timing and His plan. Realizing that it could be years before I had a baby, I started to pray to find joy in my current life circumstances even though it didn't give me my greatest desires. I prayed long and hard about being thankful for all of my blessings. I prayed that I wouldn't be miserable until I could conceive a baby. I would take pregnancy test after pregnancy test, telling myself not to get my hopes up. Each time would break my heart anyway. I would say to myself, "I know it's going to be negative, but I'll check just in case."

As a special little cherry on top, I got a new phone in December 2018, and the only piece of information that didn't transfer to the new phone was our ongoing list of baby names. Any reminder of my infertility stung. This felt like a stab to my dreams of our growing family.

My last period was December 8th, 2018. On January 13th, 2019, still without a period, I took a pregnancy test, and it was negative as I expected. I wanted to move on with my day to forget about it and just enjoy life. But I could not ignore that what I wanted the most in life was a baby, so there it stayed on my mind leaving me sad and hopeless, thinking, "Maybe in a year I'll get pregnant? Maybe two?"

While I laid in bed to fall asleep that night, I fell into prayer. I prayed again about trusting God's timing; about being joyful with what I had that day and the days to come. Those are all good prayers, prayers I had prayed for months. However, that night I felt a yearning for a baby right away and an urge to pray a different prayer, so instead of pushing those feelings away, I was reminded of a sermon I had heard some time ago. I remember a man preaching on the power God has and what it would look like if we truly trusted God to meet that level of power. Perhaps our greatest desires are His will, and maybe we should ask Him for exactly what we want; to be specific.

I figured it doesn't hurt to ask for exactly what I want. So, I changed it up, "Dear Jesus, please give me a baby this month. Please allow me to find out that I am pregnant in February. Jesus- you are all-powerful and if I don't believe that you have the power to allow me to be pregnant right away over what my body tells me I am capable of, then am I really trusting your power at all? Do I trust what you are capable of? Jesus... I WILL be pregnant next month, and there is nothing about me that isn't ready for a baby."

I stayed up a bit longer, in and out of prayer, thinking of all my stresses, what my goals were for the next day, etc., and I finally fell asleep.

I began dreaming. I saw blank spaces for a name like in the game "Hangman." I had to fill in the letters. How do I spell it? I started making guesses. V-Blank-R-Blank. Next guess: V-Blank-R-A? "yes," I know that's right somehow. Another guess. V-A?-R-A. "NO." Guess again. V-E?-R-A. "VERA," said loudly and audibly, and I shot awake suddenly, like I had been shaken. I heard God say the name Vera (Vair-uh) as clear as anything ever, and it was ringing in my ears. Somehow, I knew it was my daughter's name.

Wait, I didn't have a daughter, and I didn't really love this name. I guess I had never really considered this name. It wasn't on our list of baby names we had lost. I thought it over in my head, saying it over and over again, spelling it to myself. I tried to remember the name and specific spelling for later and fall back asleep, but I couldn't. It was sinking in that God just spoke to me for the first, and maybe only, time ever. I started to wake up more, and I realized just how vivid this dream was to me. "Vera," I think to myself, "but why Vera?" I found my phone in the dark and looked up Vera, which means faith or believe. I was shaken and confused. Joy started to bubble up inside that I could not contain. I was trying to understand and soak it all in.

I questioned myself, maybe my sanity, "Was this real? Did God speak to me so clearly that I can't deny it?" I remembered my prayer the night before; God was answering me... so clearly.

I couldn't sleep because I was so excited. I decided to take a shower, and I found myself weeping in the joy of God's promises to me. He knows the desires of our hearts, and He will provide... always. I was so thankful for his undeniable answers.

I was beside myself, and I couldn't believe it. I was having a baby... it was going to be a girl. I questioned if it would really be in February. God didn't say it would be in February, but I chose to believe it would happen in February anyway.

I held this information close to me. I didn't dare tell anyone that would doubt my experience because I didn't want anyone to ruin my joy. The friends that I did tell rejoiced with me. One friend even said that there was a time during my heartache when she was on her way to my house, and she heard God say to her, "She is coming."

Sometimes, I would doubt myself. There is always room for human error, "What if I am crazy and completely mistaken?" Then I would remind myself of the things I had learned in Sunday school about how we should have childlike faith. Or when I learned about those in the Bible that believed in Jesus and in His miracles were teased for telling others about it. These were both affirmations that I knew what I had dreamed and heard was real, and I needed not to doubt it.

I had been documenting my pregnancy tests and journey on Facebook with loved ones, but also through video. It was important to me to have these moments captured on video. I felt sure that I would get a positive pregnancy test one day, and I didn't want to miss or forget that moment. I took a test on January 21st, 2019, and it was negative. I got a urinary tract infection and had the doctor test my urine for pregnancy again on January 24th, and it was negative. On February 2nd, 2019, we were headed to my sister-in-law's birthday party, where I planned to have a cocktail. My husband ran to the store to go pick up some snacks, and I decided it would be best to take a pregnancy test to be sure I was ok to consume alcohol. It was positive.

I took another test. It was also positive. I remember the feeling like it just happened. My face turned fire hot, and I was holding my breath unintentionally in complete shock. I was in disbelief that a baby was actually growing inside of me; my child. I cried, I laughed, and I caught it all on video when I almost didn't record it at all this time because we were in a hurry to get going. I tried to collect myself for when my husband came home, and I got to tell him that we were going to have a baby. It was a beautiful moment that I also caught on video, and I will cherish it forever.

I had to get an ultrasound to know how far along the baby was. The first day of my last period was no indication of how pregnant I was. I was five weeks pregnant. It turns out that I just so happened to ovulate about four weeks later than the average woman's body would normally ovulate.

At her 20-week ultrasound, it was confirmed that she was a girl. We decided together to name our child, our daughter, Vera Love. She is now a thriving and happy toddler with all the personality, spunk, and independence of about five kids. I am forever grateful for this journey of faith and fertility, however painful it has been. I do not forget the emptiness I felt when I desired to have her. I do not take for granted that I have been blessed with a healthy child.

1. *Polycystic ovary syndrome:* a disorder involving infrequent, irregular, or prolonged menstrual periods, and often excess male hormone (androgen) levels. The ovaries develop numerous small collections of fluid- called follicles – and may fail to regularly release eggs.
2. *Follicle:* a spheroid cellular aggregation set found in the ovaries. It secretes hormones that influence stages of the menstrual cycle.
3. *Transvaginal ultrasound:* A medical ultrasonography that applies an ultrasound transducer in the vagina to visualize organs within the pelvic cavity.
4. *Letrozole:* Also known as Femara. Medication to promote ovulation and increase chances of natural conception.
5. *Intrauterine Insemination:* Sperm that have been washed and concentrated are placed directly in your uterus around the time your ovary releases one or more eggs to be fertilized.

HOLLY ADAMS

Holly Adams was born in Seattle, WA, and still resides nearby. She is a wife to a charismatic husband, mother to one wild little girl, and has hopes of growing a larger family. She has a passion for personally connecting with people, which led her to get her BA in Psychology. She is a Christian, and her relationship with God is important to her. Her fertility journey led her to be passionate about limiting the toxins we put into our bodies and chooses to sell clean beauty products in addition to her full-time job as an administrative assistant at a private school. She loves to hike, camp, get her nails done, drink coffee, and spend quality time with friends and family.

Email: hollykadams13@gmail.com
Instagram: @hollyyadams
Cleaner Beauty: www.beautycounter.com/HollyAdams

10

MY DIVINE INTERVENTION

MOM TO TWO AMAZING CHILDREN. FIANCE TO LIFE'S
GREATEST PARTNER. ENTREPRENEUR, LIFE COACH, EXERCISE
ENTHUSIAST. LOVER OF A GOOD LIFE & EVERYTHING IN
BETWEEN.

JACINTHE AUDREY BENSTRONG

I'm dedicating my First Chapter to My Daughter Klaryssah who made me a MOM!

I WAS 20 years old in nineteen ninety-nine. Young, athletic, and with a zest for life! After four years in a long-term relationship, I parted ways that summer with the person whom I thought was going to be the love of my life. Instead, that fall, while experimenting with online dating for the first time, a dare by my then girlfriends, I met the man that I would eventually marry and who would become the father of my children. But the journey to conceive wasn't that easy. I've always had a love for children and wanted one of my own someday... but that summer, everything changed.

Before meeting my husband that fall, I had noticed a change in my body. I was putting on the weight. Mind you, I had always been a solid one hundred and ten pounds of pure muscle. I was a Track and Field athlete. Running was my passion. Being competitive is what kept me going for a long time. I had a love of the sport. My fellow athletes rooting for each other. This was my family on the road. We had each other's back.

I was born on one of the smallest islands in the world, The Seychelles Island. I visited the United States pretty much every year since I was eight years old. I moved to Boston in 1995 permanently when my stepfather's contract with the US Tracking Station ended after ten years. We lived in Newton, an affluent community, and I got myself a good education. He was a mechanical engineer for NASA. He met my mother when I was four years old. I was the only daughter and had two older brothers. Sadly, my first brother died in nineteen-ninety-four from spinal meningitis and pneumonia. He was only twenty years old. My other brother, the middle child, was always the trouble maker. I was the good child, the only girl. I loved school and had lots of friends, and I was such a dreamer. I wanted to conquer the world. I always wanted to be a teacher because of the love the teachers showed to their students. It was MATERNAL. I helped take care of my little cousins on the island, and when I moved to the states, I immediately looked for babysitting jobs. I ended up taking care of my step-cousin and my neighbor's daughter. It was so rewarding!

In the fall of ninety-nine, my body completely changed on me. Somedays, I felt like I didn't recognize myself. I moved in with my then boyfriend and bought a treadmill, but I still felt something was going on in my body that I did not understand. I was always bloated around the time of my menstruation. Again, I thought this was completely normal after a while. I mean, I figured since I began my period at age nine that it was meant to be this way. It was always super heavy. I always had blood clots, headaches, backaches, nausea, fatigue. I was told that this was completely normal, and that was that.

By the time I was twenty years old, I wanted to find out more about a woman's body and the different changes women go through. In one year, I saw three different gynecologists, and all they did was give me different birth control pills and left with instructions to see them every three months. The pills never stopped my heavy bleeding, and all they did was make matters worse. I gained even more weight. That year I gained twenty pounds. I was eating healthy and exercising, but I thought the stress of a new job and new relationship was making me pack on the pounds. I really did not recognize myself. I felt bloated constantly! It was an uncomfortable feeling.

One morning I woke up with the sharpest pain in my stomach. I felt like somebody was stabbing me in the back. I was crying as I crawled to the bathroom. Yes, I LITERALLY CRAWLED TO THE BATHROOM! I've never felt *so* horrible in my life. I called my then boyfriend at work to come home right away because something was horribly wrong. Thank God he worked close by. He waited as I put on some clothes and shoes and drove me to the emergency room. Every pothole he hit on the way there made everything ten times worse. Whatever was going on inside me was NOT NORMAL at all. Once we arrived, I couldn't even walk, so a wheelchair was needed. The nurse wheeled me into a room right away after taking down all my information, and a young medical student came by to talk to me. I begged her not to touch me. She thought I was having a miscarriage because I told them that I hadn't seen my period in 6 months. I wasn't bleeding, but after an hour on IV fluid and medications to calm the pain, the doctor came in and did an internal exam and noticed a pus-like discharge. They sent me for an X-ray. The results were astounding to them. I had two grapefruit size cysts that had grown and ruptured on my right ovary. I ended up spending the night in the hospital for observation and was discharged the next day and told to stay in bed for the rest of the week.

That was the beginning of my infertility journey. By the time I was twenty-two, I was engaged and planning my wedding. I had gotten a new gynecologist who was treating me. Finally, I had gotten an answer regarding what was wrong with me. I was told I had endometriosis and polycystic ovarian syndrome (PCOS). I was sad when she let me know that my journey to conceive any children would be a very difficult one.

I had noticed that I was growing facial hair around my chin area, on my cheeks, and around my breasts. It was all due to my body having excess hormones. It was something that I had to get used to. Tweezing, shaving, and even laser removal were applied, but nothing worked to this day. Of course, it was a pain to deal with, but it became my pain and my mission. I did research. I changed my diet. I exercised. And I remained positive throughout. I honestly prayed a lot. I grew up Catholic, and prayers have been answered before, so I knew if God wanted me to have a family of my own, he was going to work some miracles.

But my journey to conceive wasn't going to be that easy! The year of my wedding, I turned 23. Yes, young to be married in 2002, but I already had a house, was working, planning my future, and babies were on my mind. Thinking I was young and fertile, I kept saying to myself. "If my grandmother, my mom, my aunts, and cousins were able to have children with no issues, I would be able to as well." But a few months before my wedding in August, I was at work and felt a weird pain in my stomach. I continued working thru the pain for the day. By the time I got home that evening, the pain was unbearable. I took a nice long, hot shower in hopes the pain would subside. I went to bed but was too uncomfortable to sleep. I took some medication to try and relieve the pain. I used what felt like twenty thousand pillows around me, slept on the couch, and walked around the house in the middle of the night, hoping the pain would go away. It had barely subsided by the time the sun came up. My fiancé was up getting ready for work, and he found me bawling in a fetal position, and all I said was, "I don't feel good, and something was happening in my stomach."

I went to the bathroom and noticed a discharge and a light smell. It was weird, and it scared me. I took a shower, dressed, and off to the emergency room we went. We waited for a while, and the pain was unbearable then. When I finally was wheeled into a room, they asked the necessary questions, put IV fluid in, and when the doctor came to see me, I was a total mess. The doctor looked at my chart and took my temperature, which was spiking because there was an infection somewhere. By the time he sent me for an X-ray, the pain was slowly subsiding. Gotta love Morphine!! When the results came back, it didn't look good. Both my ovaries had gotten worse, the cysts came back, and had ruptured....AGAIN!! I spent the next three days in the hospital, slowly recovering. The doctor suggested (while I was recovering) that I should find an Endocrinologist in order to "take care of those infected ovaries of yours." I was put on antibiotics for seven days.

I was nervous about sex for quite some time after that because it would hurt, but I didn't say anything to my husband in the time leading up to my marriage that August. So the honeymoon was a blurrr... oh well! Every month the bleeding would be worse, though. With lots of clots and super heavy periods, I went through multiple pads during the day. Tampons got uncomfortable, and then I was told by my gynecologist not to wear them until I saw the endocrinologist. I did more research to find out who was available to see me, but appointments were too far away. I didn't give up. My Faith in God was all I needed.

My maternal grandmother from Seychelles passed away in October 2002, literally months after my wedding. I grew up with my grandmother and we had a very close bond. It was the saddest and hardest time of my life. I know she's my guardian angel as well and I prayed for her guidance throughout my infertility journey.

February 2003 was one of the coldest winter months. I had gone into work on Saturday to finish some projects we were behind on, and my boss asked me to come in by 10am on Monday morning instead of 8am. It was delightful to sleep in a bit on a Monday morning and not to rush to catch the bus for work. I lived in Somerville and worked in Cambridge (the next town over), but by 7am that morning, I heard a loud bang. We had a two-family house, and my mother-in-law lived upstairs from us. My husband had already left for work since he had to be in by 6am. I listened, and I didn't hear any movements or other sounds. I had a gut feeling that something wasn't right. I got out of bed, put my robe on, and marched upstairs. I went through the back, called my mother-in-law's name, and I didn't receive an answer. I looked around the house, and I found her barely breathing and sitting on the toilet. I pulled her lifeless body on the floor and performed CPR. I called my husband at work and 911 right after. Within minutes the paramedics were at my door, and my husband followed. Curious neighbors stopped by, and sadness filled the air because it didn't look good. My mother-in-law had suffered a massive heart attack. She was transported to the nearest hospital, where she stayed for three days as medical personnel checked for any signs of brain activity. We pulled the plug and said our last goodbyes that very cold frigid sad February morning. She was only seventy-five years old.

Emotions were everywhere and extremely high for a long while now and I desperately needed a break and some good news.

When we got married in August, her only wish was that I came back pregnant from our honeymoon, and she would like a granddaughter. Well, her wish didn't come true right away. When we cleaned out her house, we found bags of new baby girl's clothing. Lots of clothes, still with tags! It looks like she desperately wanted that granddaughter, and part of me was incredibly sad because she wouldn't be able to hold and spoil her grandchildren in person, but I know she will always be with them in spirit. At her funeral, a good friend of mine who had just given birth to twins months prior asked me how I was feeling, etc. She mentioned the endocrinologist that helped her conceive her twins via IVF because she went through infertility as well. I took down the information and waited a week after the funeral to call. I was anxious the whole time. My emotions were everywhere, but I had Faith because I knew that my mother-in-law was looking down on us and sending us blessings. I got lucky, and an appointment was set up for the following week. I was nervous, elated, scared, happy, and hopefully would have some answers.

My husband took the day off to go with me to the hospital. When we met the endocrinologist, he was warm, kind, and, mind you, very attractive. Mmmmm! He read my file from the hospital. He examined me and sent me to get more X-rays. When he came back in, he said, "I've got some news, and you've got some decisions to make." If you're trying to get pregnant, it will not come easily but you do have some options. I can put you on some new birth control pills, we can have surgery to remove the cysts that keep on growing, we can remove your ovaries, and you will go through early onset menopause, or we do nothing and watch what happens in the next few months." My answer was, "let's do surgery to remove the cysts." An appointment was set up for surgery in a month's time. I felt hopeful that finally, something was going to be done to make me feel so much better.

The morning of the surgery, I was nervous and scared. But everything went beautifully. The doctor removed fifteen golf-ball-sized cysts from my ovaries. He showed me the pictures afterward. I was sent home that afternoon to recover for the next week and to come back and see him within three weeks. Another appointment was set, and I was looking forward to the next steps. It felt like a weight had been lifted, and I could see the light at the end of the tunnel. The week after the surgery was a hard recovery, but I made it through and felt so much more confident.

At my next appointment, the doctor checked to see if I was pretty much all healed up, and sure I was indeed. He wanted me to try to get pregnant on my own for the first three months after surgery. Of course, hubby and I got busy. We were like rabbits or dogs in heat. But nothing happened at all. I tried not to be disappointed, so we went for the next plan. INSEMINATION. Our insurance only covered three months of treatment. I was given Follistim to boost my hormones and really work my ovaries into overdrive. It was a wild ride. I had to give myself a shot in the leg every night, as my husband was too chicken to do so. Thank God I was brave enough and had some firm muscles from walking and running all those years! Every morning I would go to the hospital for blood work and an ultrasound. That was exciting!! NOT!! I had to be there at exactly 6am every morning because that is when your hormone level is at its peak. The nurses were always excited when the eggs in the ovaries were right and plump and ready for the sperm, but that didn't happen that cycle. The second month we tried again. Hubby went to give his sperm sample (he had millions of live sperm), thanks to my wonderful "quickie" I gave him in the "Adult Room". We had a bit of fun... I mean, why not...hahaha!! But I was all business to tell you the truth.

One Wednesday afternoon, we were driving home from running errands, and the doctor's office called, and the nurse said, "whatever you do today, DO NOT HAVE ANY INTERCOURSE! DO YOU HEAR ME?? YOU HAVE GOT FIVE VERY RIPE EGGS READY TO GO, AND IF YOU HAVE ANY SEX, YOU WILL END UP WITH MULTIPLE BABIES! You're petite. Your body cannot handle that, so we have to let you bleed and get rid of those eggs for this month." All I could do was laugh, and then I cried but then got anxious just thinking about my belly with five growing babies. I think I had a little anxiety/panic attack!

The third month the doctor asked me to come in the last minute on a Sunday morning to get inseminated because the eggs looked good to go, AGAIN! Mind you, we had tickets to go see the New England Patriots play, but I bypassed the game and sent my mother, stepfather, and my husband. I didn't ask anybody else to go with me to the hospital, so I went by myself. I was inseminated with my legs in stirrups for a few hours. I fell asleep while waiting for the sperm to make its way to my ovary. It only takes one, right? I found my way home that afternoon and just relaxed. I was trying to stay focused on other things like Lifetime movies, hahaha! But the next morning, I woke up and felt a very sharp pain. I called the doctor's office, and they told me to take some Advil and use a heating pad for the day and night. The pain eventually went away, and I didn't think of anything else. By the end of that cycle, I had gotten my period. The three months were up. We would have to wait for a few months down the road to try for IVF.

One day, I said to my husband, "That's it. I'm done for now. My body needs some rest from all the medications, stress, and everything else I was going through just to get pregnant." We both agreed to give it a rest and focus on other things. If it was meant for us to have a baby, then the Good Lord knows what he needed to do. I never stopped praying that someday somehow, it would happen. I started looking into adoption and fostering. I had that much love for children

My girlfriend, who had referred me to the endocrinologist in Boston, asked me to help her out with her twins on the weekends so she could get errands done. I had gotten extremely emotional at every visit with them. A few months later, after taking the twins for a nice long walk in the stroller by Revere Beach, I came back and literally fell asleep on the couch next to them. When I woke up, I was starving, exhausted, and felt different. My girlfriend said to buy a pregnancy test on my way home. She said, "I know you've been disappointed, but you just never know. Take the test tomorrow morning and call me."

We didn't buy the test until Sunday morning, and I didn't use it until the Wednesday after Christmas because I didn't want to get my hopes up. That Sunday was my step grandmother's birthday celebration in Plymouth. I had purchased a really cute outfit to wear, but when I tried it on, it just didn't look right

or fit properly. I felt super bloated. I thought it was just my period coming, so I didn't think twice about it. For Christmas dinner, my mother had asked me what I would like for the meal. I said I was craving something different from the norm. We went to dinner, and I literally played around with my food. My favorite wine I added sprite to it because my mouth tasted funny. Nothing looked appealing to me, and mind you, my mother is an AMAZING COOK!! She looked at me and said, "you're pregnant." I just laughed. I said, "you're funny! We've tried it all, and nothing is happening, so we are leaving it in God's hands for now."

Well, that Wednesday, I still felt weird. I took a pregnancy test (two of them), and they were positive, but I didn't want to believe it. I called the doctor's office that same morning, and they asked me to come in for some blood work. We went in, did blood work, and went on our merry way. Around one fifteen in the afternoon, we met up with a friend for lunch and a movie. Right before the movie started, the phone rang, and it was the doctor's office. It was the same familiar voice of my nurse, she said, " I hope you're sitting down for this because I've got wonderful news for you both. You're not just pregnant...YOU'VE BEEN PREGNANT! Your HCG level is through the roof. I'm going to set up an ultrasound appointment for you so we can see how far along you are. I sat down and starting crying and then laughing. I wanted to shout at the top of my lungs and call everybody with the awesome news. I had no idea how far along I was.

My ultrasound appointment was very exciting indeed! I got to see my baby, who was already formed. I was at the end of my first trimester, and I was in disbelief. Here was my baby, waving and looking over at her momma. We found out at eighteen weeks that it was a girl. My Guardian Angels, my grandmother as well as my mother-in-law, were praying and watching over us the whole time. Oh, what a blessing it was! I had such an easy pregnancy. I enjoyed watching my belly grow, her kicks, the sciatica pain (not!), the energy I had with her. I walked daily up hills, the glowing skin, the thick luscious hair growth! She was worth it! She was born on August 14th, 2004, the morning of my cousin's wedding. She came two days before her due date, exactly forty weeks. Six hours of labor, one push, and because it was a full moon and so many babies were being born that same day, my doctor said, " don't push! I'll be right back". The nurse put a full body mirror in front of me, and as she turned her back, I said, " Um, I think she's coming out." I knew I wasn't doing anything, but this girl of mine LITERALLY PUSHED HERSELF OUT OF MY WOMB!!!! Everybody stood there in shock, and the doctor came back and said, "what happened?" The nurse looked at her and said," I guess this little lady couldn't wait any longer to enter the world." She didn't cry right away because she had inhaled some meconium going through the birth canal, but before we knew it, my six-pound, two-ounce, and eighteen and a half inches long baby girl was healthy and with a set of lungs that would wake the dead was born at 10:47am!

Today I celebrate her. She's fiercely strong, independent, bossy, opinionated, incredibly smart, and, at almost seventeen years old and a Junior in high school, got her first job. She's looking at colleges, in the National Honors Society, President of the Black Student Union, got her first scholarships, a Track and Field Star, a Leader and an ABSOLUTE AMAZING HUMAN BEING I HAVE CREATED AND BEYOND PROUD OF! MY FIRST BLESSING!!!!!!

JACINTHE AUDREY BENSTRONG

Jacinthe lives in Framingham Massachusetts, a suburb of Boston with her two children (Klaryssah 16 & Danté 11) & her fiancé Jeff. She has traveled to many parts of the world & visited many US States! She speaks 6 languages (3 are her native tongue) as she's originally from the beautiful Exotic island of Seychelles in the Indian Ocean!

She enjoys traveling, hiking, movies, the beach, exercising with her Mama friends, a beautiful sunset & sunrise, spending quality time with her fiancé, family & friends & loves to entertain with dinner parties with lots of dancing! She has a Positive Outgoing Personality, Infectious Smile, friendly demeanor & is a Go-Getter in everything she puts her mind to!

Jacinthe plays a big part in Advocating for Children in the Commonwealth of Massachusetts! You can find her on the Massachusetts PTA, Antiracism Committees, Fundraising Committees just to name a few! She's a very busy mom who makes sure to involve her children in Volunteerism especially at their schools & in their community!

Jacinthe is an International Best-Selling Author with her #1 Book "(In)Fertility: Secrets, Struggles, and Successes" which reached #1 on Amazon in 13 U.S. categories, #1 in 4 Canadian categories, and #1 in 1 Australian category. The book is one of the Top 60 books sold in Canada and Top 252 books sold in the U.S. !!!!

Her motto: "Life is too short...Live Your Every Minute to the Fullest & don't forget to smile, Give Back & Pay Forward " & " It's the little moments that lasts a Lifetime "

Facebook: @Jacinthe Audrey
Instagram: @Jacintheaudreybenstrong

11

A MOTHER NEVER FORGETS

JANELLE LARA

"I don't think I'm meant to have more children... I just don't know how long I can keep doing this."

One quiet evening, I shared this news sadly with my husband. Just months before, we were ecstatically calling family members and sharing our happy news. And then, slowly but surely, one, two, and three early-term miscarriages followed one after another. Our dreams for a large family were, quite literally, going down the drain.

As a teenager, I always said I wanted six children. Knowing mothers laughed, and after I had my first, we narrowed it down to a modest four. But at that moment, one felt like all I would ever be given. It was a huge blessing, and of course, there was eons of guilt ("isn't she enough?"), but the fact is, we wanted more.

From May- November 2020, I was either pregnant or recovering from a miscarriage. And it was hard. Hard on my body, hard on my soul, and hard on my heart.

Ten years earlier, my mother, who had successfully delivered four children over the course of 14 years (and miscarried one), discovered that she suffered from a sub-clinical condition called adrenal fatigue. Within this discovery, she realized that she was low in several vital hormones. This is an issue that affects many, many women.

At the age of 24, well before I was old enough to think about testing for such things, my future husband and I took a class on Natural Family Planning called The Creighton Model. Because of our Catholic faith, we chose to use NFP in lieu of birth control and figured we'd better start to figure it out early if we didn't want to end up with dozens of kids. The Creighton Model (CrM)[1] is a natural method of family planning based on a woman's observations of her cervical fluid or mucus. (FactsAboutFertility.org*) A woman can use observations of her cervical fluid to identify the fertile and infertile times of her cycle. By observing these changes, couples can decide when to have sexual relations, depending on whether they are trying to achieve or avoid pregnancy. This method is equally as or more effective than other methods of birth control and is much, much safer for the woman than hormonal birth controls. Finally, it is successful at helping women identify conditions such as PCOS, hormonal imbalances, and failure to ovulate well before conception is the goal.

My future husband and I chose to practice The Creighton Model for the reasons listed above, but little did we know that later, The Creighton Model would actually help us solve an opposite problem... the inability to keep a child in utero.

After charting for the requested 30 days, my practitioner immediately noticed an issue. "Based on your vaginal excretions, you are low in progesterone. This could be caused by PCOS or something else, but if you were ever to get pregnant, we'd need to put you on progesterone right away."

Of course, being so young and in an abstinent relationship, I quickly brushed off the issue. Pregnancy was years away.

Just after getting married, I chose to leave an abusive work situation. While the choice was certainly best for my mental health, it was not good for our finances. My husband and I found ourselves at the poverty income level, and I could not find another teaching job. So, I decided to start a tutoring company. Immediately I got clients and was able to start (modestly) supplementing our income.

Shortly after, my husband and I were invited on an all-expenses paid trip to Cuba by his brother. Though we were still avoiding pregnancy, the Cuban rum took its toll, and we joyfully conceived our first daughter.

Our practitioner immediately put us on injectable progesterone. My husband and I weren't certain of its need, because again, I had never tested low for progesterone. The Physician at the clinic simply knew I was based on my cervical mucus. But of course, we did it anyway. Now, I realize that this Practitioner and this method brings us back to when health was intuitive, and the "healers" were those who could observe and listen to the body with keen accuracy.

As a result of her talent and attention, I had the perfect pregnancy and delivery, and at 41 weeks and five days, I gave birth to our beautiful 7lb. 11oz daughter, Adelaide Marie.

Because everything had gone so well, my husband and I didn't even think about what we might need for a second pregnancy. All I knew is that I wanted to wait a while. I was not ready to get pregnant again soon after having our daughter Adelaide. I breastfed her for two years and, in the meantime, took the business expertise I had learned building a successful tutoring company (and later a styling company) and built a multi-six figure per year company teaching women how to build a six-figure business online while working less than 20 hours per week. In doing so, I transformed our living situation financially and was able to be the stay-at-home Mom I always wanted to be. In May 2020, I finally felt that I was ready to try for our second.

Immediately, I conceived our second child, and I instinctively knew that it was another girl. We were overjoyed, and I excitedly surprised my husband with the news, and we quickly told our friends and family.

I thought about contacting our previous doctor who had prescribed the progesterone, but since we had moved from Florida to Utah, it was just something that stayed on the back burner. What could possibly go wrong? I had a perfect pregnancy last time. I just knew I was made to have babies.

However, I quickly started experiencing cramping, which I attributed to regular pregnancy symptoms. When the light spotting started, I brushed it off. However, just four days after I had made the big announcement to friends and family, the bleeding got stronger. I went alone to the hospital while my husband took care of our daughter.

There I was informed that I was having a miscarriage. I couldn't believe it but instinctively remembered the progesterone. I texted our Florida doctor, but it was too late. This pregnancy was gone.

The first cut is truly the deepest. I cried for days and felt so responsible. I knew I needed progesterone in the last pregnancy. Why didn't I request it sooner? Days earlier, we had also lost a bid on a house I desperately wanted, and coupled with the awful energy of 2020, I felt broken.

Immediately, I had a meeting with the Florida doctor, who referred me to a local doctor who was also a practitioner of the Creighton Model. He did a few tests and immediately prescribed me with both encapsulated and injectable progesterone. I was instructed to start taking the capsules daily after seeing a positive pregnancy test.

The problem was, after that first miscarriage, I would often lose babies even before I could get a positive test. I would know I was pregnant due to sore breasts, bloating, frequent urination, etc., but then would get a negative test and get my period a few days later. Some clinicians wrote it off as my body trying to get back to normal hormonally, but I knew better. Even when I did get a positive test (which I did for 2), it was too late. The dose of progesterone I was taking was not enough to be effective. I finally found the pregnancy test brand that would catch the pregnancies the quickest, and we finally figured out the right dose of progesterone, but by then, I was pregnant with my fourth child that year.

The Root Cause

I wanted to discover the root cause of my lack of progesterone. I was negative for PCOS, but the doctor I was seeing did not test for subclinical issues. So I found a Naturopathic Physician in Salt Lake who ran a full blood and gut panel. I finally felt like I had found a missing piece of the puzzle. Every other doctor had tried to find out specifically what was going on with my fertility and treated my ovaries like they were separate from the rest of my body. This doctor looked at my entire body holistically and knew that if my hormones were off and it wasn't anything wrong with my ovaries, then there was another reason. She was determined to find it. Shortly after taking those tests, I was diagnosed with a subclinical thyroid disorder and a gut issue. This also helped explain the 25 pounds I couldn't lose postpartum.

The Importance of Advocating for Yourself

Throughout this entire process, I realized how strongly I had to advocate for myself and for what I wanted. While I had an amazing team, it was a huge sacrifice to go to dozens of appointments, get my blood drawn countless times, do other alternative therapies (such as acupuncture), and almost all of it was self-pay.

I became *so* much more grateful for the company I had built, which gave me three full days off during the week and an ample income with which to see these specialists. I shudder to think of how many more babies I would have lost had I not had the resources of time, money, and my education available to me so that I could seek out those who could help and understand what they were saying.

After three miscarriages total, my husband and I decided to stop trying. I needed to get my hormones in order, I couldn't keep doing this to my body, and it was affecting my mental health. The roller coaster of getting a positive pregnancy test, only to start profusely bleeding a few days later, was too much.

However, I was now taking a thyroid medication, which made me much more fertile because it supported my body in the production of hormones needed to regulate my ovulation. It also changed my fertile signs in my charting. Confused about when I was fertile, I got pregnant yet again. I saw the positive pregnancy test on December 8th. Fortunately, we were about to go to Florida to see my family for the holidays.

My mother always said that Dr. Gramlich (my original Creighton Model doctor in Florida) saved Adelaide's life when she put me on progesterone so early in my first pregnancy. I was grateful to have found out we were pregnant when we did, just in time to pack the progesterone we had and make an appointment with Dr. Gramlich as soon as we landed. She immediately sent me to get labs done and had a prescription ready for more progesterone when I got there.

We were aggressive. I took 1600mg of progesterone/ week. That's one 200mg tablet once a day and a 100mg injection twice a week. Despite these precautions, I had no hope. I told friends and family that I was sure I would miscarry. A dear friend of mine said over dinner, "I don't know Janelle, I have a good feeling about this one." I didn't believe her.

However, slowly but surely, days and weeks went by with no blood. I remember at one point, the cramping was so bad I was sure I was miscarrying, and I even took another pregnancy test just to be sure. For the first time, my husband Roberto and I finally had the correct progesterone dosage, and we were religious about the schedule. One day, we realized we were running out of the progesterone and called the pharmacy near us. They chose to wait until late evening to let us know they did not, in fact, have the liquid progesterone we needed... but I required that injection that same evening. I frantically called Roberto. He left his brother and cousin at a restaurant and drove to a pharmacy across town at 9 pm because that was the only pharmacy that had the injectable progesterone... in the whole county! He arrived less than ten minutes before they closed, only to come home and realize they had given us the wrong needles! My sweet husband felt awful. I took a progesterone tablet that night and prayed. The following day we went to The St. Gianna Center in St. Petersburg, Fl, where Dr. Gramlich practices, and she gave us the correct needle size. While we consistently felt like we had to jump through crazy hoops just to keep this baby alive, it was so, so worthwhile.

As I am typing this, I am 22 weeks pregnant with our fifth child, another daughter. Due to our spirituality, I believe that each pregnancy created a unique and perfect soul and that we have three (maybe more!) sweet angels waiting for us in heaven, watching over us and doing God's work. It's a beautiful thought, and I can't wait to be reunited one day. Plus, after what happened in our world last year, I imagine those sweet souls are much happier in heaven than they would be here!

We still have a long way to go, but thankfully, everything with this pregnancy looks healthy and perfect. I am continuing to take 1600mgs of progesterone/ week. Every two weeks, I get my progesterone levels tested. When my Doctor tried to reduce the progesterone, we had a scare where my progesterone levels dropped dangerously low. So, despite being so far along, I still take the tablets daily, and my husband gives me the injections twice a week. Progesterone causes headaches, tiredness, and the needles can really only get injected into two places on my body, so those prime spots have begun to develop scar tissue which makes the injections more painful each time. However, it is completely worthwhile and just one of the many small sacrifices every mother makes for her children. Hopefully, before the next pregnancy, we will be able to solve the root issue of my low progesterone levels so that we won't have to do this again.

I feel so grateful for the gift of this pregnancy, and it is not lost on me how fragile life is. Skipping or forgetting a few doses is not an option for me. My medical team is incredible. The way they monitor my labs, communicate with me and have worked together with me to ensure a healthy pregnancy brings tears to my eyes.

The problem is, these types of practitioners are not typical. They are often seen as being on the outskirts of medicine, and using Natural Family Planning to recognize a progesterone deficiency without a blood test is something *very* few practitioners can even do. I had a friend who wanted to get progesterone tests done by a traditional practitioner and was told they don't do those tests until someone has had THREE miscarriages! I simply cannot imagine that lack of support and consideration for a woman's life, children, and well-being.

As women, we cannot expect others to advocate for us. We must advocate for ourselves and seek alternative solutions when traditional medicine fails. I am so grateful for my business, which allowed me to self-pay, go to countless appointments, and gave me time to do research, see doctors, etc. However, there are many free or cheap options as well. In Florida, The St. Gianna Center[2] (where Dr. Gramlich works) is a charity. When we were at the poverty level, we simply paid what we could. They never reduced the quality of care based on our inability to pay. I highly recommend googling or searching Catholic Charities Foundational Services* or other organizations that offer this quality of care, almost free of charge. There are links in the resources section of this chapter as well.

Moving Forward

My husband and I still want to heal the root cause of my low progesterone. I also want to heal my thyroid and my gut. I do not want to be on hormone replacement therapy forever. However, now that I am pregnant, I am allowing the medicine to work its magic and keep my baby alive. After I'm done breastfeeding this child, we will start the process all over, get my labs done, and see where we need to go from there.

Though I am ecstatic to be pregnant with a healthy baby, that does not replace the loss of my other children. For me, it was important to commemorate the losses. I named each child and acknowledge their due dates as they come. I have had my children come to me during prayer and meditation, and I thank God for the gift of being able to participate in the co-creation of these beautiful souls, regardless of his plan for them. I have a box for the children, where I saved the positive pregnancy tests, and little trinkets, cards our friends sent us after our losses, a painting I bought to commemorate them, and a letter I wrote to the baby after our first loss. That is how I processed, and that is how I have chosen to start my healing journey.[34]

A mother never forgets.

1. https://www.factsaboutfertility.org/wp-content/uploads/2014/09/CreightonPEH.pdf
2. https://www.stgiannacenter.com/
3. https://www.catholiccharitiesusa.org/our-vision-and-ministry/foundational-services/
4. https://www.factsaboutfertility.org/about/

JANELLE LARA

Janelle Lara is the CEO and Founder of The Part-Time CEO®. A former Teacher and School Administrator, she is now a Mother, International Best-Selling Author, Cutting- Edge Business Strategist, Podcast Host, and Guide to Six-Figure CEO's worldwide. With thousands of podcast downloads, multiple six-figures in annual sales and dozens of successful clients, Janelle is the original spokesperson for the six-figure, part-time lifestyle. Not even 30, Janelle has cracked the code to working less and making more, and she shares this code with her clients and community. Most importantly, Janelle is a wife and stay-at-home mother to two. Janelle has been featured on ABC, FOX, TaskShift and CEO Blog Nation, as well as dozens of podcasts. She is proud of her partnership with The Exodus Road, an organization that puts boots on the ground to rescue victims of sex-trafficking.

Website: http://janellelara.com

Email: janelle@janellelara.com

Podcast: The Part-Time CEO® Podcast

Facebook: http://facebook.com/janellemarie6

Facebook Group: http://makemeaparttimeceo.com

Instagram: http://instagram.com/theparttimeceopodcast

12

WHAT THE BLEEP DOES AN ENERGY HEALER KNOW ABOUT FERTILITY?!

JENNIFER LYONS, MSW: INTUITIVE COUNSELOR AND THETA HEALER

I KNOW energy healing may be something you weren't prepared to see in a collaborative project regarding fertility. You may be thinking, 'what is this woo woo?!' (And if you were, in fact, thinking that, then I just read your mind- so 1 point energy healer!)

I'm a natural skeptic myself, so I don't blame you if you're feeling some doubt about learning about and potentially adding yet another treatment or method into your journey; I promise, though, that if you stick with me and have an open mind and heart, I can lay out the most grounded and practical outline of what energy medicine can do for you physically, emotionally, and spiritually as you navigate your fertility journey. Some of my most loyal and enthralled clients start out with some apprehension and doubt, but they come in with their hearts and minds open. A client of mine came to me at the suggestion of her acupuncturist. She had no idea what energy healing was and was hesitant but was desperate to try anything to help her situation. In her first session, it was revealed that she was carrying past sexual trauma in her body that was signaling to her subconscious that sexuality and pregnancy were not safe for her. In essence, her subconscious was reliving her trauma in a loop, and in turn, her ability to achieve pregnancy was frozen. We slowly worked together to release the accumulated stress that was stored in her body. After five months of working together, she became pregnant (After four years of trying). She said she "isn't sure what exactly happened, but I do know I felt different and lighter after starting energy healing."

If you're someone who is already familiar with energy healing, awesome! I hope you are able to glean something from this as well. At the very least, it is a reminder of how life-altering and beneficial it can be, and it's a gentle nudge to continue with this type of self-care to continue to enhance your health and well-being.

WHO AM I AND WHY SHOULD YOU LISTEN TO ME?

You don't know me from Joe, so it might be a good idea to introduce myself. For all you know, I could live in a Himalayan salt cave, live on nothing but oxygen and green juice, and have my own cult that I am trying to recruit you into. Fortunately, (or unfortunately?) I am a relatively normal mom of 2 based in San Diego who eats too much chocolate and likes to take naps when I can sneak away.

I graduated with my Master's degree in Social Work in 2009 and worked in the healthcare field for close to a decade, but the work never felt fulfilling or even particularly helpful. I was bogged down by bureaucracy and paperwork, and the evidence-based modalities for therapy seemed slow and not always effective. I felt like there had to be something more. I was subsequently drawn to energy work and had what can only be described as a spiritual awakening. In the simplest terms possible, this awakening illuminated that there is more to life than just the tangible and material. I became interested in "alternative" healing modalities to complement my clinical background and became a Reiki master in 2013. My Reiki Master teacher also had a background in Social Work and was a Theta healing practitioner. I had never heard of Theta healing but decided to try it on instinct. My first session blew my mind. It was like therapy, yet it cut right to the subconscious core of long-held issues. I didn't have to delve into my childhood, my relationships, what I ate for breakfast that day. She tapped into things that were deeply buried, yet I intuitively felt the truth in what she said. I could also *feel* the effects of her working in my energy field. I felt calm, grounded, and hopeful after our session. I asked her where she learned the method because I instantly knew it was what I wanted to do for a living. I took the beginner and advanced courses and started providing sessions part-time, then shifted into doing this work full-time in 2019. I love energy work. LOVE it. It has been pivotal in my personal healing journey. It helped me shift from unconscious, defended, and neurotic to the core to a softer, more open-hearted, healthier me. It revealed who I truly am under trauma and pain and wounding. It has provided me more effective tools to navigate being human and has softened me to an intermittent neurotic who views her triggers and defenses as opportunities to heal and unwind from past conditioning. It has given me an entirely new life and perspective on the world. I feel deep gratitude that I am able to share this gift with others. I hope to share it with you, and I hope I am able to do it justice.

WHAT IS ENERGY HEALING?

Everything is energy. Anxiety and fear are energies first experienced in our nervous system then interpreted by our brains. Our thoughts, beliefs, and perceptions are at their core energetic in nature as well. We can't touch or hold onto a thought. We can't grab our anxiety and pull it out of our body with our hands (although that would be quite the relief, wouldn't it?). When unprocessed, our fear and stress show up as pain, panic, ailments, and eventually disease in the body. Energy healing is a broad term that encompasses a wide array of modalities, techniques, and philosophies. For simplicity, I will stay in my own lane and discuss the work I do with Theta and Reiki healing from my personal philosophical standpoint.

So, a quick overview.

Conscious mind: Our endless stream of thoughts and narrative about life. Our preferences, opinions, etc. For ease, we will herein refer to this as "the monkey mind" because it has a tendency to go off the rails, tell us stories that aren't true, and sometimes it likes to throw whatever poop it can find to see what sticks. (I.e., why even bother, I'm not good enough, etc. - the unhelpful thoughts we all have)

Subconscious mind: Runs our nervous system and bodily functions. Implicit memories, sensations, and fragmented beliefs and energies are also stored here. In this context, 'fragmented' refers to energies and traumas we weren't able to process in real time or beliefs and ideas we internalized without awareness due to them being deeply embedded in our culture or elsewhere in our environment from birth on. It also contains the root or foundation of belief systems that we implicitly hold that may be blocking our ability to heal, grow, and move forward. Our subconscious basically runs the show, and we don't even know what the heck is lurking there the majority of the time. While we fumble around trying to navigate the monkey mind of the conscious brain, our subconscious pumps our blood, beats our heart, breathes our breath, and potentially creates and sustains new life.

Theta healing circumvents the monkey mind and directly engages with our subconscious and nervous system. From this level of awareness, we are able to delve into imbalances, distortions, and wounds below the surface that prevent us from thriving, healing, and living in wholeness. We connect with these wounds first on an energetic level and illuminate them at a conscious level to enable deep and profound healing and energetic release. A client of mine had a very active monkey mind. She and her husband had been trying to conceive for two years. They had performed all the standard tests and procedures that determined there was no identifiable reason behind her difficulty getting pregnant. By her third session, we had discovered a core fear of happiness with accompanying beliefs that she didn't deserve to be happy, she didn't deserve a happy family, and that it would all be taken away from her if she had a child. Her monkey mind was running programs deeply embedded in her subconscious mind that she didn't deserve happiness and stability. We worked to release that fear and those beliefs and replace them with more productive ones. I didn't see her again for eight months, but when I did, she was five months pregnant and attributed the healing from our sessions as playing a huge role. Now you might be wondering how the heck you release beliefs and just replace them with new ones. This is where you have to trust in something bigger than you and a little bit of magic.

Theta healing utilizes its namesake brainwave to access a deep level of consciousness. This theta brainwave is that of meditation, visualization, and transformation. It is the brainwave of universal consciousness and deep spiritual connection. When a Theta healer taps into this brainwave with purpose and intention, it creates change at a profound energetic level. This brainwave allows us to connect to source, God, spirit, higher consciousness, or whatever term feels most comfortable for you. The label is just semantics, but the key is that the Theta healer is connecting to the most powerful energy in the universe to heal you. Their role is facilitator and witness. The healing is between your soul and divine intelligence, and the healer is lucky enough to be able to channel what is ready to be processed and released. The healer develops the use of their "clair" senses (in addition to our five major kinesthetic senses). They receive visions, downloads, and hear information that they then process through their unique lens to facilitate the healing.

If the God thing has put you off or shut you down, I understand. Theta healing is not religious in nature, but there are spiritual beliefs that accompany it. You do not need to have the same beliefs or even any belief to benefit. I mean, obviously, if you feel repelled, I would trust that. It may not be the right modality for you at this time. But if you have some interest that retracted a bit when I mentioned a higher power, don't sweat it. You truly only need an open mind and an interest in the possibilities. The rest can be as important or unimportant as you want. The only important thing is the potential for healing transformation. So please, don't throw the baby out with the bathwater. Or the energy healing out with the mention of a higher consciousness.

Reiki is the nice and mellow companion to Theta Healing. Reiki energy is soothing, like a warm hug. It is a lovely accompaniment to Theta work and helps ground the changes into your body. Reiki is mellow and allows the energy moved from Theta healing to leave your body with more ease. It grounds and relaxes. The premise is the same as Theta healing. The practitioner is tapping into a greater source of energy and channeling it to you. This modality is passed via an attunement from teacher to student. The teacher "attunes" the student to the energy, which then allows the practitioner to channel healing energy through their hands or through their intention and ritual with distant work. In distant healing, it is received however your body, mind, and spirit will best utilize it.

If energy healing isn't amazing enough already, it also gets bonus points for being effective across time and space. We don't even have to be in the same state or country, for that matter, for us to connect and for you to receive the gifts of this wonderful work. I have several clients whom I have not yet had the pleasure of meeting in person. One of them had received several unsuccessful embryo transfers and was feeling hopeless and exhausted. She also experienced chronic hip and back pain. We worked together for a year to unpack childhood traumas and patterns and to process her feelings about her fertility journey and its highs and lows. Her physical pain gradually became less acute and more manageable; she started to go several days without experiencing any. She got pregnant a year after we met.

While energy work was not an instant miracle, she states it helped her to feel healthier and more stable and to help her feel more emotionally prepared for the ups and downs of her journey and her life in general. All of this from the comfort of her home and zoom. Pretty amazing.

HOW CAN IT HELP ME?

Maybe at this point, it all sounds interesting to you but still not quite tangible or practical, and you're still unsure what this has to do with fertility. Or maybe I've already converted you, but you're dying to read more of this brilliant chapter anyway because you're enjoying yourself so much.

"Get to the point, Jennifer! How can this help me?"

Ok, ok! Remember I laid out the premise that our subconscious basically runs the show, and it is in direct control of the body processes responsible for conceiving and sustaining pregnancy? I hope you remember, otherwise I should've done a better job editing.

Anyway, the key here is that *sometimes there are subconscious emotional and psychological blocks that can contribute to experiencing difficulty getting pregnant.* Our bodies, subconscious, and conscious minds are in constant communication, and sometimes we are unaware that the messages sent are in direct conflict with our conscious desires.

If you are affected by this, you will likely have a deep inner knowing that this is relevant to you. If you have gotten every medical green light and can't find any underlying physical reason or explanation, you may have some subconscious stuff that's energetically blocking you from moving forward with ease. Heck, you may even have a lot of conscious monkey mind narrative impeding your ability to navigate the complexities of your situation as well. Energy healing can help you identify and release the psychological and emotional blocks and traumas so you can allow your body to move forward unencumbered by past wounds or heaviness you've been holding.

In the event that this isn't the case, this work can help you process both the conscious and subconscious pains, difficulties, fears, anxieties, and emotions that accompany life itself and this specific chapter in your life. I know I'm biased, but really, you can't lose here either way.

A client experienced the feeling of a deep inner knowing that she had some internal blocks that were in the way of her becoming pregnant. She's considered "advanced maternal age" and came to me after two unsuccessful embryo transfers, but I had a feeling age was not her biggest roadblock. We work together to release accumulated stress and bring back peace and calm to her nervous system. Part of that entails giving herself the space to process her fears and anxieties through writing to enable them to come to the surface and be released, so her monkey mind doesn't spin out with stories. Sometimes we have to feel to heal, and unfortunately, that includes the unpleasant stuff too. Our last session was done the day before an attempt at another transfer, and she was feeling as relaxed as she possibly could, and we are both feeling hopeful for success! She is determined not to allow past painful stories that have stayed rooted in the subconscious to limit her. My deepest wish for all beings is they won't either.

THE END OF THIS CHAPTER, BUT HOPEFULLY NOT THE END OF YOUR STORY WITH ENERGY WORK

So, there you have it. I hope you enjoyed this brief yet brilliantly written introduction to the incredibly deep and magical world of energy healing and have some idea of how it may benefit you on your journey. Of course, I can't make any grandiose claims that energy healing is a panacea that will guarantee immediate, miraculous results. Energy healing can be magical, but it's not a magic bullet. It is a complementary modality best used in tandem with other body/mind medical professionals. It has the capacity to unlock and heal long-held pain and create profound change within your body, mind, and spirit. All you need is a curiosity, a willingness, and a desire to try something a little different. You deserve to be nurtured and healed holistically. You are not just a body, or a series of tests, or your frustrations, fears, and doubts. You are not solely your monkey mind. You are an emotional being, a spiritual being, and a being of infinite capacity and potential hope. All of those parts of you are welcomed, important, and deserve to be nurtured and brought into wholeness and your highest capacity for well-being.

I welcome any questions, comments, or feedback you may have!

I wish you hope, lightness, and lots of joy and laughter as you continue forward on your path.

JENNIFER LYONS, MSW

Intuitive Counselor and Theta Healer

Jennifer Lyons, MSW, is an intuitive counselor who helps release and heal energetic and emotional blocks. Her treatments relieve stress, anxiety, and a myriad of other ailments. Jennifer utilizes a blend of Theta healing, Reiki, Spiritual Response Therapy, and her background in clinical social work to enhance the life of her clients and leave them feeling hopeful, empowered, and aligned with their soul.

Website: www.rootedinsight.com
Email: jlyons81@gmail.com
Youtube: https://www.youtube.com/channel/UCoA-mWnMI-mZW72WhBlT4TQ
- "Jennifer Lyons"

13

NEW HOPE TO TURN BACK YOUR BIOLOGICAL CLOCK

DR. KATHERINE ZAGONE, ND

I SAT THERE READING the report in tears, and anger, and shame. My assistant had just emailed the 78 page report, and I was devastated... I'm a doctor! I thought I was doing everything right?! Ok, maybe I was having gluten and dairy from time to time. And maybe I was not getting quite enough sleep. And maybe I was stressing more about work than I needed to. And maybe I skipped my supplements now and then. But still! Overall I was living healthier than 90% of America! How could this happen? What does this mean?

I had taken this test with the hopes of "hope"... that I would come back younger than I thought and be able to relieve some of the pressure of the biological clock and maybe be able to enjoy the dating process without imaging what sort of birthing partner the man across from me might be on the first date. What I got was a wake-up call.

Being 33 and single in Los Angeles felt daunting enough, and now these 78 pages were telling me that my cells are saying I'm really 37 years old! But I'm a fertility doctor! I often tell my patients that fertility is a function of health and age isn't everything. But we do know that there is an age where the reproductive window closes. Age has to be a component. I realized I might have to rethink my dream of 4 kids.

I immediately jumped into the research. What I found was astounding. Biological age, as measured by this test, is linked to reproductive outcomes in animal studies. Meaning mice whose test showed they were older than their chronological age had a harder time conceiving. I took that to mean the test is valid, and I have even less hope now.

And then I found what I'd been hoping for... hope... research that this biological clock number can actually reverse!!! While I've been a self-proclaimed biohacker for years (I try everything on myself before I recommend it to patients), it was time for a new protocol and new commitment to myself and my future babies. I knew what I needed to try to reverse my age. It was something that I had seen work so well for my clients, fasting.

I had to face the thing I'd been terrified of for years... hunger. Hangry was my middle name, and while I could make it through a few days of intermittent fasting, the thought of the level of hunger I'd need to endure to complete the type of fast shown to reverse biological age made me want to cry.

Despite the fear and anxiety, deep down, I knew this would change me in the best way. I often tell my patients that whatever we go through on our way to becoming a mother helps make us a better mother. Thinking of turning back my biological clock and buying myself time to actualize my dream was enough inspiration to embark on the fast.

Before I get caught up in my own story, let me pause and share some of my client stories that have had what some would call miraculous results from the strategy I was most afraid of... fasting.

I recently had a 29 year old patient who, three years prior, had been told her only option was to freeze embryos as her AMH was extremely low for her age and that if she waited any longer, she wouldn't be able to have her own biological children. I don't agree with this assessment, but still, how devastating to hear that at any age and as a 26 year old who wasn't thinking about babies yet even moreso. Her AMH was 1.15 at the time, and her doctor told her this was equivalent to a 42 year old. She felt her fertility was doomed. With her low number, she still managed to get one healthy boy embryo from the cycle she did with her partner. She chalked it up to fate until she recently had a yearning to try for one more embryo before her biological clock hit the tipping point for good. She really wanted a girl.

I'd love to say that the miracle this woman experienced was due to my work with her, but I simply had the pleasure of delivering the good news that she had, in fact, reversed the trajectory of her fertility and turned back her own biological clock. The miracle is this. On her most recent lab work, the first labs I ran on her, her AMH came back at 1.99. She had previously been at 1.15 and fairly consistent at that number previously. This is unheard of in the conventional "in" fertility world. She actually improved her fertility despite three years passing and, with that, increased her chances of getting more healthy embryos and perhaps not even needing those embryos in the future. I called her as soon as I got the result, and she immediately burst into tears of joy.

I had spent four hours with her during our intake process, so I went back into all my notes to figure out what worked for her. The most pronounced change she had made in her life in that time frame was fasting. She had been incorporating 2 "cleanse" days as she called them per week. This is an intermittent fasting strategy that has been shown to improve health measures across the board.

As a doctor, I had been hesitant to prescribe fasting to women trying to conceive because low caloric intake can affect the delicate balance of hormones in the body. I was starting to see that incorporated properly with the right timing and strategy that this could be an incredibly effective tool!

The second miracle story I'd love to share is of my 42 year old patient. She had two previous failed rounds of IVF at 38 and 40 years old. They had gotten either zero or one embryo which ended up not being viable. She had a history of hypothyroidism, alcoholism, and blood sugar dysregulation. She implemented a form of intermittent fasting where she basically skipped breakfast and kept her eating within a 6-hour window. Doable with her lifestyle and also effective. We also added a few more 'anti-aging' components to her protocol, including red light therapy, a detox protocol, and high dose NAD+ therapy. NAD+ therapy has been shown in animal studies to reverse ovarian aging, turn back the biological clock, and improve reproductive outcomes. After a few months of our work together, she and her husband embarked on one more IVF round and miraculously got 8 grade A embryos! This was beyond what they had hoped for!

While my patient stories are inspiring, and I could share more, I want to emphasize that everything I'm speaking about is backed up in the research. The problem is either no one has been looking for it because we didn't know it was possible or it's so new, so few people have found it.

Let's start with this article[1] released on November 11, 2020, in the journal *Human Reproduction*.

Sidenote: I am the type of doctor and woman who felt it significant that the article was published on 11/11/2020. For those in some spiritual traditions, 11:11 or 11/11 can mean "pay attention" at the very least, or even "this is blessed." I took it as a nod from the universe that I was on the right path.

The big long title says so much. Here's what happened. A group of scientists took blood from 175 women undergoing ovarian stimulation. They looked at a pattern on their DNA called methylation. This is also called an epigenetic pattern(epi-on top of, genetic-gene). What's so cool about epigenetics is that it 1) gives us information about what is happening directly on our genes, meaning we can see which genes are being turned on and off -good or bad ones, and 2) it's changeable, and we can see the changes! 3) This pattern is associated with our biological age, or the age of our cells, not just how many birthdays we had.

OK, back to the study. The scientists looked at methylation DNA patterns of these 175 women alongside how many eggs they got during the ovarian stimulation cycle. They found distinct differences in the patterns that correlated with the egg outcome. More specifically, women whose patterns showed they were biologically older (not chronologically older, though) had less eggs.

Here is what it actually means. Biological age is more important than chronological age when predicting ovarian response during a stimulated cycle, and those with a younger biological age can expect better results. We need more research. While, of course, this doesn't prove the same is true for natural conception, (we need more research), I believe it to be true and use it in my practice.

This information isn't necessarily good or bad in and of itself. Just like some women came back older biologically, some came back younger. So the next question is essentially, "what's the difference?" What causes some women to biologically age faster and others slower and still others to perfectly match agreed-upon time. We are still figuring all of those details out, but we do have research to show that it is totally possible to change the biological clock, specifically to REVERSE IT!

Now let's talk about a hopeful study. This is the first study to show turning back the biological clock is possible. This study[2] is referred to as the TRIIM study. It showed that using the biological clock measurement, a small group of humans (all men, but it's a start) were able to reverse their biological age by 2.5 years over a period of one year. The study used three medications to get this effect. Interestingly enough, two of these medications effectively mimic a fasting state in humans, supporting that fasting could turn back the biological clock. Metformin, one of the drugs on the cocktail, lowers blood sugar and improves insulin sensitivity, both very natural benefits of fasting. Growth hormone was also administered. During a fast, our bodies naturally increase growth hormone production. Who needs drugs when we really have the power in us all along. Our bodies were built with the innate mechanisms, and we just need to activate them. The third medication used in this study is DHEA, a hormone made by our adrenals glands and also already used in the fertility world with documented benefit. DHEA has also been shown to improve stress resilience,[3] meaning it effectively decreases perceived stress. One of the things we do know that accelerates the biological clock is stress. This doesn't mean you should run out and start taking DHEA. In fact, please DON'T do that. This hormone is not safe for everyone. Please speak with an educated practitioner like a functional medicine doctor or naturopathic doctor who knows your specific case.

This does suggest that mitigating stress is one tool for turning back the biological clock. Most of us don't have the power to control every potential stressor in our environment. In fact, trying to do that will likely increase stress dramatically. What we do have control over is our response to stressors. The internal dialogue about what's happening on the outside is often the difference between something being stressful vs. neutral vs. empowering. There are tons of resources and methods out there to effectively create this shift for yourself, including some of the resources in other chapters of this book!

And what's even better is that once the participants stopped the interventions, the age reversal results lasted six more months. As a doctor, this gives me an idea of what a maintenance protocol could look like. One does not need to be on a protocol constantly forever to maintain benefits. We can have our cake and eat it too (every once in a great while).

There is specific research[4] that caloric restriction also reverses the biological clock, likely through the mechanisms mentioned above that affect growth hormone and blood sugar. Caloric restriction simply means eating less calories per day. I'm not a fan of the verbiage. However, "fasting" is a strategy that produces the same biological age results and, in my opinion, allows more flexibility and also has other documented benefits like improving gut health.

Fasting also increases NAD+. NAD+ is a molecule our bodies make naturally, but levels decrease as we age. Another published paper[5] showed that by giving mice a supplement that helps them make NAD+, they were able to not only reverse the biological age but "rescue female fertility during reproductive aging." The mice that received the supplement had an improved ovulation rate, less pregnancy losses, and MORE LIVE BIRTHS! That's what we care about, more babies being born! Through testing, they also found the NAD+ group had better blastocyst quality (embryo quality) and less meiotic defects, which is a cause of genetic defects. The scientists were able to restore functional fertility in aging mice. The mice who were the same age and did not receive the NAD+ supplement showed results consistent with their age, being less live births and more genetic defects.

Now, yes, these are mice, and we are humans, but we have to start somewhere. Science is constantly evolving, especially in reproductive medicine. For example, doctors are still taught that mammals (humans, mice, dogs, all mammals) are born with all the eggs they will ever have. Research in the last two decades has shown that mammals across a few different species actually make new eggs and that those new eggs are ovulated and used to create healthy babies[6]. The same mechanism that makes these new eggs has been identified in humans. This suggests that age-related reproductive struggles and even menopause are not a function of running out of eggs but rather some other mechanism we've yet to pinpoint. I share this to show how the field is evolving and to offer hope as we get closer to figuring out how to work with these mechanisms and eventually massage this reproductive window. We might be closer than most think.

Jonathan Tilly, the researcher who found mammals can make more eggs, also took his data and combined it with the caloric restriction research to see if caloric restriction or fasting could improve the reproductive outcomes in mice[7]. Guess what? It did! The aging mice who participated in caloric restriction had measurable improvements in egg quality and quantity, and their offspring were more likely to survive after birth than the age-matched mice who didn't do caloric restriction. Again, it's mice, not humans, but when properly supervised, a medical fasting program has almost no risk and lots of potential upside for many women who feel they have no control over their age or reproductive window.

Let's go back to the human research on reversing the biological clock. A more recent study[8] uses a larger number of humans and gives me even more hope and doesn't even use medications! This study was able to show a 3.23 year reversal in ONLY 8 weeks! And only using diet and lifestyle interventions. The diet used in the study was nutrient-dense, mostly plant-based, with some high nutrient animal foods like eggs and liver. It also utilized lower carbohydrate levels and intermittent fasting, one of the fasting strategies that has worked well for my patients. The lifestyle interventions included 30 min of exercise 5 days per week and twice-daily breathing exercises to elicit a relaxation response and mitigate stress and had participants aim for at least 7 hours of sleep. Sounds so simple right?

Let us summarize. We have a way to measure our biological age. That biological age is a better reflection of our reproductive timeline than our chronological age. We can reverse our biological age. Reversing our biological age may translate to a longer reproductive window.

Fasting can help turn back the biological clock and potentially extend the reproductive window.

Decreasing perceived stress may also help reverse biological age. Diet and lifestyle interventions alone may be enough to improve your biological age dramatically.

Now a few caveats. While the research presented here is entirely positive about fasting and fertility, fasting is not for everyone. There is research that shows lean women who fast may negatively impact their fertility which is why it's important to work with a doctor or educated practitioner in this realm[9]. We also know that extreme restriction like from an eating disorder has this same negative effect. But when done properly and timed appropriately both for the length of the fast and at the proper time during the menstrual cycle, fasting improves multiple health markers and outcomes in women without disrupting reproduction and, as we've discussed throughout this chapter, may improve reproduction[10].

The details are that as women, we don't want to fast during or around ovulation, and we also need enough calories and carbs leading up to our menstrual cycles in order to make enough progesterone. Progesterone is essential for fertility. If a woman is underweight, it is also not advised to fast as this can have detrimental effects on fertility. And absolutely no fasting during pregnancy or breastfeeding. Beyond those restrictions, fasting can look a number of different ways. It can be a restricted feeding window during the day. For example, 12 hours of fasting and 12 hours of eating is a very basic place to start if you aren't already doing that naturally. Eating one meal a day a few days a week can also be a fasting strategy. The more extreme fast would be a five day water fast, meaning only consuming water for five days. While a water fast is highly effective at healing the body, this is not recommended without adequate preparation and medical supervision.

I've seen it in the research, and I've seen it help patients, but will this approach help me? I faced my biggest fear-hunger. I created a protocol for myself that would be both doable and hopefully effective. I planned on two five day fasting mimicking diets over two months. The fasting mimicking diet is low in protein and low in calories. It allows the body to access the benefits of fasting without the suffering because I still ate food throughout the day. In between the fasting mimicking days, I did 2-3 days per week of intermittent fasting, only eating between noon and 6pm. I did go above and beyond here and test my ketone levels through a simple fingerstick. I was able to be in ketosis for at least a few days after each fasting mimicking diet stint. Being in ketosis meant my body was burning fat for fuel. This also meant my blood sugar and insulin were likely low, which we know from the research supports reversing the biological clock. I also had plenty of feast days or days where I ate carbs and calories galore with no regard for timing. Feast days are important too, and not just for mental health. The variation is therapeutic as well.

I also added a supplement to boost my NAD+ and added a B-complex with some methylated folate. I know I have a gene mutation that makes my body require extra folate in the methylated form. These methyl groups attached to the folate are part of what regulates the DNA and the biological age. Deficiencies in methylfolate in people with this specific MTHFR mutation can accelerate aging. I've known this. I just hadn't chosen to really take care of myself the way I know I should... until now.

After eight weeks of the above protocol, I retested myself. I wasn't sure if it would be long enough to see a difference. I definitely had not been perfect with the food. Exercise was sporadic. Honestly, I only took my two supplements about 70% of the time. I had made conscious efforts to decrease my stress and even had a daily mantra, "I get younger every day."

It was judgment day. My assistant emailed over my results as soon as they arrived. I didn't even give myself time to think or stress. I opened the email immediately, scrolled to find the number, and burst into tears again. This time was tears of joy. In eight weeks, I reversed my biological age by approximately two years!! It wasn't the 3.23 years from the study, but I'll take it! Hope!! Hope for my future family! And then it really hit me. This meant hope for women everywhere. Hope that we could have some control over our biological age and reproductive window.

The benefits extend beyond just biological age. My cells being younger translated to everything being younger and healthier. My blood sugar numbers improved. My thyroid numbers improved. My skin improved. My libido improved. My energy improved. And, oh yeah, I lost 10lbs and have kept it off.

These results were consistent with what I had seen in my patients and the research. And go figure, it worked for me too! I just had to actually do it!

I had seen my patients get healthier through our work together. That translated into better fertility, easier times getting pregnant, and, I think, healthier babies because we do pass down this epigenetic pattern I spoke about. So if you're thinking, "can this help me conceive RIGHT NOW"? The honest answer is "most likely yes." Just make sure to speak with your practitioner about your specific case. If you are underweight or have certain conditions like low blood sugar or hypothyroidism, fasting may not be for you, or you may just need careful medical supervision.

Then the questions started flying through my mind. What if women started implementing these strategies in their 20's? How much can we rewind the biological clock? What would it take to add five or even ten years to the normal reproductive lifespan? We don't have these answers yet, but what we do have is a little more power over how we create our lives and our families.

I think about all the decisions we make based on our chronological age and reproductive window. Maybe trying for a baby before we're really ready. Maybe jumping to IVF and sometimes influencing our career choices and relationship choices as well. Perhaps just putting too much stress on ourselves to do it all and do it all NOW.

I envision a world where we, as women, have the knowledge of our biological age and know how to reverse it so we can enjoy this journey of life with at least a bit more peace and spaciousness. This journey inspired me to create MyFertilityAge.com so every woman can find out her biological age and then learn what to do to rewind her biological clock

---

1. https://www.mdlinx.com/journal-summary/young-women-with-poor-ovarian-response-exhibit-epigenetic-age-acceleration-based-on-evaluation-of/2tclFHhUTFj7sKmsRsnAZh
2. https://onlinelibrary.wiley.com/doi/full/10.1111/acel.13028
3. https://www.elsevier.com/about/press-releases/research-and-journals/hormone-levels-contribute-to-stress-resilience
4. https://www.ncbi.nlm.nih.gov/pmc/articles/PMC6515465/
5. https://www.ncbi.nlm.nih.gov/pmc/articles/PMC7063679/
6. https://www.sciencedaily.com/releases/2017/09/170916080143.htm
7. https://www.newscientist.com/article/dn17701-fasting-could-extend-female-fertility/
8. https://www.medrxiv.org/content/10.1101/2020.07.07.20148098v1.full.pdf
9. https://pubmed.ncbi.nlm.nih.gov/11334904/
10. https://pubmed.ncbi.nlm.nih.gov/11334904/

DR. KATHERINE ZAGONE, ND

Dr. Katherine Zagone, ND, combines the mind of a doctor and the heart of a healer to serve couples and women in their journey to conceive their healthiest baby and build the family of their dreams.

After witnessing family members struggle with infertility for years, she felt compelled to find solutions for her patients in similar agonizing situations.

Her holistic approach provides a nurturing experience while addressing medical, functional, environmental, emotional, and energetic causes of infertility.

She is also the medical director of Gentera Center for Regenerative Medicine in Beverly Hills, where she utilizes advanced regenerative therapies for cutting-edge, but still natural, fertility optimization.

Dr. Zagone also co-founded MyFertilityAge.com to support women in turning back their biological clock before it's a problem.

Dr. Zagone graduated top of her class from Southwest College of Naturopathic Medicine. She received her Bachelors of Science in Health Science from Benedictine University in IL, where she graduated summa cum laude.

As a belly dancer and champion for feminine power, she embodies the fertile goddess and helps her female clients access their own embodiment to promote fertility.

Every visit with Dr. Zagone is a healing experience in itself.

Website: https://www.MyFertilityAge.com

14

FAT/QUEER FERTILITY: MY FERTILITY JOURNEY AS AN OVERWEIGHT LESBIAN

EARLY CHILDHOOD EDUCATOR, MAMA TO ONE BEAUTIFUL
KIDDO (NON-GESTATIONAL PARENT), ONE RAINBOW BABY,
AND STILL WANDERING THROUGH THIS INFERTILITY MAZE

KATHLEEN PARÉ, M.ED

"I have this feeling I will not be able to get pregnant one day, just like Auntie." -Katy, 1 3

"Don't say that Katy, you'll be just like me. I wanted babies, and I had babies!" -My mother

I CAN'T REMEMBER a time when I DID NOT want to be a mother. All of the strongest people in my life are mothers. I grew up in a home where it was necessary for me to be raised by more than one mother. I saw strong women all around me, and much of their strength, in my little girl opinion, came from their ability to nurture not only their own children but me and my sister as well. I only knew of three women who had trouble getting pregnant when I was young: one of my mother's best friends, my Auntie, and my Noni (my maternal grandmother). I only knew of one woman who did not end up having biological children of her own: my Auntie. These things were talked about in hushed tones after I was supposed to be in bed. These "problems" were a secret, and you didn't talk about these "problems" that **WOMEN** had in mixed settings. I grew up being told by society and the women around me that when, and if, I wanted to get pregnant, I would. I also got the very clear message that if a woman couldn't conceive a child, it was her fault, and she was broken.

I didn't "come out" as a lesbian until I had finished undergrad. I had one boyfriend in the 6th grade, and other than that, I had so much social anxiety it just didn't appeal to me. Looking back, I am sure if I had even known that it was ok to like and love girls, I would have been more open to dating in my teen years. I grew up Catholic. We went to church every Sunday, and I taught CCD. While I never personally heard anyone say being gay was a sin, that is the stance of the Catholic Church. I didn't grow up knowing anyone in the LGBTQIA[1] community, or if I did, I didn't know it. My parents didn't say there was anything bad about people in this community. In fact, I have a feeling that it wouldn't have been a problem, but it just was a non-issue because it didn't exist in my community out loud. During my undergrad at Simmons College, I met the most obnoxious woman. She was loud, liked to be the best at whatever she was doing, and I felt like she was smarter than me. Nicole vied for my spot as the know-it-all and most mature. It annoyed the heck out of me. However, we had friends in common, and then we had a class together. As I started spending more time with her, I realized that I really enjoyed spending time with her, but we were still just acquaintances. Through a series of events, we ended up rooming together senior year of college, and we got really close. In fact, I wanted to spend every moment with her.

Even when I did come out, I don't think I ever thought about how being a lesbian might change parenthood. My dreams of parenthood had always involved me being single. I had never imagined parenting with anyone else, let alone another woman who would potentially fill the same roles that I do.

Fast forward to 2010. On July 2, 2010, I married my wife. This was an amazing day for me. I never imagined that I would meet someone that I would want to spend the rest of my life with and who would want to spend the rest of theirs with me.

At the time we got married, Nicole was 28, and I was 25. Nicole had just finished her Master's in Severe Special Education and had just started teaching. I was nannying and getting my Master's in Early Childhood and Creative Arts in Learning. At this point, we couldn't afford to have a baby, but we started doing all the researching, preparing, and nesting. Now, in the LGBTQIA community, the conversations around conceiving, pregnancy, and childbirth are somewhat different than those for a couple where one partner already has sperm, and one partner already has an egg. We started to join conception and parenting groups that were for the LGBTQIA community. The first recommendation we got was to buy a book called "The Essential Guide to Lesbian Conception, Pregnancy and Birth; By Kim Toevs and Stephanie Brill." At the time, it was one of the best and most thorough books we could find.

At this point, we started a conversation that is also somewhat unique to the LGBTQIA community. Nicole and I are both cisgender female queers[2]. We both wanted to carry a baby and have the experience of giving birth. So, this led to a conversation around who would become pregnant first. Nicole is older than me by three years and has type 1 diabetes. We talked to her doctors and did research. We found that it would be healthier for Nicole to carry a baby when she was younger and would be less likely to have medical complications. With this knowledge, the decision was made that Nicole would carry our first child when we felt ready to start the process. Knowing that we were going to be ready in the near future, we began to have other conversations that many families trying to conceive in the LGBTQIA community have.

The first conversation we had was whether or not we would use a known donor[3] (someone you know or are an acquaintance willing to donate to your family) or an unknown donor (donor sperm that is bought through a sperm bank). At the time that we first started this conversation, we didn't know anyone we could ask to be a known donor. Also, using a known donor comes with its own risks, even though it is less expensive overall. We did look at several websites where you can find people who are willing to donate sperm to you, but for the most part, the people who donate on those sites want to have a role in your child's life (i.e., uncle, co-parent, etc.). This was not something we were looking for, and we felt really uncomfortable with the idea that we wouldn't have a lot of medical knowledge about the person donating.

Although we did not have a ton of money, we were young and optimistic. We decided we would use an unknown donor. We chose a local sperm bank in Cambridge because we could pay $700 dollars a vial for unwashed (this means you get the sperm in its natural state) donor sperm if we picked it up ourselves. This was something we felt that we could make work at the time.**The average price of unknown donor sperm in 2021 is $900-$1000 a vial (marketplace.org).

Nicole and I also talked about at-home insemination[4] vs. **in-office insemination**[5]. From what we had read in our book and from talking to others trying to conceive in the Queer parenting community, there was no clear consensus about which alternative was better in terms of becoming pregnant. Still, anecdotally there is some evidence that the more you can replicate actual intercourse, the more likely it is to work. At home ICI[6] (intracervical insemination) insemination, without a midwife, has little to no cost. You can purchase an at-home insemination kit, but many people get a baby syringe (not the squeezie top kind) in order to perform the insemination. There is an out-of-pocket expense if you want to inseminate at a doctor's office. It tends to run between $200-$400 per visit if you are doing a basic ICI insemination.

Nicole and I decided that because we had no indication that she would have any trouble conceiving, we would use donor sperm from a local bank and try to conceive at home. In 2012 we decided we were ready to try. Nicole started documenting her cycle. We went to the sperm bank website that we had decided on and began to look for a donor. We were mostly looking for someone with a similar background to me so that the baby would look similar to me. In order to get any information beyond the basics, including genetic testing, you have to pay more money. We got our selection down to 3 choices and then paid the $30 per donor to see their long information. Part of how we ended up choosing was that we wanted a donor that would be open to the child being able to contact them someday if they were interested. Looking for a donor is complicated. People put what they feel are their most attractive qualities on the sheet, but you don't actually find out that much about the actual person.

On the day she was ovulating, we went and picked up a cryogenic tank with two vials of sperm from a sperm bank in Cambridge, MA. We thawed the first vial (in a vial of donor sperm, you get 1mL of semen. In a fresh ejaculation, you get anywhere from 2 to 5x that much.) and inseminated the first night of ovulation at home with a baby syringe, a guide from our handy book, and my cell phone flashlight. As the person who was trying to make sure that everything was going in the right place, there was a lot of pressure. I would recommend practicing pre-having the sperm on hand. The pressure was immense to make sure that I was doing everything right. This was not only because we wanted a baby desperately, but also because of the cost.

Nicole spent the next day with her legs in the air watching tv, and we repeated the process again. We very impatiently waited ten days and broke down and took a pregnancy test in the bathroom at a target and hysterically cried when it said negative. We waited eight more days, and we got another negative, and Nicole got her period. We were sad, but it was only our first try.

We repeated all of this for one more cycle, without the result of a pregnancy. We were still young at this point and knew we had plenty of time, but we also had a lot of student loan debt and not a lot of money. We were crying one day in the presence of a friend who said, "I can do that for you!". Nicole and I looked at each other and said, "That's very sweet, but we can't do that!". On our way home that night, we discussed whether or not we thought he was serious. Could a person do that without wanting anything in return besides a friendly relationship with the child?

Using a known donor can feel like a less expensive option, but in truth, it comes with a lot of emotional expense. As we had found out, looking at the known donor websites, the costs may come in the person wanting to have a bigger relationship with the child than you want. You have to think about if the person will change their mind during the pregnancy. You can have them sign a known donor agreement, but it does not hold much weight in court. Would the known donor be willing to sign their rights away as soon as the child was born?

So after a lot of discussion amongst the different parties, after a lot of therapy, legal advice, and a lot more discussion and therapy, we found out that yes, a person can and would do that. After the first try inseminating at home with fresh sperm, we were pregnant.

Nicole's pregnancy was the best, hardest, most thrilling time in my life. I was going to get to be a mom!!!! I had always wanted that, but I was not going to be **THE MOM**. Let me say this, being the non-gestational parent[7] bites. No one asks how you are, you don't get to feel any of the special things first, and you don't get any of the praise. As much as I tried, it was really hard to swallow the jealousy surrounding my wife being pregnant. It was totally irrational and raw. Nicole was so understanding, and we did a lot of therapy in order to work on feelings around becoming parents. I loved going to all the appointments and talking to our baby at night after Nicole had fallen asleep, BUT this is not how I imagined becoming a mother would be!

On August 3rd, 2013, my baby, Theo, came into this world!! He was born via c-section because my wife had developed preeclampsia which was not totally unexpected given her type 1 diabetes and her high-risk pregnancy. What was unexpected was that, even at 38 weeks, Theo was not a fully baked cookie and gave us a scare. He was blue and not crying when he came into this world. He finally perked up a little but was destined to spend his first hours on a c-pap in the NICU and has continued to be somewhat of a rebel when it comes to doing things that aren't on his timeline!

When I went down to the NICU to see Theo and report back to Nicole, I was told that I couldn't see my baby because I was not the Mother. "The Mother had just given birth!" I was told this by a flamingly gay nurse at a hospital known for being good to LGBTQIA families. I was devastated and furious!! It would be the first time that I would be told I am not the true mother of my child, but not the last. When we were finally able to all be together in our hospital room and out of the NICU, we were able to feel overjoyed with our new little fella and couldn't believe that we were parents.

Next came the hardest part for me. Because Nicole and I were married before The Marriage Equality Act was passed, we needed to complete a second parent adoption[8]. A second parent or step-parent adoption is a process by which a marriage partner can adopt their partner's biological or adoptive child without terminating the first legal parent's rights. This is vital to LGBTQIA couples, even today in 2021, because if you leave your state or travel outside of the country and something happens to the gestational parent, the non-gestational parent may have no rights to their child. This is also another added cost when creating a family in the LGBTQIA community. The average cost of a second parent adoption is anywhere from $250-$3000[9]. Our second parent adoption cost $5000 because we used a known donor. We needed to do a donor agreement beforehand, termination of the donor's parental rights, and the second parent adoption. Our lawyer was amazing at what she does for a living, but she was not sympathetic and barely listened when I vocalized how hard things were for me.

This meant, not only was I not the gestational parent[10], but I was also going to have to adopt my own baby. For weeks before this happened, my wife and I had fights. She was trying to be a voice of reason, but all I could feel was the anger and the injustice of having to adopt my child because of the fact that my name, as another woman, on our baby's birth certificate was not enough! I would do it over and over again. I needed legal rights to our baby! This adoption day was weird and overwhelming! Everyone at court wanted us to take pictures and be ecstatic, but I was Theo's Mama already. This was just a piece of paper for protection!! We HAD to have this paper because our families didn't have the same rights as other families and because the man who had given us the material to make our son needed his rights protected (this part was very valid and important).

During the first months of Theo's life, I discovered that biology does not make a person a parent. I bonded with my baby, I fed my baby, I bathed my baby, and I LOVED my baby. But, during Nicole's pregnancy, the idea that I needed to be pregnant and give birth only became stronger and more dire. I felt like I desperately needed those experiences in order to be a true mother still. It did not help that the world around me was still telling me that I was not Theo's true mother. Now, I have had several people come right out and tell me that I am not his mother, but mostly it was small, subtle things. "Oh, which one of you is mom?" or "Oh, no, I meant, which one of you is the REAL mom?" I was the f***ing REAL mom! We both were the real mom. I had not contributed DNA, but in every other way possible, I was a part of the process and my baby's mother.

Then right away started the questions: "When would we have another?" "Didn't we want more kids?" "Isn't it better to have them close together?" etc. There was barely any time to breathe between successfully creating this little miracle and when we were *supposed* to make the next.

As it goes in our lives and in our marriage, life took hold, and we were very busy raising Theo and being integral parts of our jobs and families. I was nannying for a wonderful little girl full time while taking Theo with me, and Nicole was getting seniority at her teaching job. We sold our condo and bought a home with my sister and her family. I also was a PCA for my sister, where I brought Theo as well. It didn't feel as though we had time or money to start expanding our family. My need to carry a baby ebbed and flowed as time passed. I had totally gotten to see that I didn't NEED to carry a baby to be complete, but the want to do that was still very strong, and our family didn't feel complete. So the spring before Theo started kindergarten, we started talking more seriously about what we wanted for our family. I still craved being pregnant and carrying a baby. Nicole and I wanted to expand our family, and Theo was in agreement as well.

So, in the spring of 2018, I started tracking my periods and ovulation. Nicole and I had a conversation with our known donor and asked if he would be willing to help us again. He said he was willing, and we decided to move forward and begin trying in July. At that point, I was 32 years old and had no risks or reasons to believe that I would have any trouble getting pregnant. However, I am **FAT**!!! I have been fat since I was 8 or 9 years old and not just chubby, fat. I haven't been under 200lbs at 5' 10" since I was 13. However, I have never had any risk factors and have always been relatively healthy, minus needing an appendectomy at 16, and they lanced some cysts on my ovaries while in there. Knowing, however, the medical and social narratives in our society about it being harder to get pregnant when you are overweight, I went to my PCP to talk about my plan to get pregnant and whether or not she felt there was any reason that it might be harder for me as a fat person. She said that there was no indication that I should have any trouble getting pregnant and that she thought we should go ahead and proceed. That actually much of the research around being fat and pregnant had more to do with complications during pregnancy, not in actually getting pregnant. I did mention to my doctor that I had a history of cysts but that nothing had ever come of that and that I had pretty regular periods.

With the ok from my PCP, my wife and I went ahead and made plans to start inseminating. We did our first at-home insemination in July. Everything went smoothly, and we inseminated on what I felt were the two peak days of ovulation for me. While tracking my ovulation before starting to inseminate, I did notice that the peak days of my cycle, according to the ovulation strips you pee on, didn't fall within what most of my research suggested it should. I also noticed that the ovulation strips never seemed to reach the peak color that suggested you were most likely to ovulate. I noted that in the back of my mind, and we went with what the data was suggesting. We waited 14 days to test, and I got an unclear result. There was a very faint 2nd line on the pregnancy test. I was ecstatic, but because it was pale and we weren't sure, we decided we would repeat the test after a few more days, but the next morning I got my period. The sadness was overwhelming. It was my first try, but I so wanted it to happen and was extremely dismayed by that faint second line.

We repeated this for two more months, but with a definite negative on the tests. During this time, we did more research on how best to approach the insemination: Was my butt up high enough, or was it up too high? Should we use the baby syringe method still or buy a kit? There has been some luck in the LGBTQIA community with using a menstrual cup after insemination to keep the sperm from coming back out. Should we try that? Should I start doing basal temperature as well? Or maybe I was too stressed out?

By the fourth insemination, I was starting to get really down on myself because, after the fourth insemination, I once again got what looked like a positive result on my pregnancy test. That faint second line was back. We were so excited, and the next day I didn't get my period. Two more days, and I didn't get my period, so I took another test, and the second line was gone. I tried to tell myself that maybe something was wrong with the box of tests, and I would go to the store and get more tests the next day. I woke up in the middle of the night feeling like I needed to go pee, and there was my period. I sat in the bathroom as tears streamed down my face. Why was I broken? Why wasn't this working? We had already gotten pregnant with Theo at this point. Why had Nicole been able to get pregnant and I couldn't? Why couldn't I have this one thing that I desperately wanted all of my life? Nicole suggested that maybe I was not the person whose contribution to the process was not working. That, after all, as my then 5.5 year old would gladly tell you, the sperm and the egg have to do their dance in order to make a baby. You can't make a baby with just one of these ingredients. I immediately dismissed this idea because our donor had helped to create more than one baby at this point, so it must be me.

We decided to take a month off for Thanksgiving. Maybe I needed a break. Maybe we all needed a break. The break didn't make me feel any better. I had one goal. That goal was to have a baby. I was picking apart and analyzing how I could make that happen every step of the way. The thoughts were all-consuming and what was worse was that multiple people I knew and was friends with were all getting pregnant. It felt supremely unfair and unjust!

We decided to try again before Christmas with no luck. We tried again in January and finally, SUCCESS!!!!! Every inch of me screamed, "I have done it. I'm not defective!!!!" We told immediate family and Theo, but we explained to Theo that sometimes things can go wrong when growing a baby, so just because I was pregnant didn't mean that we would actually end up with a baby. Of course, I said all that to my son with complete confidence that I would end up with a beautiful baby at the end of my pregnancy. I made it almost ten weeks exactly.

On March 22nd, 2019, I got my son ready for school and dropped him off at early care. I got back home to take a quick shower before I went upstairs to work with my sister. I went to the bathroom and realized I had some spotting. I called Nicole and checked in with her to make sure that was normal. She said that it could be, and I went ahead and took my shower. I had just gotten out and was walking across my kitchen to head to get dressed when a gush of blood poured down my legs. At that moment, I knew that I was losing my baby. Sobbing, I called my wife and told her I was headed to the emergency room. I quickly wiped myself up, threw on clothes and a pad, grabbed my wallet and car keys. As I ran up the stairs, I called to my sister what was happening and that she would need to get my mom to fill in for me. I could barely see as I choked back tears and drove to the emergency room. I walked into the ER and explained what was happening.

While everyone was very nice and kind, there was a lack of support. I was not once offered a female provider or female nurse (I get that it's the ER, but...), I was not offered fresh pads, and I was bleeding A LOT, and I was not offered anyone to wait with me till my partner arrived. Finally, Nicole arrived. Of course, I broke down again. I was taken for an internal ultrasound and told to go to the bathroom, so my bladder was empty. As I sat on the toilet, I could hear the techs in the hallway laughing and joking about their babies. I went to stand to flush and felt my whole hope slip into the toilet, and before I could do anything else, the automatic flusher went off. I don't think I would have wanted to see what was in the toilet, but at that moment, my choice was taken from me, and it was devastating!

The one female nurse I did encounter during my ER visit didn't know why I was at the ER. At first, she chatted about off topic things.

She couldn't find a stretcher that had stirrups, so she flipped a bedpan upside down and told me it works the same way. When she finally understood what was happening, she began to recount her story of miscarriage history. She told me that she had 13 miscarriages during the course of trying to have children and that she had two healthy kiddos. While I totally got that she was trying to relate to me and tell me there was light at the end of the tunnel, all I heard at that moment was that she had 13 miscarriages, and that felt devastating. I was not offered any kind of mental health support during my visit to the ER or after.

When I got home, I spent the weekend in bed, grieving the loss of our baby. But life cannot come to a screeching halt when you have a five year old who wants you and when you have to go to work to make ends meet. I picked up the pieces and went to my appointments. We tried two more times, and the grief around trying and the waves of anger were so hard to bear. My PCP finally referred me to a fertility doctor.

When I finally got my appointment with a fertility doctor at my local hospital 3+ months later, they told me I would be sent a paperwork packet to fill out in the next couple of weeks. When the packet came, I started to fill the papers out, and my anxiety welled. I suffer from some intense anxiety on a regular day, and my miscarriage and not being able to get pregnant had greatly intensified this anxiety. This packet was all aimed at heterosexual couples. Ok, lots of self-talk, because most things are geared toward heterosexual couples. Give them the benefit of the doubt.

On the day of my appointment, I walked into the hospital by myself (Nicole couldn't get the day off from work). I walked by people with balloons for new babies, because you have to walk through the maternity ward. I entered the women's health clinic, and it was filled with pregnant women and mothers with new babies. I waited for an hour plus to go in (I was a little early), and the nurse came to bring me into my appointment. "No partner?" she said. "No, I am married, but my wife couldn't be here today." The nurse folded up the sheet from my packet about male information and put it aside. She then asked me questions about exactly how we got pregnant with Theo. There is a tell that I can pick up on when someone starts asking questions that are purely voyeuristic, and I could tell this was one of those times. The nurse asked me about whether or not I've been pregnant, then said, "Oh yes, I read on the notes you've had a miscarriage." She got me on the table and then started taking my blood pressure. As she took my blood pressure, she warned me that the doctor is very "academic" and that she's going to tell me I can't get pregnant because of my weight. I explained to the nurse that my PCP said that's not true, that I have a regular cycle. The nurse's response was that she was just warning me, that her commitment was to her patient, and she wanted to warn me. Then the nurse asked me what I wanted from the visit. My answer was that I wanted to know what my options were, I wanted support, and I wanted help.

I find myself alone and waiting, again. My anxiety through the roof, I tried texting and talking to Nicole. Nicole told me that I could leave if I wanted to, but I was still willing to try. The doctor comes in talking about weight, but I don't totally catch what she's saying. She's older. She starts talking very clinically. My mind is racing. "Concentrate Katy." The doctor says we can do a three-day test and that she can check my A1C, my thyroid. She says she's not sure why I'm there, that I got pregnant, that I should keep trying, that because all of my documents state that I am in a same sex marriage, insurance won't pay for much.

I have to have been trying for a year, and there is no documentation of my interaction with sperm because we attempted at home. The doctor kept pushing about my having to pay for things out of pocket but didn't ask me what my willingness to do so was. I was holding back tears, and I couldn't understand why she was being so forceful. She asks what I am hoping to have help with. I told her that we have been trying for a year, and she told me that I have to have 12 interactions with sperm. Ok, I needed to hear that. The little time when I was pregnant doesn't count. She adds in something weird about how she guesses I could say I was bisexual. The doctor says over and over again that they won't do in-office IUI with fresh sperm. I say we understand, and I told the nurse I would be willing to buy donor sperm from a bank. She tells me that doing the insemination in-office will cost at least $1000. I ask her if she's worked with same sex couples before. Yes, but they pay for most things out of pocket... That's not what I asked. I am feeling more and more sick. She tells me to come back for this three-day test. I ask what that is. She finally explains it. She tells me to go home and try more at home and that I will probably get pregnant. I realize as I walk slowly back to my car that the money piece is her way of pushing me out the door. I feel ashamed of my body. Why couldn't you have just held on to her (me talking to myself about the baby)? I wouldn't be here enduring this subtle or not so subtle homophobia.

Needless to say, after talking with my wife and our different support systems, we began looking for a new fertility doctor. We got several recommendations for a clinic that had offices both locally in Worcester and in the town where Nicole works, which would help to make it easier for Nicole to come to the appointments too. We made the appointment, and I felt much better after talking to the office assistant about my concerns. She assured me that they worked with a lot of LGBTQIA couples and were open to all families. When we got the packet from the office, the wording on the paperwork was much more inclusive, except that my wife would need to register as a patient as well. This makes sense for couples where one person has sperm, and one person has an egg, but in our case, none of Nicole's materials would be used, so it seemed like an extra unnecessary step.

When we arrived at the appointment to meet the new fertility doctor, she was once again over an hour late. My anxiety was rising. We first talked to the doctor. I explained my history and why we were there, and that I had not had a great appointment with the last doctor I saw. So the first thing that came up with the doctor was once again my weight. In order to proceed at all, I would need to see a nutritionist and agree to work on losing weight, now again, at this point, I had no health risks, but I agreed to this while starting to tear up. I had been prepared, but I still began to cry. I asked the doctor what information she had that my weight would be the reason behind my infertility. She said that women who are obese and with a certain BMI often don't make enough hormones. I asked her if there was any indication this was true for me. She told me we wouldn't know until we could get the tests done. This part was a little mind-boggling for me as I couldn't get the tests done until after I agreed to see the nutritionist and lose weight...

The next issue was that we had performed the inseminations at home instead of in-office. She would have no proof of my having interactions with sperm, except for my miscarriage. I explained that there was content in my medical record from when I asked my doctor about getting pregnant. She said it didn't matter. Tears kept flowing as she told me we would need to perform five in-office inseminations out of pocket before insurance would cover my infertility. I asked her if that was true for heterosexual couples, she told me that it was different because they knew one partner had sperm and one had an egg. I said, well, what if my known donor filled out something saying that he had donated, no it didn't count. At this point, I am hysterical. We didn't have $1,200 x 5, purely because insurance wouldn't believe that we had access to sperm, purely because we are queer.

Nicole tried to explain why I was so upset. She didn't get it or didn't want to. Nicole mentioned we could switch our insurance plan. I was so upset, my wife has type 1 diabetes, and my son has epilepsy. We couldn't just change insurances easily. We had to make sure everything was covered. This doctor clung to us being able to change insurances, and it was the plan. We would set up my nutritionist appointment and testing, and then we would use hormones and do in-office, and hopefully, we could soon skip right to IVF. My head was spinning. We talked to a very nice nurse who was understanding, and we left. I shouted and yelled in the parking lot. I was angry, but I wanted a baby. I would do what she said.

We got through the nutritionist, the testing, and I started losing weight, and just as I was supposed to have my first round of hormones and in-office insemination, Covid hit. I was once again devastated. I was supposed to get my baby finally, but I couldn't imagine having to be pregnant or give birth without Nicole. We talked and decided it would be best to wait until after Covid ended, which at the time we thought would be a few months.

Now, we are almost at a year of Covid and almost two years out from my miscarriage. Not having been able to finish my fertility journey has been beyond frustrating, but at the same time, I have had a lot of space and room to breathe. I have been able to talk to my wife and think about what we really want in terms of parenting, and I have been able to get a better team of healthcare providers. I am currently undergoing some tests for Polycystic Ovary Syndrome[11]. It turns out those cysts I had lanced back in high school may have been more indicative of a bigger problem. I am working on losing weight and getting my type 2 diabetes[12] (newly diagnosed December 2020 and highly associated with PCOS) under control. Most importantly, I am working on being the most healthy I can be in the body that has gotten me this far in life.

My fertility journey has changed the way I think about the world and what makes a person a mother. I am lucky that I have been able to be a mother regardless of my having been able to carry a child myself. I have changed a lot of my thinking around what the impact of a biological connection means when it comes to MOTHERHOOD. I know for sure that I am not finished with my fertility journey, but I will not let it consume me! Every day I talk to myself about where I am on this journey, and every day it changes a little, but every day I know that I am not broken, and I am not defective. I am human, and my maze has had many dead ends, but I continue to find hope in twists and turns that make my unique path worth every moment of travel.

---

1. *LGBTQIA:* Lesbian, Gay, Bisexual, Transgender, Queer (Questioning), Intersex, and Asexual (Agender)
2. *Queer:* Queer is an umbrella term for sexual and gender minorities who are not heterosexual or are not cisgender.
3. *Known Donor:* A person you know who is willing to donate sperm to you.
4. *At Home Insemination:* Is an opportunity to attempt to achieve pregnancy in the comfort of one's home through an intracervical insemination (ICI). The sperm sample is drawn into a needleless syringe, the syringe is inserted into the vagina, and the sperm is expelled onto the cervix.
5. *In-Office Insemination:* See at home, but takes place in the doctor's office and hormones are usually offered.
6. *ICI (Intracervical Insemination):* Inserting sperm near the front of the cervix, similar to intercourse.
7. *Non-Gestational Parent:* The parent who did not carry the baby.
8. Second Parent Adoption: A second parent or step parent adoption is a process by which a marriage partner can adopt their partner's biological or adoptive child without terminating the first legal parent's rights.
9. https://www.familyequality.org/resources/average-adoption-costs-in-the-united-states
10. *Gestational Parent:* The person whose uterus was used for the nurturing and development of an embryo into a baby.
11. *Polycystic Ovary Syndrome:* A hormonal disorder common among women of reproductive age. Women with PCOS may have infrequent or prolonged menstrual periods or an excess of androgen hormone levels. The ovaries may develop numerous small collections of fluid (follicles) and fail to regularly release eggs.
12. *Type 2 Diabetes:* An impairment in the way the body regulates and uses glucose as fuel. This long-term (chronic) condition results in too much sugar circulating through the bloodstream. Eventually, high blood sugar levels can lead to disorders of circulatory, nervous and immune systems. It is highly associated with PCOS.

KATHLEEN PARÉ

Kathleen Paré has a Master's Degree in Early Childhood Education from Lesley University and an undergraduate degree in Sociology from Simmons College. Katy lives with her wife (Nicole) and her son (Theo), who is seven years old. They live in Worcester, MA, with their bunny, two kitties, and a leopard gecko. Katy's wife carried their first son, and when it was time to expand their family, she began her journey with infertility and miscarriage. Katy is passionate about ending the stigma around infertility and miscarriage.

Email: kathleen.pare@yahoo.com
Email: pare.robillard@gmail.com
Instagram: katypare

15

A WINDING ROAD ILLUMINATED BY ANCIENT WISDOM

KAYLEE STEIFF: AYURVEDIC FERTILITY SPECIALIST

Everyone's journey down the path of fertility begins in a different place. For me, it began long before I even knew I wanted to be a mother. In fact, for many years, I believed in my core I would not be. I felt very strongly that I did not want to birth my own children physically. Sometimes I wonder if this belief, as well as some of the others I held about my own body, cycle, and womanhood, aren't what contributed to the fertility struggles I would later experience.

As a young girl, I remember feeling a lot of shame around my body, especially when it started bleeding. I, like many young girls, was subliminally taught that periods were not something you talked about. It needed to be kept a secret. So, every month I was flooded with anxiety. I had to cover my changing body, keep a secret stash of pads and tampons with me, and be sure to wear dark colors so I would never have a visible leaking fiasco. All of this shame and secrecy began to build resentment in me towards my cycle and towards being a woman in general.

Not long after they began, my periods became more and more troublesome. The cramps and fatigue were the most memorable symptoms. The fatigue would set in a couple of days before my period. I would often complain of an overall ache and say that I felt like "I had been hit by a bus." Then the cramps would come. The intense pain would double me over often throughout the day. The pain was so bad I often would miss a few days of school every single month. For almost two weeks of every month, my moods would swing from ecstatically happy and unable to sleep to incredibly antisocial, crying alone in the dark and sleeping for 20 hours straight. My disdain for my womanly body grew month after month.

Although I didn't know whether other women dealt with the same issues because no one talked about it, I felt in my heart that something was not right. Our wombs were created to carry a child, but we should not be miserable every month that we are not growing one. So, I went to see an OBGYN and discuss what I was experiencing. I was told that every woman experiences her cycle differently but that my symptoms were nothing to be concerned about. Then, at the age of 15, I was told "it would be best" to get on hormonal birth control, that it would help settle or even eliminate my period so that I could enjoy life more. This answer felt confusing to me. I could not wrap my head around adding more hormones to my teenage body. But, being a naive child and not knowing of any other solutions, I followed my doctor's orders.

For the next five years, I was on one form or another of hormonal birth control. Every few months, I would go back to the doctor because my symptoms weren't improved or because the side effects of the pills were unbearable. They would switch me to a new brand with a different ratio of hormones and hope for the best. I was growing more frustrated with the doctors and with my own body. I began feeling like no one, not even myself, truly understood this menstrual cycle thing, and it was hopeless. I was just going to have to learn to live with this torture every single month. At the age of 20, I was fed up. I asked the doctor for a low dosage option because the side effects were worse than the symptoms, so I just wanted it to prevent pregnancy now. Not long after I started the new birth control, I began feeling very sick. I never tracked my cycle and often had no idea how long my cycles were, but I knew it had been a bit since I had actually had a real period. That's when I found out I was pregnant with my son.

During my pregnancy, I had found a passion for health and wellness. I studied holistic nutrition and became a certified Health Coach. After his birth, I refused to go back on birth control. I wasn't sure what I wanted in the future as far as fertility, but I knew I no longer wanted to put artificial hormones into my body for any reason. Through the process of pregnancy and giving birth, I had become much more aware of my body than ever before. I started to realize the magic that is the womb.

A few months after giving birth, I began experiencing abdominal pain throughout the month. In one instance, the pain was so intense and sharp I almost dropped my baby boy when I fell to the floor. I rushed to the hospital, certain something was extremely wrong. I told the emergency room doctors what had been happening and that I was sure it was something with my womb. Their diagnosis, based on no evidence at all, was that I was constipated. They insisted I do an enema before they would run any further diagnostic test, so with tears of pain streaming down my face, I complied. After a useless enema and waiting for hours, they performed an ultrasound and then a CT scan. They found multiple large cysts on both of my ovaries. The immense pain they assumed was from one or more cysts bursting. At that point, all the hospital could do was to offer me painkillers and tell me to follow up with my OBGYN.

When I went to see my OBGYN, I was offered very little as far as hope or solutions. She very matter-of-factly told me the cysts I had would continue to burst and cause pain, most likely around ovulation every month. She informed me that I most likely was not having an actual ovulation, or the release of an egg, due to the high number of cyst I had. Her one and only suggestion for management of this condition was to place me back on hormonal birth control. When I refused, she gave me an ongoing prescription for painkillers and sent me on my way. As she predicted, I suffered from painful "bursts" for the next few months.

For years it felt like every time I saw a Western medicine doctor, they looked directly through me. It felt like I was just a number to them, one more birth control prescription. I felt as if they did not truly care if I had a solution for the slightly annoying problems I was experiencing; I mean, I wasn't dying. But, at this point in my journey, I wasn't hopeless anymore. I knew I didn't know the exact answers, but I did understand my own body better. Plus, I had gained a new wealth of knowledge about health and nutrition. The answers had to be there somewhere!

I became determined to get in the best physical shape of my life. I began a rigorous weight lifting and a cardio routine. I would spend two hours a day in the gym, and I loved it! That was my alone time, and I would not miss it for anything! I was also eating a very typical "bodybuilder" diet that consisted of high protein meals, lots of eggs, protein powder, and other supplements. I would work extremely hard all week and then reward myself with a beer or two or six on the weekends. I had dropped lower than my pre-baby weight, I had muscle definition in all the right places, and overall I felt pretty great. Although the way I was living and eating did not fit what I learned in school to be a "healthy lifestyle," all I saw was the physical results. Plus, the painful bursts each month had stopped! In fact, my periods were barely noticeable at all. I finally loved my body, but that love was very conditional.

As my son grew, I felt the tug at my heart. I had always said I didn't want kids, but my oldest was a pleasant surprise. He changed me for the better and lit up my world in a way I never knew was possible. My head began to fill with the ideas of more children. I was kinda doing great at this mom thing, and he would be an amazing big brother. Maybe I *need* to have more children so that he won't be lonely. Plus, I had already gone through it once. The second time would be a breeze, right? So, the man I was with and I decided we would stop trying to prevent further babies. We weren't actively trying to make it happen, but if it was meant to be, we would be ecstatic.

My cycles had not been regular for a long time, so I never really knew when I would be ovulating or when my period should come. Those early pregnancy symptoms rocked me, though. I could smell onions from a mile away, and they made me gag. Moving from lying to standing or vice versa would almost always make me vomit. I am also pretty sure if someone looked at my boobs too long, they would hurt. That's how sensitive they were! Although physically I felt awful, I was so full of joy. I never expected it to happen this soon, but I immediately began thinking of names for this little growing being in my belly.

When I called the doctor with excitement to hear this little heartbeat, I was disappointed. After being unable to give them an exact date of my last period, they wanted to wait two more weeks before seeing me for the first ultrasound, to be sure the baby was big enough to detect. I impatiently marked the date on the calendar with a big red heart.

About a week before the ultrasound date, I woke up to a sharp pain in my side and blood between my legs. I immediately knew in my heart that I would never get to hear that heartbeat. The pain I felt that day has no comparison because the physical pain came with such immense pain in my heart as well. I said goodbye to that beautiful baby soul as I flushed the toilet a few hours later. At the time, I thought that would be the hardest moment of my life. I wasn't sure I would ever recover. Then over the next couple of years, I said goodbye in the same way to three more baby souls.

After my last miscarriage, I wasn't sure that I could keep going. I began thinking maybe it wasn't supposed to happen, and I should just be grateful I have my oldest, who was now four years old. I wanted to be grateful, I wanted to run and play with him, but I hurt. I physically hurt a lot this time, not to mention the emotional hurt. It was hard to get out of bed. The abdominal pain continued to get worse, especially if I moved, and before long, I became lethargic with fever. I was rushed to the hospital and put on IV antibiotics for a severe pelvic infection. After a few weeks of recovery, I returned to the OBGYN for more ultrasounds to see how I was healing. The doctor sat me down in his office and delivered my first official infertile diagnosis. He informed me that not only were the cysts still a problem, but now my fallopian tubes have closed due to the inflammation, and it was not reversible. He told me I would never have any more children and that I would be on high estrogen birth control for the rest of my reproductive years.

I felt my heart sink to my stomach. I may not have wanted children in the beginning, but I did now. I got a glimpse of the magic that is a women's cycle and ability to give birth, and I was not ready to give up on that for myself. But, instead of wallowing in a feeling of hopelessness like I may have in previous years, I was filled with faith and a little furry. I was angry that these Western medicine doctors only offered drugs and a negative prognosis. Through my journey so far, I had gained faith that there were answers out there, and I would go down every avenue until I found the right one. So, I not so politely told the doctor, "Challenge accepted." and walked out of the office with a new drive to not just *live healthily* but to *heal* my womb and my spirit!

I went back to a form of medicine and healing I had heard about briefly in school called Ayurveda. Ayurveda is the ancient form of wellness and healing from India and has been practiced for over 5000 years continuously. In Sanskrit, it means *science of life*. It takes a very holistic view of health and encompasses the mind and spirit as well as the physical body. Ayurveda fosters self-awareness and empowers the individual to take charge of their own wellbeing. This system honors that we are all unique individuals. We are all made of different proportions of the stuff of the universe; in Ayurveda, this stuff is referred to as elements, doshas, and energies. The goal in Ayurveda is first and foremost prevention, but if a disorder has occurred, then the goal is to dig deep to find the root cause of the disorder or imbalance in the elements, doshas, and energies. What Ayurveda does not do is simply ease symptoms or prescribe a one size fits all solution. To prevent future imbalances, Ayurveda teaches how to live in sync with cycles of nature, including our own cycles as women.

I dove headfirst into learning everything I could about Ayurveda, convinced that a system that has been around for that long must have answers that Western medicine has missed. Over the next few months, I became my own great experiment. I took the little lessons I had learned through my journey and combined them with the ancient wisdom of Ayurveda. I began to overhaul not only my diet but my lifestyle and my mindset. I focused on self-awareness and got to know myself on an intimate level. Then I learned how to find my own unique form of balance. Finally, I learned how to live in sync with my cycle instead of fighting against it. I began to fall deeply in love with my body, my cycle, and the power it possessed. Six months after that doctor called me infertile, I became pregnant with my youngest son.

The Ayurvedic System

Every time I kiss that little boy good morning, I am reminded of the amazing power of the female cycle as well as our bodies' natural abilities to heal themselves when cared for deeply. Now, as an Ayurvedic Fertility Specialist, I walk with women through the three-phase system I used so that they can also heal their cycles and strengthen their fertility.

Awareness

Self Awareness is the foundation on which all health can be built. The more you know about how your unique body reacts to things such as food, weather, temperature, emotions, noises, and sensations, the easier it becomes to make the right choices or preparations.

I always recommend that everyone work with a practitioner to discover their dosha or their very unique constitution of body, mind, and spirit. Not knowing your unique makeup is like going sailing in the middle of the ocean with no navigation system. Your dosha is like your own unique North Star. Like life, going sailing is never a straight journey. There will be ups and downs, gusts of wind, and turbulent times. But, like the North Star, your dosha gives you something to aim for. It is your personal beacon of health and wellbeing.

Another great step on the road to this deep level of self-awareness is a food journal. Keep a notebook with you and write down everything you consume, then take it a step further. Everything is connected, so take note of how you were feeling both physically and emotionally when you ate. What time did you eat? What was the environment like that you were in while you were eating? Take note of how you felt immediately after finishing and then again in about 30 minutes. Also, make a note in this food journal about your elimination. I know this can also be a taboo subject in our society, but your elimination offers a lot of insight into the health of your digestive system. At this phase, do not worry about making any changes. Simply observe.

You also want to begin observing your cycle closely. I'm sure if you have been on a journey of fertility for any length of time, you have heard this. I would like to challenge you to take a less clinical approach to this for a few months. Yes, we know temperature and cervical mucus can help us know when you are ovulating, but how do your energy levels feel on Day 1, Day 8, or Day 21? Were you able to be super focused and get a lot of creative work done, or was your head a little foggy? Did you *feel* light in your body today or more heavy? What was your appetite like? Did you have any specific cravings? Did you comply with those cravings or not, and how did that feel? All of these little things offer you clues as to how your unique body ebbs and flows throughout the month. Observing and learning these patterns is going to be instrumental in finding the imbalances that may be occurring, healing them, and then harnessing the power of your cycle.

Balance
The next phase is finding your balance. This *balance* will look different for everyone based on your unique constitution. The good news is now you have your north star of health, your dosha. In this phase, you will take small baby steps to steer your health into more alignment with your dosha.

The first baby step is almost always an Ayurvedic cleanse, especially if pregnancy is your goal. Through daily living, we accumulate some toxins in our bodies. Even those who eat exceptionally clean and use all-natural home and beauty products will encounter toxins in their food and environment. Our bodies, specifically our digestive tract, are designed to process and eliminate most of these toxins (some of the new human-made chemicals can be difficult). The problems begin to occur when the amount of toxins begins to build up. A few signs that you may have some built-up toxins are a white coating on your tongue, fatigue, acne, eczema, loose bowels, or constipation. This build-up can happen for a few reasons. If the amount of toxins you are exposing yourself to is higher than normal or coming in faster than your body can handle. Two, if your digestive tract is not functioning properly (this could be for many reasons), your body will not be able to eliminate the toxins. So, by doing an Ayurvedic cleanse, you will effectively be giving your body and digestion a break from incoming toxins for anywhere from 3 to 21 days. You will also be implementing some practices such as abhyanga (self-massage) to aid the body in eliminating any toxins it currently has. After your cleanse and you ease back into "normal" living, your digestion should be stronger than before and ready to tackle any incoming toxins (in reasonable amounts). Although I highly recommend an Ayurvedic cleanse to everyone, I am not going to give you the protocol in this book. Ayurveda truly honors the individual. Therefore each one of your cleanses would look different, and I cannot safely give general instructions. I strongly recommend working with a practitioner to determine the perfect cleanse for your body.

The next baby step in finding your balance is to begin living more in sync with the cycles of nature. To align more with the daily cycles of our world, you can adjust your sleeping and eating habits. Ayurveda recommends rising with or slightly (think an hour or two) before the sun. This is when most humans' brains are the most active, and it is a good time for meditation and creativity. When the sun is the highest in the sky (around noon) is when your digestion is the strongest, so Ayurveda suggests eating your largest meal of the day at this time. Then it is best to get to bed before 10 in the evening. Just as at noon, your body is primed to digest food. At midnight, it does its best digestion or processing of all the information and emotions you experienced during the day; being in a deep sleep at this time is helpful for that process.

The next step is to look at specific doshic imbalances. This topic alone could be an entire book, but I am going to attempt to summarize it for you. You are made up of your own unique proportions of doshas; vata, pitta, or kapha. These doshas can be described by elements of our world; earth, air, fire, water, and space. Then we can go even deeper by describing those elements with specific traits such as dense, mobile, hot, moist, or light. These traits all have balancing traits; mobile and stable, hot and cold, wet and dry, dense and light. In Ayurveda, we use these balancing traits to help someone achieve health, or return to their unique state of health, their dosha. There are a million ways that these traits and, therefore, doshas can manifest for each of us. As a very simple example, let's talk about skin since it is easy to see. If your skin is appearing dry (easily cracking), then the solution would be to add moisture to it. This is essentially how Ayurveda approaches any imbalance in the body, mind, or spirit. We look for the trait, element, or dosha, which is being exacerbated, and we use the opposite to balance it. Finding these imbalances and healing them is again going to be very specific to you, but you are on the right track now that you are becoming self-aware, ridding your body of toxins, and getting in sync with nature.

Cycle Optimization

This final phase is where the magic begins to happen. At this point, you have been tracking your body's reaction to inputs like food, environment, and sensations, so you should almost be able to predict the future. Do you know how you will feel this afternoon if you eat a cold salad for lunch and it's wintertime? You've also been paying closer attention to how you feel throughout your cycle. Do you know what days you crave socialization and when you'd rather have alone time? Now you start to sync your life and your diet with your menstrual cycle.

Let's start in the follicular phase. This begins as soon as you finish bleeding, so approximately day 5 of your cycle. This is known as a very kapha period and is all about building your juiciness and your confidence in who you are. This is like your own personal springtime. You will most likely feel your energy growing as your new uterine lining does. It is a great time to work on activities like brainstorming, planning, and starting new projects. This is a great time to begin waking earlier and getting more movement into your day. It's great to include spices in your diet like ginger and cinnamon to stimulate your digestion during this phase.

Your ovulation phase is next, and it begins with the release of an egg. This shorter phase is dominated by the pitta dosha. It's going to feel like summer. This is when you are your hottest, physically and metaphorically. Your endometrium becomes flushed with blood, and your body temperature will rise. You will most likely feel your most confident and social during this time. This is a great time for communication and collaboration! For me, this is when I love to schedule press or speaking engagements. Because you are "running hot" during this time, it's a great time to include cooling foods into your diet. This is the perfect time for smoothies if you like them. Peppermint tea is also a wonderful cooling treat. You could also try cooking with coconut oil during this time.

After ovulation, you move into your luteal phase or your own personal fall. Your energy may begin to wane, and you may feel a desire to be less social. The heat slowly tapers off. This is a great time to shift your focus to more detail-oriented tasks and to finish up loose ends. Personally, I find myself wanting to clean and organize during this phase. This a great time to include some extra magnesium into your diet to help prevent cramps once menstruation starts. I also love to use this time to prepare for the next phase, like prepping healthy meals and freezing them so they will be quick and easy when I am on my period. During the last few days of this phase, the vata dosha will suddenly spike. This is the mobile force that will tell your body to let go and begin bleeding.

Then you enter the menstrual phase of your cycle. I understand the flow of emotions that might come with your menstrual flow if you were hoping for a baby. Let them flow. This is a great time of release for both your physical body and your emotional one. But I encourage you to look at your menstrual flow as a blessing. It is a great expression of what is going on within your body. It really is like a vital sign. This is an opportunity to become even more self-aware. Make a note of your symptoms and how heavy your flow. Is there a smell to your flow? What specific emotions keep coming up during this time?

These things are all telling you more about what is happening with your doshic balance. This is a great time to focus on rest and rejuvenation. Include more warmth and moisture into your routine with hot teas and baths. Eat warm, moist, nourishing foods, and maybe include some ghee in your cooking.

Now continue to lean into these phases each month. The more you sync your life with your cycle, the easier they both become. Keep paying attention to your own body and listen when it sends you messages. Write in your journal about the positive attributes each phase brings to you. If you can shift your mindset around your cycle and really begin to view it as the blessing it is, the more it will return the blessings.

If you're on a fertility journey of your own, hopefully, my story can give you some hope. As you can see from this book, there are many paths you can take to become a parent. Do not lose faith that your body and spirit can heal when provided the right nourishment. And do not be afraid to reach out for help! You do not have to travel this road alone!

KAYLEE STEIFF

Kaylee Steiff is an Ayurvedic Fertility Specialist, speaker, best-selling author, and founder of Feminine Elements. Ltd. She is passionate about helping women live in alignment with their menstrual cycles and embrace the power of their periods. She personally struggled for years with her reproductive health. When she found Ayurvedic medicine she was able to balance her hormones, heal her cycle and strengthen her fertility and now she is passionate about helping other women do the same.

She has been studying Ayurveda and women's health for over 10 years. She graduated from the Institute for Integrative Nutrition in 2011. Then she studied birth and bereavement with Still Birthday and became an Ayurvedic Postpartum Professional through the Newborn Mothers Collective. She believes learning is a lifelong pursuit and continues her education in Ayurveda and Ayurvedic Yoga Therapy through Yoga Veda Institute.

Kaylee was born and raised in central Ohio where she now raises her two boys. She spends her free time homeschooling her boys, reading books, and chasing her hyper dog. You can also occasionally find her sneaking off to explore local breweries as she is also a craft beer enthusiast.

Website: www.feminine-elements.com
Email: kaylee@feminine-elements.com

Facebook: www.facebook.com/feminineelementsfertility
Instagram:www/instagram.com/feminine.elements

16

TRAVERSING THE VALLEY OF INFERTILITY

HOW A PLAN OF INTENTIONAL FERTILITY LED TO NATURAL CONCEPTION AFTER SIX YEARS OF INFERTILITY

LACEY WESTERBY

IT IS hard for me to believe that, not long ago, I wasn't sure I could even, *if ever*, get pregnant. Now, here I am with a sweet girl who lights up my husband and I's entire world. But it hasn't always been like this. I haven't always been here experiencing the mountaintop splendor of these tried for, prayed for, cried for mama days. I was deep in the shadows of the valley before I reached this mountaintop.

Merriam-Webster defines a valley as an elongated depression of the earth's surface, usually between ranges of hills or mountains; a hollow depression. Further, the definition of a depression is a place or part that is lower than the surrounding area. And hollow is defined as an unfilled space: cavity, hole[1].

I often refer to my six-year struggle with infertility as a valley. From the mountaintop of newlywed bliss, through the barren depression of endometriosis (endo)[2] and infertility, and finally back to the mountaintop of long awaited mama-hood. That valley, that depression, that low-point—was marked by emptiness. A hollow longing in my heart to become a mama.

When you are deep in the valley of infertility, it is difficult to see ahead. The mountaintops in the distance are covered in clouds. You have to search for hope, for faith. I believe that we all have our share of valleys in this life. But when we emerge from those valleys, we come out with something gained, something we would never have gained had we not gone through it.

Just a Girl with Killer Cramps

My story began long before I was concerned about fertility. Much of my youth and young adulthood revolved around my monthly cycle, as my periods came each month with a vengeance. They were heavy, and they were *painful*. When the cramps kicked in, it was all I could do to not double over in pain. I'd become ghostly pale, sweaty with the chills, and nauseous to the point of vomiting. I popped Advil like they were Skittles and would remain in the bathroom for hours, hunched over on the toilet. I'd bloat up like a balloon, going up an entire pant size, and I suffered from terrible hormonal migraines[3]. If I curled up in a ball with a heating pad, the pain was a bit more bearable. This was my typical period. Every month, like clockwork.

Sure, I got good at managing it; it's what you do when it's your normal. I did my best to live a regular life, but I missed school once in a while and bailed on social events during my period. This normal stayed with me through adulthood. I'd call in sick to work, curl up in the fetal position on my office floor, and rearrange entire vacation plans around my period.

My killer cramps and intense periods were something I had come to terms with and learned to deal with over the years. While I had my mama's empathy and understanding, she also told me what she knew to be true: heavy, painful periods ran in our family. Apparently, I just happened to draw the short straw in the genetics game when it came to my menstrual cycle. So, I learned to live with my normal. Month after month. *Year after year.*

I told every single doctor I ever had about my extreme pain during my periods. I was told to take Midol instead of Advil because that would help get rid of the pain. I was told my period was normal, heavy —*sure*, but normal because it was regular every single month. I was told my ovaries were posterior, and that was the cause of my significant lower back pain. I was put on birth control to help manage my heavy, painful periods in college. I was told endometriosis wasn't a concern for me because I didn't exhibit all the symptoms associated with it. I was even told, *"you would know if you had endometriosis."*

First Comes Love, Then Comes Marriage, Then Comes...

Fast forward a few years: I married my best friend, and we intentionally set out to enjoy our marriage for a while before adding kids to the mix. We wanted time for us as a couple; to travel, build up our savings, and feel a bit more settled. I wanted to be in a really great place in my marriage before changing up that dynamic.

I never saw any women in my life struggle to have babies, at least not publicly. Therefore, I grew up with the mindset that being able to have a baby, as a woman, should be a given. I had no reason to believe otherwise, and I thought I still had plenty of time to become a mama. Five years into married life and I recollect telling my husband that the only gift I wanted for my 30th birthday was to be pregnant.

The thrill of finally making the decision to start a family was exhilarating. The dreaming and planning and preparing started to take hold. The visions and discussions about how we would raise our kids together were the topics of conversation. Our whole life perspective shifted to center around the idea of starting a family. We never imagined it would be so difficult to conceive a child. Infertility wasn't something we ever anticipated having to address. It was not part of the dream of starting a family—*it was never in the plans.*

When we first started trying to conceive (TTC), it was no big deal; we weren't in any big rush. We figured if it happened, it happened. We didn't want to "work at it." A few months went by, and I started to wonder why we weren't having any success with conception. I decided to check in with an obstetrician-gynecologist (OB-GYN) for a basic wellness visit and to discuss preparing my body for pregnancy. My doctor reassured me, and I felt pretty confident that, in time, we'd get pregnant.

Six more months went by, and *nothing*. Maybe we just needed to time things a bit more closely. I started charting my cycles to be sure we were hitting our prime window of opportunity each month. *Now we were starting to "work at it."*

Another six months...*nothing*. Time for another wellness check. This time the doctor agreed to do some basic hormonal blood work. She didn't seem too concerned, so I figured I shouldn't be either. But, just in case, I tightened up the reigns a bit on our diet and improved my supplements.

Somewhere along the road after that appointment, I fell into a pattern of self-diagnosing. I think I wanted a baby so bad, and I had no answers as to why we weren't conceiving, that I convinced myself there must be something wrong with me. *I had to be broken somewhere.* Sure, my hormone blood work came back normal, but was it *optimal*? Could my thyroid be out of whack? I think I might have symptoms of adrenal fatigue[4] or maybe leaky gut[5]? I suppose it crossed my mind that I could have endometriosis to some degree, but, remember, I'd asked all the doctors and was always told it wasn't likely in my case.

I finally set up another appointment with my OB to address my concerns. She ran a thyroid panel[6] and told me to relax. I think she could sense that I was searching for answers, so she recommended that my husband run a semen analysis[7] as well. Both of our tests came back normal.

The excitement of starting a family together eventually waned into worry and anxiety. That worry turned to doubt; the doubt led to fear and defeat. Those dreams of starting a family began to feel tarnished. Infertility was a hardship—it was suffering a loss, restructuring dreams, and working through a multitude of solutions my husband and I never envisioned for our future together. At that point, most people close to us were aware of the fact that we'd been trying for a while to have a baby. We had their support, but their well-meaning comments didn't always land softly on my heart.

"Well, at least you're having fun trying!"
No, not actually. Timing intercourse, fertility testing, the pressure mounting...it kind of felt like a job. Not fun. *Not really.*

"You just need to relax. Then you'll be able to get pregnant. Stop stressing about it."
I wish it were that easy, but trying to conceive and not conceiving sort of causes the stress in the first place.

"You just need to quit trying. When you stop trying, you'll get pregnant."
Um, *ok.* But in the meantime, I wasn't getting any younger. And the longer we prolonged finding out why we were struggling, the further out the end goal got.

My doctor mentioned trying out Ovulation Predictor Kits (OPK)[8]. That would really narrow down the prime window of opportunity, right? Maybe we were just doing it all wrong? *Timing* it wrong? Who knew getting pregnant was so technical?

More Than a Painful Period

The next move, medically speaking, was to assess my reproductive organs with a laparoscopic surgery[9]. A quick, easy, routine day-surgery with my OB-GYN to look for any anatomical abnormalities that might be interfering with our attempt to get pregnant. It sounded easy enough, but surgery was a big milestone for me. I still had my tonsils and my appendix. I'd never even broken a bone or been hospitalized, *ever*. Surgery and anesthesia, it was all new to me and a bit scary.

My doctor didn't rush me, she suggested it in the spring, and I needed a few months before I was ready for that next step. All in all, my first-ever surgery wasn't that bad. I was in and out of the operating room in about 45 minutes. My pain level was minimal, and my recovery was quick.

But I wasn't prepared for the diagnosis. My doctor was shocked to find stage 4 endometriosis[10] covering my reproductive organs, creating a web-like mess of scar tissue everywhere. She said that my case was in her top 5 of worst cases she'd seen in her 20+ year career. *Not that I wanted those bragging rights.*

According to Dr. Tamer Seckin, a world-renowned laparoscopic deep-excision endometriosis surgeon, "Endometriosis is a...disease in which endometrial-like tissue is found outside of the uterus in other parts of the body...This tissue, which normally lines the uterus, is associated with monthly menstruation and is often characterized by abnormal painful and heavy periods, as well as pelvic pain, severe cramps, and pain with sex." [11]

Endometriosis affects millions of women worldwide. An estimated 1 in 10 women experiences endometriosis during their reproductive years. There is no known cause and no known cure[12]. Family history and genetics most likely play a part in developing endometriosis. It is often misdiagnosed as irritable bowel syndrome (IBS)[13] or written off as a regular heavy period. Endometriosis accounts for a staggering number of infertility cases in women, often keeping the odds of getting pregnant via natural conception at less than 1%[14]. Endometriosis can go unnoticed for years[15], just as mine did.

In receiving the diagnosis of stage 4 endometriosis, I felt a sense of relief amid the disappointment. All of a sudden, with the assessment of my doctor, my normal wasn't *normal* anymore. My pain was justified. It was ok to admit the hurt that came with my periods every month. *It wasn't my fault or a weakness.* It was a real thing, a real condition that I suffered from. There was gratification in knowing I wasn't crazy.

With that diagnosis, I was empowered to learn as much as possible, change what I could, and move forward with knowledge and acceptance. For twenty-plus years, I didn't have that. I felt alone and isolated at times because no one *"got it."*

I Just Wanna Be a Mama

After that diagnostic surgery, my OB-GYN told us she couldn't do any more to help us and referred my husband and me to a fertility specialist, a reproductive endocrinologist (RE)[16] whom I couldn't get an appointment with for another *three months*. Those months of waiting to see the RE were a roller coaster ride, emotionally speaking. I felt liberated in finally knowing why we were struggling to conceive and empowerment in being able to make a plan moving forward. But then there was disappointment, guilt, and even resentment building.

How could I not know that I had endometriosis for 20 years? Why didn't I push harder to get diagnosed sooner? Would the outcome have been any different? Will we even be able to conceive naturally now?

Some days I was just fed up, angry, and frustrated that we couldn't just get pregnant already. I was irritated by the position endometriosis had put me in. I was saddened with grief for something that may never be. In a matter of just a few years, I went from being excited about *finally* being ready to start a family to feeling like a ticking time bomb was about to go off in my uterus.

Infertility took me to places I never thought I would go; to places filled with guilt, shame, and envy. Guilt for feeling like the one that was broken. Shame for feeling like my body was incapable of doing what it was supposed to do. And the envy of those for whom it came easily. It took me to a place of heightened insecurities and brokenness. Would someone ask me if I looked pregnant in this outfit? Was my body broken beyond repair? *Infertility was ugly.* It had a way of exposing all of my flaws. My fears. My doubts. My weaknesses in my faith. It gave no guarantees. There was no concrete answer or quick-fix solution. It led to depression and anxiety, defeat and loss.

What were simple joys for mothers of babes were like daggers to the heart for a yearning wanna-be-mama. A beautiful pregnancy announcement invoked a flood of tears. A tote of second-hand maternity clothes caused a full-fledged meltdown. Watching a mother cradle her newborn baby in a store sent me outside sobbing. I could be truly overjoyed to hear of a friend excitedly expecting, but my heart also hurt. Because in another's blessing, I was *painfully* aware of what I didn't have. I just wanted to be a mama, and it wasn't supposed to be this hard.

Going All-In: Forging My Own Path to Motherhood

Eventually, our appointment with the RE came around, and I felt better getting some direction. However, I wasn't stoked about a second, more intense excision surgery[17] to remove the endometriosis and the associated scarring that had manifested all over my reproductive organs for the last two decades of my life.

After surgery, the RE recommended that we keep trying to conceive naturally for a few months before starting an in vitro fertilization (IVF)[18] procedure. He was concerned that my horribly scarred fallopian tubes[19] might not be able to incubate an embryo properly. In addition, the damage to my tubes increased the risk for a tubal pregnancy[20] tenfold. On top of that, a recent test indicated that my Anti-Müllerian Hormone (AMH)[21] had dropped significantly post-surgery.

Thus, we knew, if natural conception wasn't going to happen for us, we would have to bypass all other forms of fertility treatment and start with the most intensive option there was—IVF. This was a tough pill to swallow, and I felt like I needed time to pray, to soul search what we were willing to consider moving forward. My type-A, investigate all the options, personality needed time to just *be still*[22] for a moment. I needed to prayerfully consider which path to motherhood I was meant to take.

In a span of six months, I underwent two surgeries for endometriosis and learned that IVF would be our best shot at conceiving. I knew my husband and I needed some time to process everything, and my body needed time to rest and recover. We decided to prioritize improving my health and healing over adding a baby to our family for a few months. We took a break from all the cycle-charting[23], temperature-taking, and ovulation predictor kits, and it was refreshing.

Before I started trying to become a mama with all my might, I was guilty of thinking it'd be easy to get pregnant. I couldn't comprehend what it meant to want something so desperately but have no control in being able to bring that desire into reality. So, while my husband and I committed to trying on our own for a bit longer, we were also fully relying on God to bring us the desire of our hearts.[24]

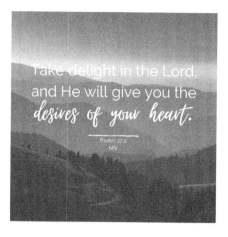

Once I accepted that my pain, my health issues, my infertility had a cause and a name, endometriosis, I found *power* in that knowledge. I dove into learning all that I could about endometriosis and its impact on fertility. Specifically, what, *if anything*, I could do or change in my daily life to make a difference in my healing. I explored all possible paths to becoming a mama—domestic and international adoption, adoption through foster care, and IVF. My husband and I prayed, *intensely*, for guidance.

I believed that God had plans for my husband and me to become parents. Specifically, I felt the Holy Spirit leading me toward carrying our own child in my womb. Therefore, I began to prepare myself mentally and emotionally for IVF. We did a couple of consults with our RE and started preliminary testing, which sent me down more research rabbit trails. The more I researched, the more I realized there was so much I could do to improve my fertility—even with low AMH and endo-scarred reproductive organs.

While I was placing a whole lot of faith in God to bring me complete healing from endometriosis and fulfill the desires of my heart to become a mama someday soon, I decided that I wanted to do my part while I waited on God to do His. I became consumed with researching and replacing all things plastic in our home. I learned more about how we could tweak our diet and include whole foods to improve our chances of naturally conceiving. I explored DIY fertility massage[25], acupuncture[26], and the use of essential oils[27] for fertility.

I became committed to doing everything in my power to provide the best environment for my body to conceive a baby naturally, as God intricately designed it to, or at least set it up for success in the event that we would need to pursue IVF. But I also knew, deep down, that the whole baby-making thing wasn't in my hands...*it was in His.* I was intentional about allowing room for God to work in my life while I began to make small shifts towards improving my fertility.

I implemented my own holistic[28] approach to healing from endometriosis and improving our odds of conceiving with or without the assistance of IVF, and I prayed for healing daily. I made massive changes with nutrition, exercise, and self-care. I prioritized building up my marriage, and I worked at strengthening my faith and my resolve. I was shifting into an organic, nontoxic lifestyle with an "all-in" approach to the natural conception game that I began to refer to as Intentional Fertility.

Intentional Fertility

I felt like my husband and I were at a crossroads. We were either going to be able to have a child naturally, or we wouldn't. I wanted to say that I gave it everything I could to go the natural route before we followed other paths to parenthood. My entire life became about conception.

It took a full nine months before I felt the small shifts were starting to take hold, becoming a part of our daily life. I found that every improvement created a ripple effect, further improving other areas of my health and well-being along the way.

The specifics of the changes my husband and I made are too lengthy to include in this single chapter, but I can give you a brief understanding of what Intentional Fertility looked like for me. Please know, I am not a doctor, and I am not advising you on what you should or should not be doing. I am simply sharing some of the lifestyle shifts my husband and I made in our endeavor to get pregnant naturally.

- **Curating a Team**: I knew that I couldn't go about the Intentional Fertility thing all alone; I needed a support network. My husband was on board, my prayer warriors were praying diligently, and I was working with an OB-GYN and RE. I found a therapist to help me through the heavy emotional aspects of infertility. I started treatment with an acupuncturist and a chiropractor[29], and I added in a functional medicine nutritionist[30] to assist with supplementation and customized hormonal testing.
- **Eating for Fertility**: I meticulously removed all inflammatory foods[31] from my diet, significantly lessening my endometriosis symptoms. I increased fertility superfoods[32] to balance hormones for optimal fertility, further boost our chances of natural conception and embryo implantation[33], and support retaining a pregnancy. I crafted an incredibly nourishing and healing diet by removing sugar, dairy, gluten, caffeine, and soy while adding in high-quality meat and produce, fertility smoothies packed with superfoods, herbal teas, and other nutrient-dense foods[34] like seaweed, bone broth, fermented foods, and healthy fats.
- **Reducing Toxic Load**[35]: I swapped personal care and cleaning products for less toxic versions. I cleansed our home of all things plastic and replaced them with glass or metal. Toxic cookware and kitchen items were traded for nontoxic equivalents. We improved our water filtration with a multi-stage under-the-counter drinking water system and shower filters and upgraded our fabrics to organic cotton. I created a less toxic home, a safe place, for my body to fight off the toxins it was dealing with.

- **Choosing Fertility-Based Practices and Movement**: I applied various practices to enhance my fertility: fertility massage, lymphatic drainage[36] techniques, detox baths[37], daily walks, fertility yoga[38], conception meditation[39], castor oil packs[40], and more. Essentially, I slowed down my exercise regimen tremendously and prioritized sleep above movement. I listened to what my body was telling me, giving it gentle movement most often and choosing rest when needed.

- **Prioritizing Sleep**: I initiated a bedtime routine that I religiously adhered to, shutting down all electronics a solid two hours before bed and winding down purposefully. My evenings consisted of a lavender and Epsom salt bath, snuggle time with my hubby, reading a book, and spending quiet time in meditation or prayer. As I learned how foundational sleep was to my health and hormones, sleep simply became a non-negotiable for me.

- **Reducing Stress**: I learned that essential oils for aromatherapy[41], bath salts, and roll-on blends were imperative in helping me find a more relaxed state whenever anxiety bubbled up. I incorporated a short yoga or meditative breathing session at the end of most days. I became very intentional about stepping back from anything that might cause my body, be it physically or emotionally, any sort of stress.

- **Reinforcing my Faith:** My faith grounded me and reminded me of the greater purpose I had in Him while I was walking the valley of infertility. It kept me looking up at the mountains on the other side when it would have been so easy to continue looking down. *I leaned hard into my faith.* I dug deeper to rely on God fully and grabbed on tighter to the Promises I clung to in the Bible. I knew I needed to reinforce my connection to Jesus so that when all the walls came down, and I found myself in my lowest moments, I wouldn't have to search for Him. I prioritized daily quiet time for prayer, devotions, and meditation. I listened to encouraging Christian podcasts and worship music. It was in the depths of the valley of infertility that I experienced some of the deepest, most personally emotional, meditative, soul searching, and soul-filling prayer. This deeper prayer experience stretched me and helped me to process very real emotions. I *knew* God was good. I *knew* He wouldn't leave me to figure it all out on my own, even when I tried to do just that[42]. I knew, I knew, *I knew* that my pain would not be wasted; that He would use my story for His glory; He would use my hurt for *good*. [43]

- **Supporting My Spouse**: I didn't want to become so self-focused on my healing that my marriage suffered. I needed my husband in my corner; I needed him to feel loved when I struggled to express affection. I put my energy toward drawing closer to my husband rather than pushing him away and isolating myself. Infertility took our marriage to a whole new level, in an eerily beautiful kind of way. We were raw and vulnerable with one another. My big, burly, man of a man let down his guard in ways I had never seen before; I saw his heart ache for mine. He prayed for me when I couldn't find the words. He felt strength when I was weak. He heard the Holy Spirit speak directly into our lives when all I heard was silence. We bared our souls in sharing our fears and hopes and dreams and faith in this struggle. We envisioned our future since the beginning of our marriage and we worked hard to bring that vision into reality. We made plans for our family-to-be, and we had to change, adjust, and rework those plans. We fortified our marriage on strength and intention; we lived a beautiful, messy life while we walked the valley of infertility *together*.

With all of these changes, I turned myself into a natural, holistic mama-in-waiting. I learned that I had the ability to change the outcome. I didn't need to sit in agonizing chronic pain caused by endometriosis every month. I could play a part in my healing. I could detox my body to set it up for conception success. I could remove the things in my life that were hindering my fertility. And over time, I felt a difference. All the improvements and adjustments were starting to add up. The overwhelm of change started to give way to a season of hope and health.

Soon Intentional Fertility started to feel routine, and I found myself desiring a time of rest and renewal. I decluttered my home and my schedule. I focused on being still—nesting, reading, gardening; nourishing my soul with a slower pace. As I committed myself to Intentional Fertility, I was committing myself to self-care.

Be Still & Know...

It was in this season of stillness and acceptance that I truly surrendered it all—my pain, my dreams, my desire to be a mama—to God. I vividly recall laying on my bedroom floor, with a castor oil pack on my abdomen, listening to worship music while breathing deep into a meditative prayer[44] when a particular song started to play.

The lyrics stirred my soul, and my whole perspective on my fertility journey pivoted as tears streamed down my face.

The words spoke of being refined by the fire, struggling to praise God in the tough times, and knowing that God was able to do anything—perform miracles, move mountains, save souls. Additionally, the song spoke of the unanswered prayers, the missing miracles, the mountains unmoved. Could I still choose to put my hope in Him in these downtrodden times? Could I trust Him with my life, even if He didn't choose the path I was praying He would for me? Could I sing praise and worship to a God that I knew could remove this infertility from my life, even if He chose not to?

As the song profoundly moved me, I felt an emotional release, a burden lifted. I let go of expectation. I had been praying and hoping and secretly wishing for God to make me a mama, but in this one powerful, Holy Spirit-filled moment, I literally threw my hands up in the air and praised my God—not knowing if He would take infertility away from me or not. I relented the control I was grasping for and quit trying to prepare for a future I had intended for myself. It was the moment I said, *I felt,* "Ok, God, You got this. And in the meantime, I'm going to choose to live, to *enjoy,* my present circumstances. And if You choose not to make me a mama in the way I thought You were going to, You are still my God. I know I will be a mama, someway, somehow, but I surrender what that looks like to You. I trust You to make it happen in Your will. My hope is in You...it is well with my soul[45]."

I continued to walk in the mucky valley of infertility after that ultimate surrender. I continued to pray, each and every day, for God to bring my husband and me a baby in whatever way He chose. God's grace gave me the patience and persistence to wait on Him and His timing. I still fully expected God to speak in the silence as I pleaded for Him to take away our pain and yearning and bless us with the desire of our hearts. For I knew those desires of my heart, *He* placed them there. In the silence, I continued to fall back on one thing, *hope.* Hope in the Promises of my God; hope in the future I knew He had planned for me[46]. Hope to bring me peace beyond understanding[47].

And one day, God broke through the silence. He handed me my very own miracle. My husband was out of state for work; I was a couple of days late on my period, so I decided to take a pregnancy test. I honestly can't tell you why because over the past six years of infertility and disappointment when it came to pregnancy tests, I had made it my habit never to take a test before I was at least five days late. I just didn't want to get my hopes up, *ever.* But this time was different. *In every single way.* Because this time, the test was positive. And the test I took the next day, just to be sure, was positive. And the next one I took the day after that, and the day after that, and the day after that, *they were all positive.* Five positive pregnancy tests later, and I was still in a state of disbelief.

We were told our chances of naturally conceiving were significantly less than 1%, yet, against all the odds, I was holding a positive test in my hands. A solid nine months after living out Intentional Fertility on all levels. Two months before we were scheduled to start IVF. Six years after my 30th birthday. Six years of TTC. Six years without a single positive pregnancy test.

In one perfect, extraordinary, miraculous, dreamlike instant, my entire life shifted from all things Intentional Fertility to intentional pregnancy. I was in awe, pure wonder, and amazement. And I was ready, so ready, *to just be.* To bask in the miracle we had been given. To love on our sweet, precious baby growing in my belly. To transition from wanna-be-mama to the real deal as fully present as possible.

From Valley Views to Mountaintop Miracles

If you are standing where I was not all that long ago, desperate to try all the things in order to fall pregnant, I pray that my story brings you hope in the hardship. Know that you are not alone. I was on that side of infertility just yesterday, it seems. Now I'm navigating a whole new terrain as a mama. It is magnificent and beautiful, and ever-changing. While I had to rely on God fully, pray harder than I ever had before, and trust in His timing over my own, there was also so much I could do, so much I could change. You don't have to feel helpless in the struggle of infertility —there is plenty you can do in the waiting.

This is my story. My path is unique, as is yours. Still, we are similarly connected by this valley we have traversed. A great deal of my story is about change and growth, learning and knowledge, transformation and surrender. It is about a complete overhaul of my life in a desperate attempt to find fertility. It is about miraculous healing and fully surrendering to God. My journey, a season of wilderness, of trudging through the valley of infertility, was a period of pain and hurt and suffering in my life. Equally, it was a time of searching for the streams in the wasteland[48], for trusting that God desired to make me a mama, and for believing in miracles.

Six years of infertility, and this is what I've learned about valleys:

1. They are not infinite. No valley on this earth is never-ending. Eventually, you come up out of the valley and ascend the mountain on the other side.

2. They are fertile ground. The rocky, rugged mountaintop itself is quite barren. All the good growth, lush vegetation, and diversity of plants exist in the valley where the fertile soil and nourishing water lies. The valley is where growth happens.

3. They make the mountaintop views that much sweeter. Overlooking the tear-stained valley summons a sense of gratitude and contentment that simply wouldn't exist without first navigating the gorge to scale the mountain.

As we drove home from the hospital, with our brand-new babe in the car seat next to me, in an act of serendipity, that same song from my moment of complete surrender came over the radio. I beheld my baby girl sleeping soundly in her seat, and the tears welled up in my eyes. My Intentional Fertility journey had unfolded to become one of intentional pregnancy and, ultimately, just as I had hoped and prayed for, one of intentional motherhood.

I was finally a mama.

---

1. https://www.merriam-webster.com)
2. *Endometriosis (endo)*: A condition in which tissue that normally lines the inside of the uterus grows outside the uterus. This tissue usually is found on reproductive organs in the pelvis, but can show up in other areas of the body.
3. *Hormonal Migraine*: Migraines, intense headaches, caused by variable hormone levels.
4. *Adrenal Fatigue*: A syndrome that results when adrenal glands are not functioning properly. Most often caused by periods of intense stress.

5. *Leaky Gut*: A condition also known as "intestinal permeability" that occurs when the gut lining becomes compromised, allowing particles to enter the bloodstream that shouldn't, leading to an inflammatory response.

6. *Thyroid Panel*: A lab test ordered to analyze thyroid function, measuring the hormones associated with thyroid health.

7. *Semen Analysis*: A test that examines the health and viability of sperm, also known as sperm count.

8. *Ovulation Predictor Kit (OPK)*: A test that predicts ovulation by detecting the level of luteinizing hormone in urine.

9. *Laparoscopic Surgery*: A diagnostic procedure used to inspect the organs inside the abdomen with a laparoscope, a very small tube-like instrument with a light and camera that sends real-time images to a monitor in the surgical room.

10. *Stage 4 Endometriosis*: The "severe" stage of endometriosis. This stage usually involves deep endometriosis implants or adhesions on the reproductive organs, usually involves other abdominal organs or ovarian cysts, and in rare cases can be found outside of the pelvic region

11. Seckin, MD, T. 2020, June 23. Endometriosis: Symptoms, Causes, and Treatments https://www.drseckin.com/endometriosis

12. Facts about Endometriosis. Retrieved from http://endometriosis.org/resources/articles/facts-about-endometriosis/

13. *Irritable Bowel Syndrome (IBS)*: A disorder that includes symptoms of cramping, abdominal pain, bloating, gas, and diarrhea or constipation.

14. Endometriosis and Pregnancy. Retrieved from https://endometriosisnews.com/endometriosis-and-pregnancy/

15. Facts about Endometriosis. Retrieved from http://endometriosis.org/resources/articles/facts-about-endometriosis/

16. *Reproductive Endocrinologist (RE)*: An OB-GYN that specializes in endocrinology (hormone system) as it relates to reproduction.

17. *Excision Surgery*: Excision surgery fully removes damaged tissue by scalpel dissection as opposed to ablation surgery, which burns away the surface of endometriosis adhesions.

18. *In Vitro Fertilization (IVF)*: A form of Assisted Reproductive Technology that retrieves mature eggs from ovaries, cultures them with sperm in a lab setting, and after a period of incubation, transfers a fertilized egg (embryo) to a uterus.

19. *Fallopian Tubes*: The tubes that carry the eggs from the ovaries to the uterus.

20. *Tubal Pregnancy*: A pregnancy in which a fertilized egg implants in the wall of a fallopian tube instead of the uterus.

21. *Anti-Müllerian Hormone (AMH)*: A hormone produced in the ovarian follicles that reflects ovarian reserve (egg count). A low AMH level indicates a diminished ovarian reserve.

22. Psalm 46:10 New King James Version "Be still, and know that I am God; I will be exalted among the nations, I will be exalted in the earth!"

23. *Cycle-Charting*: The act of charting a menstrual cycle to record its length as well as observe signs of ovulation with basal body temperature and cervical mucus.

24. Psalm 37:4 New International Version "Take delight in the Lord, and He will give you the desires of your heart."

25. *Fertility Massage*: A type of massage designed to improve fertility.

26. *Acupuncture*: A therapy that involves inserting thin, sterile needles into acupuncture points on specific meridians of the body. Acupuncture increases blood flow and has been shown to improve reproductive function.

27. *Essential Oils*: Highly concentrated oils made from various parts of plants that have been shown to have many health benefits.

28. *Holistic*: Addressing health as a complete system rather than parts.

29. *Chiropractor*: A health care practitioner that specializes in the manual manipulation of the spine to improve mobility and function of joints and the nervous system.

30. *Functional Medicine Nutritionist*: A form of medicine that tackles the root cause of health concerns with nutrient-dense foods and customized supplementation.

31. *Inflammatory Foods*: Foods that can cause or worsen inflammation in a body, including sugar, refined carbohydrates, alcohol, unhealthy fats, gluten, and processed meats and dairy.

32. *Fertility Superfoods*: Foods that nourish the egg and the sperm as well as assist in balancing hormones.

33. *Embryo Implantation*: The implantation of a fertilized egg into the wall of the uterus.

34. *Nutrient-Dense Foods*: Foods that are rich in vitamins, minerals, and other nutrients important for health.

35. *Toxic Load:* The amount of toxins in a body, accumulated from foods eaten, environmental factors, or other toxic exposure.

36. *Lymphatic Drainage*: The lymphatic system naturally eliminates cellular waste from the body through daily movement. However, circumstances can cause the lymph system to stagnate and may require lymphatic drainage techniques to assist in its function.

37. *Detox Bath*: A relaxing bath with detoxifying ingredients, such as Epsom salts, bentonite clay, or essential oils, that help to remove toxins from the body.

38. *Fertility Yoga*: Physical postures, breathing techniques, and meditation that specifically promote reproductive health.

39. *Conception Meditation*: The act or process of meditating on concepts surrounding ovulation, conception, and fertility.

40. *Castor Oil Packs*: A cloth soaked in unrefined castor oil that is placed on the area of the body needing healing and then covered with a heating pad. Castor oil packs used for endometriosis and fertility are placed on the abdomen, increasing blood circulation to reproductive organs while also improving the body's detox pathways and reducing inflammation.

41. *Aromatherapy*: The use of essential oils for therapeutic purposes.

42. Deuteronomy 31:8 New International Version "The Lord himself goes before you and will be with you; he will never leave you nor forsake you. Do not be afraid; do not be discouraged."

43. 2 Corinthians 1:3-5 New International Version "Praise be to the God and Father of our Lord Jesus Christ, the Father of compassion and the God of all comfort, who comforts us in all our troubles, so that we can comfort those in any trouble with the comfort we ourselves receive from God. For just as we share abundantly in the sufferings of Christ, so also our comfort abounds through Christ."

44. *Meditative Prayer*: A quiet prayer experience in which a person listens for God to work in their lives by focusing on the Promises of God in His Word.

45. Psalm 62:5 New International Version "Yes, my soul, find rest in God; my hope comes from him."

46. Jeremiah 29:11 New International Version "'For I know the plans I have for you" declares the Lord, "plans to prosper you and not to harm you, plans to give you hope and a future."

47. Philippians 4:6-7 New International Version "Do not be anxious about anything, but in every situation, by prayer and petition, with thanksgiving, present your requests to God. And the peace of God, which transcends all understanding, will guard your hearts and your minds in Christ Jesus."

48. Isaiah 43:19 New International Version "See, I am doing a new thing! Now it springs up; do you not perceive it? I am making a way in the wilderness and streams in the wasteland."

LACEY WESTERBY

Lacey Westerby is the Country Wife behind *Country Wife Chronicles* (*CWC*), a blog started with the intention to build a community of wildland fire wives while sharing a heart for Jesus and all things simple and slow; rustic and rural. In recent years, the content of *CWC* shifted as it became Lacey's voice through a diagnosis of endometriosis and infertility; she shares her story to help others find hope in the hardship and *Streams in the Wasteland*.

Lacey describes herself as an introvert, a bit of an old soul that believes strongly in sharing our stories to unite commonalities and learn from one another. It is this passion to help other women naturally improve their fertility that inspired her to develop Intentional Fertility, a working blueprint of intentional efforts aimed at optimizing conception.

After six years of infertility, Lacey and her rugged hubby, Jon, are blessed to have the desire of their hearts, a sweetheart miracle baby girl. Lacey and her family have returned to her Nebraska roots after six years of living in the South to build their homesteading dream and live out her life's mantra, Psalm 46:10, "Be Still & Know."

Additional Info
Blog: https://www.countrywifechronicles.com
Email: countrywifechronicles@gmail.com
Relevant Publications:

Streams in the Wasteland: 31 Days of Devotions for Finding Hope in the Hardship
31 Days of Scripture: Praying Through Infertility PDF
Facebook: https://www.facebook.com/countrywifechronicles
Instagram: https://www.instagram.com/countrywifechronicles/
Pinterest: https://www.pinterest.com/countrywifeblog/

17

THE IVF ROLLER COASTER RIDE

LISA CHIYA

ONE OUT OF eight couples will grapple with infertility-related issues. For me, that's not just a statistic- I was one of the eight. Like so many before me, my journey has had its fair share of ups and downs. Trying to conceive when your body won't cooperate is an emotional, physical, and financial rollercoaster. There were many days when I thought I would never be a mother. On those days, I was grateful for my career. My years of work in the infertility industry emotionally prepared me for our journey.

My name is Lisa Chiya. I am the Founder and President of The Genesis Group. We are a well-established egg donation and surrogacy agency in Southern California. Our agency has helped thousands of intended parents build their families. When I started working in this field, I never would have guessed that I would need my own services one day.

Most of us don't grow up imagining we will need an egg donor or a surrogate to build our family. You just assume that things will work out like they do in the movies. Growing up, it was never a question of whether I wanted to have children. I always had a strong maternal instinct. My mother passed away when I was two years old from a brain aneurysm, which forced me to grow up quickly. My memory of her is faint, but I feel fortunate to have known her for even a short period of time. I know she loved me, but not being able to recall the love of a mother cemented my desire to have children. In my heart, I knew that life would not be complete, or rather life would be empty, without the pitter-patter of little feet. Luckily, my dear husband always wanted a large family too. But after years of trying to conceive, we knew we needed to invest the time and resources to undergo IVF. I will not bore you with the IVF details. I will just say we spent more money than we allocated. We underwent countless cycles at various clinics to finally have twelve embryos, six of which genetically tested normal and six that were not tested at all.

On July 2, 2015, we transferred two embryos that were not genetically tested. After the dreaded two-week waiting period, my reproductive endocrinologist confirmed that I was pregnant. And at the six-week heartbeat confirmation, I heard two heartbeats. I couldn't believe that both embryos took!! Of course, I was ecstatic, but my joy was short-lived. The following week we found out that the second embryo no longer had a heartbeat. It was a sad setback, but we were grateful that we were still pregnant with a singleton. I believe that loss set the tone for the rest of my pregnancy. My pregnancy was physically uneventful but emotionally torturous. Every week I would hope for the best but expected the absolute worst. We did not share the news with a single soul until we were about twelve weeks pregnant. But even then, I didn't let my guard down. In the back of my head, I still knew anything could happen. A part of me just couldn't believe that I was really pregnant. If I am being honest, I regret not enjoying being pregnant. The miracle of life was happening, and I wasn't able to fully appreciate most of it.

At our twenty-week anatomy scan, my perinatologist was really enthusiastic about my progress. He told me everything was looking great and asked if I wanted to know the sex of the baby. I did!!! I have always wanted a little girl. But my heart told me that I was carrying a baby boy, and on March 14, 2016, my incredible son was born.

Nothing prepares you for motherhood. The miracle of life is beautiful. But the first few months were the most challenging days of my life. The fourth trimester is brutal; the lack of sleep, constant worrying, hormonal surges, and the physical recovery. The days were long, but the weeks were lightning fast. Even with the lack of sleep, I yearned to grow our family. We desperately wanted a sibling for our son. We wanted our children to know the joy of having a brother or a sister.

I have one sibling myself: a younger sister. We have not lived in the same city for more than twenty years. In fact, we currently live about 3,000 miles away from each other, but we speak daily. I've known for all of my life that my bond with my sister was not common, and our relationship is rather unique. When you grow up without a mother, you learn to lean on each other. She is two and a half years my junior, but she was like a mentor and teacher to me my entire life. She would teach herself something, then turn around and teach me. She taught me how to drive a car, cook, put on make-up, sew, and braid my hair. I was so lucky to have a sister like her. There isn't a single thing we wouldn't do for one another. She has stood by my side through it all. She is my person. I have always wanted my son to experience that kind of kinship and know that kind of pure love.

When my son was about six months old, we started preparing for another frozen embryo transfer (FET). We were planning for a November or December transfer, but my body had other plans. In October, I was diagnosed with Graves' Disease. The diagnosis stopped me dead in my family-building tracks. In a matter of a month, I lost twenty-five pounds. My heart palpitations were so bad, and I felt like I was having a heart attack at all times. I couldn't walk upstairs without feeling winded. My endocrinologist was surprised I wasn't experiencing something called thyroid storm because my hormone levels were so severe. I felt betrayed yet again by my body. I was told that pregnancy was not an option and that I would have to wait a minimum of eighteen months to reassess my health. Eighteen months?!? I couldn't wait that long, and I knew I would need to find a surrogate and continue my journey for a sibling that way. The idea of complete strangers helping my family and me with something so personal was at once absolutely beautiful and terrifying.

I was fortunate to find a surrogate quickly. Our surrogate was a young woman with a big heart. I will call her Olivia for privacy reasons. The journey with Olivia and her husband, Steward, started off really well. We met each other, and we immediately agreed to work together. We transferred the two genetically untested embryos, and she became pregnant on the first attempt. It was a surreal feeling. Olivia was pregnant with our baby, but I wasn't tormented like I was with my pregnancy. The weeks moved so quickly, and I felt like I was cheating. We were pregnant, but I wasn't feeling the side effects of the hormones. I wasn't taking shots daily. I wasn't gaining weight. I had mixed feelings. I was excited about the pregnancy, but I was worried and wondered how Olivia was treating the baby. I would speak to my surrogate weekly to see how she was doing. At six weeks, we heard one beautiful heartbeat. Everything was going perfectly. Around the eighth week of gestation, Olivia asked me the strangest question. She asked if I was allergic to milk. "No", I replied, and asked, "why?" She said she would have mild cramps every time she had milk. So, I just asked her to stop drinking milk and thought nothing of it.

However, the more I thought about it, the more it caused me concern. All surrogates need to take medication for the first ten to twelve weeks of gestation to carry the pregnancy. I called her two days later and asked when she expected she would need her progesterone in oil (PIO) refill. It was that day I found out that she had stopped taking her PIO and started taking the suppositories. All surrogates need to take progesterone and estrogen to help create the placenta.

Progesterone in oil PIO is known to have the highest efficacy and absorption rate compared to vaginal suppositories. The issue with PIO is that it must be administered by a long intramuscular needle daily. No one likes needles, but this is part of the surrogacy process. I found out that Olivia had been taking the wrong dosage of her medication for the past eleven days!!

I can't remember the whole conversation. It is all a blur. I remember calling the monitoring IVF clinic immediately and begging for an ultrasound to be performed. Most clinics perform ultrasounds from six a.m. to ten-thirty a.m. daily. I was calling at four p.m. I begged a nurse coordinator I had become friends with to call the doctor back to the clinic to perform an ultrasound. I was fortunate to know the physician as well. I was praying and hoping that the placenta had developed enough to be able to sustain the pregnancy. Olivia and her husband rushed to the clinic. She only lived a few miles away from the monitoring clinic. However, before she could get to the clinic, she started gushing blood uncontrollably. She knew something was terribly wrong, so she called me. I told her we needed to be 100% certain, so they performed the ultrasound and confirmed the worst. I cried silently on the phone while her husband sadly told me no heartbeat was present. I wanted to scream at Olivia. It took every ounce of composure for me not to scream, "YOU killed my baby." How could she be so cavalier with my baby's life? I said nothing more than I have to go and proceeded to hang up the phone. I was numb.

Deep down, I knew she was mourning too. She was physically experiencing the miscarriage, but I didn't care. I was stone cold. I crawled into bed and called my husband to share my grief. I selfishly was hoping he would be able to carry some of the weight that I was feeling. He was devastated but did his best to keep our spirits up. I couldn't get out of bed for days. I lost my appetite. I saw the world in gray hues. I mourned the loss of our baby. I played the "what if...?" game in my head and blamed myself for things I could have done differently. What if I called her more often? Maybe I would have found out that she was taking the incorrect dose of medication. What if I had called sooner? Maybe we could have salvaged the pregnancy. I should have policed her more. In hindsight, I should have asked what medication she was taking daily and confirmed she took her medication.

My next stage of grief was blame. I didn't understand how a rational human being could start taking a new medication without instruction. As a surrogate, you are the protector. The only way to mess up being a surrogate is to take the medication incorrectly. And since this was my first surrogacy journey as the intended Mother, the impact of its failure was more severe for me at the time. This was a very difficult time for me. I had lost faith in surrogacy. How could I even continue on with my own career? How could I advocate to use a surrogate when I couldn't trust the use of a surrogate? I became resigned to the idea that I would need to wait eighteen months to see if I could transfer into myself again.

Days turned into weeks, and weeks turned into a month. I realized that I needed to find the why. I needed to find the silver lining. I wracked my brain. I ultimately decided that it was because I never fully understood the grief that my intended parents often experience when needing to find an egg donor or surrogate. The mourning of their fertility and genetic legacy. The feeling of never experiencing pregnancy. I had never really experienced that mourning phase. I made myself believe this all happened so I could better understand and empathize with my clients. I desperately needed to find the reason. It was the only way for me to rationalize what transpired.

Living in a dark space, you become accustomed to the darkness. I realized that I was depressed, and I needed to stop feeling sorry for myself. I need to live in a space of gratitude. It was like a lightbulb. Sometimes you just need to quiet the mind and be thankful. I started by being thankful that I could breathe. I could walk. I had a beautiful baby. My son! He was the reason to be grateful. My beautiful baby boy helped me find my way back. He truly saved me during this dark period of time. I hugged him tighter and kissed him more, and he reminded me that I needed to be grateful for life. I made one of my favorite movies quotes my mantra, "Get busy living, or get busy dying." I needed to get busy living.

In order to start living, I needed to find forgiveness in my heart. I haven't spoken to Olivia since the miscarriage. We stopped speaking because I was so hurt by what transpired. I tried to understand her side of the story, so I wrote her an email that I never ended up sending. I guess my biggest issue is that she never admitted her wrongdoing. She blamed the clinic and miscommunication with her nurse. Sometimes I want to reach out to her and see how she is doing. I want to apologize for shutting her out. I know she grieved too. I am still trying to find the courage to reach out. If I am being honest, I don't know if I ever will. I think too much time has passed to open up old wounds.

It took a long time for me to get back on the proverbial horse. I had Post Traumatic Stress Disorder. But I knew my desire for my son to have a sibling would eventually overcome –"my fears". I was apprehensive, but I was on a mission to find an experienced surrogate. I believe when you put intention and energy out into the universe, the universe will provide. When I was ready, a previous surrogate became available. An incredibly strong woman named Margaux, who had previously carried quadruplets, came into my life. I found comfort knowing that she was a successful surrogate a few times before. She knew the drill, but her determination to carry quadruplets really inspired me to trust again. From our initial match meeting, she was able to put my nerves at ease. Margaux was a genuinely kind person. She was everything I was hoping to find in a surrogate. She was also a consummate professional. She helped me heal from the trauma of the previous journey. She was comforting and fun to be around. I will always be grateful to her and everything she did for my family and me. She restored my faith in surrogacy.

After the initial medical screenings and legal contract were executed, we decided to transfer two embryos. Unlike the previous transfers, we decided we would transfer two genetically tested girls. My husband and I have always wanted a daughter. The idea of potentially having a daughter made me giddy. Like clockwork, Margaux became pregnant on the first attempt. Margaux was on top of everything. She was so good about communicating every detail of the pregnancy and the medication she was taking. I found so much comfort in the level of details she shared. The two weeks of waiting seemed to fly by. When we tested Margaux's HCG levels, we found out we were PREGNANT. We were going to have a baby girl. My husband and I were over the moon. The pregnancy was moving along beautifully.

At the confirmation of heartbeat, the doctor noticed a pool of blood next to the healthy embryo. The official diagnosis was a subchorionic hematoma, which is fairly common in pregnancies. I had one during my pregnancy as well, and we weren't too concerned about it. The doctor just wanted Margaux to take it easy for the next few weeks. We figured it would resolve itself. The first trimester whizzed by, and I started to feel confident about the pregnancy. This was about the time most people share the good news with their families. We just didn't feel comfortable yet. The trauma from the last surrogacy journey still weighed on us. We decided to wait to share the good news until after the anatomy scan, which is done at twenty weeks of gestation. We had just two more weeks before we would share the good news.

A few days later, on a warm October day, I was in the driveway about to leave for work when Margaux called me to tell me something was wrong. She said that the doctor found something called a molar pregnancy. What is a molar pregnancy, and what did this mean? As I would soon learn, a molar pregnancy is an abnormal form of pregnancy in which a non-viable fertilized egg implants in the uterus and will fail to come to term. I wouldn't realize the gravity of her words until a day later. How was it possible to have a molar pregnancy? We had transferred two embryos that were supposed to have been genetically tested. We later found out that one embryo was genetically abnormal. I felt cheated. I paid thousands of dollars to test embryos that were supposed to be genetically normal. This is all inconclusive because we didn't test the tissue, but we believe that the embryo had sixty-nine chromosomes (most likely one egg and two sperm), a tripolody embryo, which then turned into a mass called a molar pregnancy. In other words, Margaux was carrying a healthy fetus, but next to that healthy fetus was this diabolical molar mass. The prognosis was devastating. Margaux's OBGYN recommended to terminate immediately because of the risks associated with molar pregnancy.

We decided to get a second opinion. We found out that the odds for a healthy full-term delivery were very small. Some of the likely scenarios were the surrogate could develop cancer, thyroid storm, or worse, death. Also, the baby could have been delivered extremely prematurely. So much so, in fact, that the baby's very survival would not have been guaranteed. So, after getting a second opinion, the choice was clear on paper. I still did not feel comfortable being the one to make the choice to terminate the pregnancy. I discussed all the facts with Margaux and asked her to make the decision. I grew up without a mother, and I couldn't stomach the idea of something happening to Margaux. I would never be able to live with myself. I did not pressure her at all. I told her I would support her decision, regardless of which direction she went. Ultimately and rightfully, she decided to terminate the pregnancy, and at twenty weeks, we lost our baby girl. The termination was risky as well. We had to get a specially trained doctor to perform the termination. There were more than a dozen doctors involved, and she was made aware of all of the possible complications. Fortunately, everything went according to plan, and she made a full recovery.

Just 11 months after mourning the loss of our other baby, we were mourning the loss of our baby girl. I still think of her. We had given her a name. For closure, we wrote goodbye letters to her. We decided to go outside to read our letters to each other under the moonlight. It just so happened to be a full moon. The moonlight cast a perfectly circular halo around our home. It was magical and beautiful. We told her how much we wanted to meet her and how much we loved her. I apologized to her for not fighting for her survival. We cried and held each other in silence.

That night seems like yesterday. I still feel the weight of that guilt. I still sometimes wonder what would have happened if we pushed forward. Was there a scenario in which all would have worked out? I harbor no ill will toward Margaux. She did the best she could and made the best decision for her health and her family. To this day, I think about Margaux often. I didn't do another journey with her. I wanted to, but I was so afraid that the same thing could happen again.

I was hoping the third time would be the charm. After spending so much of our financial resources, we were really starting to wonder if we were fools. However, my husband and I felt we just needed to keep forging ahead. We both have very strong personalities and usually don't take no for an answer, so on we went to search for our next surrogate. Luck smiled upon us when we met Betty. Betty is literally the sweetest person. She is such a kind soul. Betty is always apologizing and over-accommodating. We couldn't ask for a nicer surrogate to carry for us. When Betty was physically ready, we again transferred two embryos. We decided to transfer two boys this time because statistically, there was a lower chance of another molar pregnancy. We were so fortunate to learn that Betty was pregnant with a singleton. The pregnancy was fairly easy for Betty. She loved being pregnant, and the pregnancy progressed at lightning speed. And at every milestone, we were told that everything was fine.

After the twenty-week anatomy scan, we discussed sharing the good news with our family. My husband wasn't ready. He literally wanted to wait until the baby was born. I protested that it wasn't fair to our family and friends to let them know after the baby was born. Throughout our journeys, my husband has always been my silent pillar of strength. I think I took his strength for granted. He never showed me any sign of weakness. He always put on a brave face and held me, and supported me whenever I needed it. The only time I recall him crying was the night we read our goodbye letters under the moonlight. Of course, he wanted to wait to tell everyone. He was traumatized too. In hindsight, I should have given him more patience and grace. I sometimes forget that I wasn't the only one hurt in our journey. We did eventually settle on telling everyone at thirty-two weeks. The family was shocked but so happy for us. They now joke that we ordered our baby via Amazon Prime.

At thirty-eight weeks, Betty and my husband went to her last perinatologist appointment visit. It was seven a.m., and by eight a.m., I was told that I needed to meet them at the hospital. Betty's amniotic fluids were dangerously low. Our perinatologist didn't want to take any risks. He had seen a recent case in which the baby was deprived of oxygen, and it didn't end very well. We raced to the hospital. We called our OBGYN to let her know what was happening. We left several messages with her, with no response. By ten a.m., Betty wasn't allowed to be checked in without our OBGYN's blessing. At ten-fifteen a.m., I called the OB's office and threatened legal action against them if something should happen to my son. I told the receptionist I would include her in this lawsuit if she did not assist me. I was livid that our OB was not taking our perinatologists' recommendations seriously. I finally got her on the phone, and demanded her to review the records. After much back and forth, we were finally admitted into a L&D room at three-thirty p.m. They started the induction, and my son was born at four a.m. Betty's delivery was so easy. She pushed once, and our son came flying out - a perfect little man with ten toes and ten fingers. I was in disbelief that this was really happening. We were finally a family of four! He arrived a few weeks earlier than expected, but all turned out OK. He was on the small side but perfectly healthy in every way.

After the dust from this last pregnancy had settled, we realized that we must continue for one more cycle in order to have a baby girl. We were down to our last two remaining female embryos. Because we still had not fulfilled our dream of having a little girl, we sought out the assistance of another surrogate. Emma was the most perfect surrogate for us. We connected on almost every level. Our children were of similar ages. We shared the same family values. We absolutely loved spending time with their whole family. Emma was small-framed, and during our initial medical screening, the doctor recommended that we only transfer one embryo. The night before the embryo transfer, I felt very strongly that I needed to call our doctor and advocate for the transfer of two embryos. I told my husband, "I don't know why, but I don't think this is going to work."To this day, I regret not calling to transfer two embryos. We transferred one girl embryo, and Emma became pregnant, but the pregnancy did not make it to the heartbeat confirmation. Unfortunately, the pregnancy fizzled out within the first two weeks after our embryo transfer.

Now we only had one more girl embryo left, and we had some decisions to make. Should we attempt to do another transfer with Emma? Should we try to find another surrogate and try with her instead? We only had one girl embryo left, along with two boys. We thought maybe we should transfer one girl and one boy embryo. After many discussions and going back and forth, we decided to transfer just the one remaining girl embryo into Emma. It took about four months for us to get Emma's body ready for another embryo transfer, and in November 2019, we attempted to transfer our last girl embryo. We were very hopeful and excited about this transfer. We did our best to remain positive about this last transfer and tried our best to envision a successful cycle and welcoming our baby girl to the family. As is too often par for the course, we were greeted with devastating news. The morning of the transfer, a few hours before the scheduled transfer, our clinic called to tell us our last girl embryo did not survive the thaw. We were asked whether or not we wanted to cancel our transfer or if we wanted to thaw one or both of our remaining embryos. We only had two boy embryos left. Our surrogate was on her way to the clinic, and she had been taking meds for the past two weeks to prepare her body for the transfer. We didn't want to just cancel the cycle at this point, so we all decided to transfer the last two remaining embryos.

After the embryo transfer, we quickly learned that we were indeed pregnant with a baby boy. After our initial heartbreak, we celebrated the pregnancy and prayed for a healthy pregnancy. The pregnancy moved along perfectly. When you experience so many trials, you sometimes start to question what you are missing when everything is going according to plan. And on March 14, 2020, the universe threw us another curveball. The city of Los Angeles came to a grinding halt because of Covid. There was a full-fledged global pandemic amongst us. The school shut down. The restaurants closed. The freeways were empty. We were not allowed to attend any of the OB appointments. The pregnancy was experienced through FaceTime when it was allowed. Emma did her best to share all of the milestones with us. We felt so removed from the pregnancy. The delivery date quickly came upon us. During the delivery, the hospital warned us only one parent was allowed to stay at the hospital. I decided to go since I was a trained Doula. I was not allowed to leave the premises once I arrived. Emma tirelessly labored naturally with a mask on. She had such a hard time breathing that she broke vessels all around her neck. I was in awe of her strength. She was a superwoman on a mission! And on August 1, 2020, Emma delivered the most perfect little human being.

I remember driving home from the hospital with our little angel. We had transferred every last embryo we had, and now our family was complete. I no longer needed to find another surrogate. There was no need to go to any more ultrasound appointments. I didn't have to pay for any more embryo transfer. I was finally done. There was a time that I didn't think I was going to be a mother. Today, I am the mother of three incredible boys. The roller coaster ride of IVF, surrogacy and motherhood has been full of challenges, but I feel beyond blessed. I am sincerely grateful to be living in a time where this technology exists and in a country in which surrogacy is an option for me. These boys are my entire world. They make everything in life so much better, and I am grateful to be their mommy.

LISA CHIYA

Lisa Chiya is the Founder and President of The Genesis Group. She oversees the egg donor, surrogacy, frozen egg bank, and specialized directed egg donor search programs. Lisa brings over 20 years of third-party reproductive management to the Genesis Group.She is also a Founding member and board member of the Society for Ethics in Egg Donation and Surrogacy (SEEDS). She has a deep passion for family building and feels honored to be in a position to help so many Intended Parents find their way to parenthood. Lisa is a proud parent to three beautiful children via IVF and surrogacy.

18

CHIROPRACTIC CARE FOR FERTILITY IN MEN

DR. MARTHA K. MEKONEN, D.C

It Takes Two to Tango

PREGNANCY IS A BEAUTIFULLY comprehensive and transitive experience which the human body undergoes to produce and support a growing baby. We find that most of our attention lands on the woman's reproductive system such as their eggs and womb when defining fertility. However, there's more to the picture. The male reproductive system plays a pivotal role in fertility because the egg cannot be fertilized **without sperm**. The preparation of all three is essential to creating life. According to the Urology Care Foundation, more than 1/3 of fertility problems stem from men[1].

Thus, when considering fertility, both male and female reproductive systems need to share the same level of importance.

The Power of the Nervous System

Fertilization is a process in which the sperm penetrates the surface of the female egg to divide, multiply, and develop into a fetus. Before looking at the cascade of events that occur during pregnancy, we need to further understand what controls all these processes in both the female and male body, The Nervous System.

The Nervous System is divided into two parts; the Central Nervous System (CNS) which includes the brain and spinal cord, and the Peripheral Nervous System (PNS) which includes the nerves that connect the brain to the rest of the body. The brain controls and transmits voluntary and involuntary signals throughout the body to optimize function and balance of all 12 systems of the body. An extension of the PNS is the Autonomic Nervous System (ANS) which stimulates involuntary responses via the sympathetic (fight or flight) and parasympathetic (rest, digest, and relaxation) pathways. The goal of the ANS is to maintain *homeostasis*[2] via sympathetic (excitatory) and parasympathetic (inhibitory) responses.

In looking at the neurological process of an erection, the sympathetic nervous system releases chemical mediators to stimulate sexual arousal by increasing the heart rate, blood pressure, and breathing while the parasympathetic nervous system increases the blood flow to the tissues of the penis to create an erection. As sexual arousal increases, activation of both PS and SP will increase until he no longer has control meaning he has reached his climax and ejaculates. The release of the semen is stimulated by the height of the sympathetic nervous system while the loss of the erection is a relaxed response due to the inhibition of the parasympathetic nervous system.

When stress is added, whether it be physical, emotional, or chemical, the body will respond by releasing a hormone called cortisol which is produced in the adrenal glands. The CNS and ANS are both directly influenced by the internal and external stressors of the body. Cortisol's role is to regulate normal functioning amongst the cardiovascular, circulatory, and reproductive system. An increased amount of cortisol levels can biochemically affect the function of the male reproductive system and sexual desire. Chronic stress levels can affect the production of testosterone and result in low sex drive or dysfunction with erections. It can also have a negative impact on the production and maturation of sperm.

The Infinite Clock

Puberty is seen very differently between the female and male reproductive systems. Women are born with all the eggs they are ever going to have because they are not able to produce any new eggs. Just think about this, if you are a female and you are carrying a baby girl, you are essentially carrying your future grandchildren as well since all of your daughter's eggs are in her ovaries. At birth, the female body carries about 2 million eggs, but once they reach puberty, only about 25% of her egg pool will remain. Although her body may be essentially ready for conception, her egg count will diminish in quantity and quality with age. As she progresses in life, 1,000 immature eggs are projected to die each month. Once the woman exhausts her egg supply (menopause due to the decreased production of estrogen), her ability to carry a child ceases hence she is on a biological clock[3].

Men on the other hand, are on a completely different cycle. The objective of the male reproductive system is to make, store, and transport sperm. Once puberty begins, the testes will increase testosterone production and produce millions of sperm cells every day. Although most men are capable of producing sperm as they age, the quality (size and shape) of the sperm tends to decrease with age. Sperm production is a critical phase in the male reproductive tract. If production is altered whatsoever, it can decrease the likelihood of the sperm surviving during its journey to form semen and get ejaculated and to stimulate fertilization. Male fertility is directly related to the making and the delivery of sperm. All of these processes are controlled by the nervous system and the biochemical conditions of the internal and external body.

I was treating a patient who was trying to get pregnant with her partner. She was doing everything she could to try to prepare her body for IVF. Chiropractic, massage, acupuncture, diet, yoga, and meditation were all part of her daily practices. After three rounds of IVF, her stress levels were through the roof, not to mention her motivation to try another round of IVF was drastically low. Prior to starting the next round, we had started to see her partner as a patient. His sperm count was underlooked since his number just made the average range. He became consistent with his care and also implemented a healthy diet, yoga, and acupuncture to his wellness regimen. He started to notice a change in his energy levels, mood, and overall outlook on drive and motivation. A few months later, they decided to give it another try naturally. They got pregnant! Both of them worked on themselves to get the best possible outcome. Majority of the time we think that the female body needs to be regulated when considering fertility, but it takes two to tango. At times, male sperm production could be underlooked due to their ability to produce millions of sperm everyday. This is why it is important to fully analyze the quality of the sperm when considering fertility[4].

Causes of Male Infertility

Male fertility typically does not get the attention it deserves, when realistically, they play a huge role in the pre-pregnancy phase of life. There are a multitude of factors that can directly affect healthy sperm production and delivery. Here are some common causes to male infertility[5]:

- *Low hormone (testosterone) levels* will result in poor sperm growth and production in the testes.

- *Sperm disorders* directly affect the sperm count. In looking at the quantity, sperm count is directly affected by quality of sperm such as sperm motility (ability to swim) and morphology (size and shape). Both genetics and lifestyle choices such as smoking, alcohol, drugs/medications can result in a low sperm count.
- *Damage to the male reproductive system* due to an infection, surgery, trauma, or birth defect can cause blockage in the sperm pathway therefore decreasing the number of sperm being released.
- *Retrograde Ejaculation* is when the semen goes into the bladder rather than out of the penis. Normally, the nervous system stimulates the muscles in the bladder to close during an orgasm. In the case of a retrograde ejaculation, the bladder is open which allows for the semen to enter rather than exit from the penis. Sperm production may be normal as far as the quality but due to the lack of nerve innervation, the route is now altered. Any obstruction or blockage to the male reproductive tract will inhibit the sperm from leaving the body.
- *Varicoceles* is when the veins located in the testes become swollen. This process inhibits proper blood drainage resulting in an increase of temperature in the testicles. If the testicles are too warm, the sperm will not be able to undergo production, therefore resulting in a low sperm count.
- *Chromosomes* carry genetic information. During fertilization, the female and male chromosome come together to create a gene expression (DNA) of the fetus. Since the sperm carries half of the genetic expression of the offspring, any changes in the number and structure of the Y chromosome can affect fertility in males.
- *Use of some medications* can change the way sperm is produced and the function it serves as far as its delivery through the male reproductive system.

- *Emotional, chemical, and physical stress* directly affects how the body operates. When the body undergoes imbalances (stress), how the body responds and regulates those imbalances can really justify the overall well being of the body. When information is being altered due to the lack of communication between the mind-body, the body tends to shut down or detour away from the normal processes. Therefore, making it harder for the mind to react to normal bodily functions.

The Importance of Spinal Alignment

The nervous system is a network of nerves that transmits and carries information to and from the brain through the spinal cord and to the whole body. The spinal cord passes through the spinal column, which consists of 33 bony segments that protect the nervous system. Nerves endings that are attached to the spinal cord transmit information through the small openings in the vertebrae known as the vertebral foramen. Each vertebra has 2 vertebral foramen (one for each side of the body) at every level of the spine. Nerves transmit information by either entering or exiting the spine in hopes to reach its respected destination (cells, tissues, muscles, organs, or organ system). This complex interaction between the brain and body ensures optimal function of the body. Essentially the nervous system is the electrical wiring of the body.

The spine shape and structure consists of different curves to accommodate different organs and their regions. The spine is divided into 5 different parts: cervical, thoracic, lumbar, sacral, and coccyx. The thoracic spine directly connects to the rib cage, while the sacrum and coccyx both sit within the pelvic inlet. All of these bony structures have a huge influence on posture and how the physical body supports and protects itself structurally. Each region generates a kyphotic or lordotic curve meaning the curve is in a flexed or an extended position again to support the corresponding organs within that region. The spine is stabilized and supported by the muscles and fascia that are attached to it. Over time, the soft tissue structures will adapt to the environment the body is placed in. For example, if you are someone that constantly sits and works on a computer, over time you will start to notice changes within the spinal regions. Your neck may be protruding forward and in a flexed position while your shoulders are rounded. Your mid back can be in a hyper-flexed (hyperkyphotic) position while your lower back is in a hypo-extended (hypolordotic). This position is how your body compensates due to the increased stress added from being in that position for long periods of time. Since nerves are constantly transmitting information through the spine, changes to the curves in the spine can directly affect how the nerves function and operate. Misalignments, also called subluxations, in the spine can cause irritation to the nerves. Nerve irritation can alter mind-body communication by disrupting the normal function of the body.

The function of the nervous system is to maintain homeostasis in the body. In life we are directly and indirectly affected by stress. Stress can be presented as physical, emotional, and chemical stressors that can affect the body internally and externally. Physical stress can start from your birthing process. How you were brought into this world directly affects how your nervous system operates and develops. As you grow, your body can undergo changes that can affect your body in your adult years. Accidents, injuries, and surgeries also have an influence on how your physical body functions as far as alignment of your spine. Posture plays a huge role in maintaining nervous system functionality. Pelvic alignment, specifically sacral alignment, has a direct correlation with the function of the male reproductive system. If the nerves that operate and regulate sperm production and sperm flow are irritated at the site of the spine and pelvis, the likelihood of the nervous system stimulating that process is far less compared to if alignment is intact. Emotional and mental stress such as your thoughts, can manifest by inhibiting normal neurological function. Finances, relationships, work, and emotional distress can affect sexual drive and arousal. Meditating, breathwork, exercising, and finding good coping mechanisms can all be impactful in improving the mental state of mind. Chemical stressors and toxins can be influenced by types of foods you eat or are lacking, drugs/medications, and the quality of sleep. How the body breaks down and uptakes these byproducts is influenced by the quality and quantity of these substances. Processed foods, alcohol and drugs, and environmental toxins can have a negative effect on sex drive and arousal. In conclusion, traumas, thoughts, and toxins can all greatly affect the neurological control and stimulation of the male reproductive tract. Eliminating these stressors can increase the communication between the brain and body and therefore improve the function of the nervous system.

Improving the Function of the Nervous System

The communication between the brain and body is reliant on a plethora of pathways. These pathways travel to different regions and innerative cells, tissues, organs, and organ systems throughout the body. Information to and from these regions travel through the spinal cord and up to the brain. The skeletal spine that is protecting the spinal cord has many bony articulations that have the capability of shifting throughout your lifetime, in other words, having bad posture. This "shift" can directly irritate the nerves that pass through the spine resulting in a miscommunication with the brain and body. Subluxation[6] can lead to an inflammatory response in the spine and throughout the body. Reducing and eliminating the interference will sharpen the communication by reducing inflammation and creating optimal function in the body.

Chiropractic Medicine directly promotes spinal alignment by removing nerve interference to the spine through spinal manipulation called adjustments. Adjustment can be done in many different ways, with different modalities (hands, activator, pelvic blocks, drop table), and by different types of Chiropractors (Diversified, SOT, Upper Cervical). Typically a chiropractor will use their hands to feel and assess the spinal alignment through palpation. The spine is best felt when the body is in a relaxed state, so taking a few deep breaths prior to the assessment will help to stimulate the relaxation phase. The chiropractor will use their hands or a device to deliver a fast impulse of force into the spine to place the segment that is "out of alignment" back into place. Depending on the person, an immediate response can be felt such as an increase in spinal mobility, decrease of pain/tension, and an increase in mental clarity. Soreness may also be present due to the direct changes that have been implemented to the spine. Chiropractic care focuses on nerves, muscles, and bones in regulating both voluntary and involuntary responses throughout the body. The body is an extraordinary organism. The brain has an ability to control and respond to a multitude of stimuluses at the same time via the nervous system. Reducing nerve interference from the spine can improve this communication therefore promoting optimal functioning of the body.

Benefits of Chiropractic care for Fertility in Men

Chiropractic adjustment helps to regulate the nervous system by promoting communication between the brain and body. The origin of the nervous system varies amongst the different systems. The Central Nervous System is located in the brain and spinal cord while the Peripheral Nervous System is located everywhere else. Specifically the Sympathetic and Parasympathetic Nervous System is located within the spine. Sympathetic is in the thoracic spine while Parasympathetic is in two locations (hence the word "para") cervical and sacral spine. These nerves regulate involuntary responses throughout the body. The male reproductive tract can greatly be influenced by stimulating these three spinal regions. Subluxations within these regions can result in difficulty producing and transferring sperm and/or difficulty with achieving and maintaining an erection. According to a case study published in *the Annals of Vertebral Subluxation Research*, 53-year old male with a history of erectile dysfunction and chronic low back pain, received 2 months of chiropractic care which resulted in not only diminishing his low back pain symptoms, but improving the function of his erections[7]. Adjusting the cervical, sacral and pelvic spine can stimulate relaxation in the body by increasing blood flow to male reproductive organs. Adjusting the thoracic spine can stimulate excitation in the body by regulating heart rate, blood pressure, and breathing. Through these adjustments, the body will undergo better blood flow and a reduction of inflammation. Any interference to these areas can result in undesired neurological sexual responses. When considering fertility, nervous system control and regulation should be the first things that come to mind.

Proper nerve flow can stimulate a balance in hormones. Testosterone is a hormone produced in the testes. It serves as the precursor in the production of sperm. The production of testosterone is stimulated by two hormones found in the brain, follicle-stimulating hormone (FSH) and luteinizing hormone (LH). Stress can cause misalignments in the spine that can result in hormonal imbalances. As a stress response, the muscles in the body can tense up and shift the joints within the spine. Misalignments in the spine can alter neurological stimulation and production of FSH and LH leading to a decrease in the production of testosterone which can result in a lower sperm count. Chiropractic care is beneficial in stimulating proper neurological responses in balancing and regulating hormones as well as decreasing physical stress.

Regular Chiropractic care is highly recommended throughout life. Routine adjustments to your spine are necessary because of the amount of stress we display each and every day. Gravity is constantly running against our body, shifting structures to accommodate to the environment. Regular daily processes and repetitive stress can directly influence the way your body functions. This is why spine health and alignment need to be taken seriously when it comes to improving the way the body functions, especially when it comes to fertility. Chiropractic adjustments can boost the ability of the body to prepare and create life. Remember, fertility consists of three major components: the sperm, the egg, and the womb. They all have a specific and important role in creating and bringing life into this world. The things you do to your body today, greatly affect the outcome of your body tomorrow. No one part should be overlooked or underlooked because all three need to be considered in boosting fertility. This includes preparing both the male and female body prior to this empowering, yet delicate phase of life.

---

1. https://www.urologyhealth.org/urology-a-z/m/male-infertility
2. Homeostasis: the state in which the internal body maintains stability through regulating the systems of the body despite external and/or environmental stressors.
3. https://www.infertile.com/beating-biological
4. https://www.merckmanuals.com/home/men-s-health-issues/biology-of-the-male-reproductive-system/puberty-in-boys
5. https://www.urologyhealth.org/urology-a-z/m/male-infertility
6. Subluxation: a slight misalignment of the vertebrae which can impair the optimal expression of the nervous system caused by physical, biochemical, or psychological distress.
7. https://www.vertebralsubluxationresearch.com/2017/09/04/reduction-in-frequency-and-severity-of-erectile-dysfunction-and-chronic-low-back-pain-in-a-53-year-old-male-utilizing-the-gonstead-technique-a-case-study/

DR. MARTHA K. MEKONEN, D.C.

Dr. Martha K. Mekonen, D.C., is a Webster Certified Chiropractor that specializes in perinatal and pediatric care. She obtained her B.S. in Neuroscience at the University of California Riverside. She then received her Doctorate in Chiropractic at the Southern California University of Health Sciences. She co-founded Life Adjusted Wellness - a center focused on empowering and uplifting women through quality chiropractic care. During the first few years in practice, Dr. Martha enjoyed encouraging and supporting pregnant families through her work as a birth doula. As a first-generation Ethiopian-American, she is most passionate about educating and providing equal access to care for pregnant mothers, families, and marginalized communities. Dr. Martha envisions a future where expecting families are able to make well-informed decisions and have control over their pregnancy and postpartum journeys.

Website: www.lifeadjustedwellness.com
Email: hello@lifeadjustedwellness.com
Facebook: facebook.com/lifeadjustedwellness
Instagram: @lifeadjustedwellness, @movement4mamas
TikTok: @lifeadjustedwellness

19

MEXICAN SOBADAS AND FERTILITY
THE BODY AND SPIRITUAL JOURNEY THROUGH FERTILITY BASE ON INDIGENOUS KNOWLEDGE

METZTLI LOPEZ TORRES, MA

"Nuestros viejos, los mas sabios y antiguos, los primeros que caminaron estas tierras, nos enseñaron que la palabra tiene que compartirse con humildad y respeto al oído y corazón de las personas, sin importar el sonido de sus voces ni el color de su rostro, pero también con las plantas, las piedras y los animales, el sol, el agua, la luna, las estrellas y con nuestra madre tierra"

Palabras de curandero tenek de Veracruz

(Martinez;2006:60-61)

My Journey into Women's Health

I REMEMBER A LONG TIME AGO, a friend of mine that was a Reiki practitioner and tarot reader did a reading about my spiritual life, and she told me something that totally resonated with me. She told me that my spirit was old and I was living my last human life. This was the fourth time I was a human and sent to this world to share my experiences. During my other human lives, I learned and got experience, and that was why this time, I was sharing knowledge and knowing things that other people my age didn't understand. This is one of the reasons why writing this chapter was important for me; to continue sharing.

At the time my friend told me this, I had been on my path as a healer for a long time. I learned from *curanderas* and midwives in my home state of Veracruz. Since I was a child, my mother took me to ceremonies among powerful and wise healers. I didn't know that many years later, that would become my path in life. As a child, I always looked with respect and admiration at all the healing the *curanderas* were doing and talking about. Still today, I have fond memories of those times of my childhood among these women.

Another big reason for understanding healing in a different way was, in greater part, due to my family. My family has used Traditional Mexican Medicine as our main medicine before using allopathic treatment. My mother's grandfather was a healer, and we can say we have that in our veins. I guess that's why it is not strange that my family accepted my path as a healer. I have always received support from them in this calling.

Also, I grew up in the southeast part of Mexico in the Mesoamerican territory. The name of my city is *Xalapa* that means *water in the sand* in nahuatl. This village was formed by four different indigenous groups: Totonacas, Aztecs, Chichimecas, and Toltecs in 1313. It is surrounded by small towns, mountains, and rivers. The combination of location, resources, and indigenous traditional healers was an ideal scenario to begin my calling into women's health. My mother's family comes from a strong Totonaca heritage. That is the strongest indigenous lineage in me.

My hometown is in the heart of the cloud forest. This means it rains almost daily, but the climate is sub-tropical. The weather is perfect for growing coffee beans, bananas, limes, guavas, and many other fruits of the tropics. I grew up among fruit trees, rivers, flowers, plants, birds, butterflies, and animals. When you grew up in nature the way I did, it just becomes normal to learn through observation how living things are interconnected and the strong bond we have with nature all the time. It was green year-round, and the cycles of life were present every season.

At the age of 17, I got pregnant. I remember I had care from an OB, but also wise indigenous women in my area gave me so much information about how to take care of my pregnancy using herbs and the importance of movement to help the baby engage in the pelvis. During those months of pregnancy, I became fascinated with the traditional –indigenous- pregnancy, delivery, and postpartum world, and I decided I wanted to be a midwife. Since then, I have dedicated my time and life to study women's health from an indigenous perspective.

I started to look for an option for midwifery school to attend after having my baby, but the only option was to move to San Miguel de Allende in the state of Guanajuato. This central State is 12 hours away from my hometown, and when I spoke with them about the possibility of bringing my baby with me, they told me that was not an option. I would need to sacrifice taking care of my baby to go to school and study midwifery. Of course, that wasn't an option for me. I didn't want to leave my newborn to go and study away for three years. Also, economically was something I couldn't afford. I had to come up with a different plan to pursue my goal.

I made one of the best decisions I could make at the time. I started my bachelor's in Anthropology at the local University as a way to academically research about midwifery and Traditional Mexican Medicine, and I started to learned midwifery through local midwives of the area. I would then have the academic and empirical background I needed to pursue my path.

This turned out to be a perfect combination because I gained an academic title to become a researcher on topics of my interest. On the other hand, I was learning and practicing from the most experienced midwives I knew. The theory came from academia and the praxis from the midwives.

Traditional Midwifery in Mexico was called, until recently, Mexican Midwifery. In Mesoamerican areas of Mexico, there are female midwives (*parteras*) and male midwives (*parteros*) who learn about midwifery through their own mother or because they got the divine called to become a midwife through dreams. In both cases, we are talking about Traditional Midwifery.

Traditional midwives (women and men) were very popular and well-respected figures before the colonization. They were –and still are, in some towns- the ones with knowledge to provide information and care about women's health through all cycles of life. They support women with the most common problems related to the reproductive system. This goes from menstruation to menopause.

Most women want to go with a midwife to deliver a baby because they feel safe and respected under her/his care. Another reason why midwives are popular in Mexico is that they can help women who have fertility problems to get pregnant. Midwives help women with infertility problems by prescribing herbs and providing specific *sobadas* on the body and uterus. A well-versed *partera* and or *sobadora* will know if a woman's uterus is in a correct position only by touching the outside of the pelvic area. From this perspective, a tilted uterus will cause problems from menstruation to fertility. The midwife or *sobadora* will assess the position and health of the uterus through the *sobada* to further fix it.

All of these skills and experiences are the ones I learned during my time as a student midwife that later on let me focus only on *sobadas* which are one of the services I provide here in the United States.

The uterus as a physical and spiritual place of care

The uterus is an organ in the pelvic bowl. This organ is small and has the ability to expand during menstruation and during pregnancy. Once that this process is over, the uterus will return to the regular size but not always to the same place. The uterus is a suspended organ, which means it is attached to different ligaments in the pelvis. It tends to move based on pregnancy, postpartum, exercises, weight, age, and etcetera. It is like a balloon made of layers of muscle that expand and contract during the person's life.

When the uterus is not in an optimal place, the person can suffer from infertility, painful sex, miscarriages, and menstrual problems, among other issues. That's the reason why in Mexican culture, it is common to look for a *partera* or *sobadora* to have a womb massage that will help to place the uterus in an optional position, and by doing this, the organ will start working properly. Once the womb is manipulated and moved by the hands of the *partera* or *sobadora,* an improvement will start.

A *sobada* in the womb is a non-invasive therapy. This "massage" is done on the abdominal area using deep pressure on the client's body to picture the place and health of the main organs in this area, including the uterus. Once the uterus is detected by the skilled hands of the *sobadora/partera,* the next step is to slowly move it if needed. The *sobada* is safe on most bodies, but it is considered a deep tissue work.

Sometimes the uterus could be toward one side or the other. Sometimes the uterus can be very low –prolapsed- and this is known in Mexican culture as *"matriz caída"*. When the uterus is not in an optimal position, the person can start suffering from symptoms like frequent urination, incontinence, painful period, painful sex, infertility, miscarriages, and the list goes on. But it is only the sensitivity of the hands of the *partera* or *sobadora* that can feel the uterus externally through this technique.

Once the problem is detected, the practitioner will use a series of movements to reposition all the organs that need alignments, and the last one will be the uterus. The sobada is not done only on the uterus. It has to be done in all the abdominal area and most of the time in the whole body. This is the traditional way it is done by traditional *sobadoras* or *parteras* in Mesoamerica.

Once the *sobada* is done, the client will have to follow some recommendations from the *sobadora* or midwife. Most of the recommendations are related to diet and the use of herbs to help improve the problem. There is not a magic formula that will work for all clients. That's the reason why this treatment is tailored based on the person. For some people, one *sobada* and maybe taking a tincture for one month will be more than enough. For other ones, it could take months or years based on severity.

During my years as a researcher, I can attest to the testimony of hundreds of women getting pregnant using *sobadas* and drinking custom-made herbal blend teas provided by the midwife or *sobadora*. These women attend from 1 to 10 *sobadas* and, after years of infertility, got pregnant. These cases differed from case to case.

In my personal practice as a *sobadora,* I have the chance to help women getting pregnant after unexplained infertility. My experience in the United States has been mainly with clients in Los Angeles and San Diego, California, from 2018 to the present -2021-. My clients have different backgrounds and different health issues, so it is hard to use only one example to explain all the variables. On the other hand, this means that sobadas can be done to all kinds of people who are looking for this care and it is not discriminatory to one group of people base on race, sex, or gender.

I will mention two examples to have an idea of the timing and care using *sobadas* as a treatment. The first case is a woman who had a baby seven years ago, and she was struggling to get pregnant again for the last two years. She is in her 30s, with no medical conditions, no menstrual problems, and no "evident" problem. After three months under my care, she got pregnant following my recommendations of diet and herbs along with a monthly *sobada*. This case is more or less easy and very common in my practice. The second case is a woman in her 20s with a history of PCOS, never been pregnant, and with other health issues related to diabetes. In this case, we have been working on helping her body to have a regular menstrual cycle, keeping a normal level in her glucose test results, and improving her lifestyle to finally be able to work on the pregnancy. We have been working together for one year. As you can see, there are many things in between, but the health of the client always improved while we are working on the goal that is pregnancy.

It is important to mention that my practice in the United States is different from the one provided in Mexico. This is because the diet and lifestyle of people here differ greatly from the people in Mexico. While in Mexico, the sole care that a *sobadora* or midwife provides to help people get pregnant works very fast. Here in the United States, I will sometimes recommend receiving an acupuncturist's care or a naturopathic doctor along with the *sobadas*. I have found that working collaboratively with other practitioners results in better outcomes. Every case is different, and sometimes it is necessary to have the support of other specialists for a better result.

The work of the *sobada* or any other healing modality of Mesoamerican Medicine is also a spiritual journey through emotions kept in the body. During a *sobada*, the release of emotions is a key component for healing. This is not only about working with the uterus as an organ but more about understanding the womb as a recipient of emotions. The connection that we make with our womb and body, in general, is essential in the healing treatment. If the client continues having a disconnection with her body and her spirit, it is very hard that a *sobada* will work. It may put the uterus in an optimal position but from our understanding –from an indigenous perspective- getting pregnant and having a baby goes beyond the physical part of it. It's a combination of the physical and spiritual world all connected in the body.

In the indigenous perspective, a baby has a spirit. Only through a real connection with the world of the spirits can we call the baby's spirit when there is no apparent problem. Many of my clients don't have a medical explanation for their infertility or miscarriages. This is one of the reasons why this type of work is essential to go deeper into understanding the body and pregnancy in a whole different way. We will look into the physical part and the spiritual component of the client.

If there is something I have learned very well from my *maestras curanderas* was to work always in alignment with the spiritual world, to pray hard, and call the energy of the elements to support the work I do. For the indigenous people, we are not only flesh or body. Half of everything is in the realm of the spirits, and only in a healthy and safe spirit, a new life can grow. This is the reason why also working with the spirit and in the spiritual world is so essential.

A person can go through the very expensive treatments and several IVF rounds, but if her spirit is not aligned to receive the spirit of a new life in her body, then the chances of failure are bigger, based on the indigenous perspective. This is the reason why this type of healing is also recommended in the case of IVF procedures in order to get the body and the spirit ready for the process. The *sobada* will help to align the physical, spiritual, and mental components to get a person ready for the pregnancy.

Another key element is the way a person takes care of the uterus. In Traditional Mexican Medicine, the recommendations of *sobadoras* and *parteras* are to keep the uterus warm, protected, "happy" with warm drinks and meals, self-care, and in constant communication with the messages from the womb. The messages of the womb range from menstrual cycles, the color of the blood, and strong cramping before or during menstruation among others. The healer will collect this information and interpret the symptoms.

Also, protecting the uterus from coldness is essential. For example, I recommend that my clients avoid cold drinks or cold food in the morning if they are trying to conceive or if there are problems related to their menstrual period. I do not recommend walking barefoot on a tiled floor or hardwood floor any time. Warm baths, saunas –or sweat lodge-, vaginal steaming, or foot baths can be very beneficial if the patient has fertility problems related to *frialdad* in the uterus. If the pregnancy occurred is recommended to eat warm soups and broths daily during the first 12 weeks to avoid a miscarriage.

I want to mention that I also have been using *sobadas* for myself. I had the honor to received *sobadas* from my *maestras* in Veracruz and in Yucatan. My maestra *partera*, who taught me Mayan Massage, helped me by moving my uterus 18 months after the delivery of my second baby. I literally felt and heard a "pop" when she used her technique on my uterus. She told me that if I continued without care, I would have problems getting pregnant in the future. I wasn't trying to get pregnant at that time, but six months later, when I did, I got pregnant on the first try. I'm sure the work she did on me was very helpful to achieve my pregnancy.

How Parteras and Sobadoras learn to treat fertility problems

For centuries people from Mesoamerica territory (from the center to the south of Mexico, Guatemala, Honduras, Belize, El Salvador, and northern Costa Rica) have used similar techniques to heal the body and the spirit. All of these techniques are intimately related to nature under the understanding that the spirit of a person and the body are one. The relationship of humans with nature is at the center, playing a delicate balance between healing and disease. In this case, nature goes for all living and non-living things around us that are part of Mother Nature and the cosmos.

The people or experts in these healings arts are called by different names based on the specialty of healing, technique, and ground of expertise. For example, a *partera* (midwife) is the specialist in women's health from pre-conception to menopause, but they are also well versed in health problems related to infants and children. Other specialists are the ones called *hueseros* (from the word in Spanish *hueso* = bone), which are the people who know how to take care of bone fractures and bone misalignments properly. Their job looks pretty much like what a chiropractor does, and they also work with children to older people on any problem related to bones. Another category among these healers are the ones called *sobadoras. These* are the ones who know a different way to *sobar* (the closest concept to *sobada* in English would be massage) the body of a person based on the disease to aim for a faster recovery.

The *sobada* is a Mexican Massage in the same way that we can talk about Tai Massage or Swedish Massage. It has specific techniques and requires training and practice to understand the body from this perspective along with skills to provide it. It was developed by indigenous healers after years of practice and a deep understanding of the human body. And it was commonly used as regular healing care before the arrival of the Spaniards to Mesoamerica.

Today this technique is used by healers to help the body and spirit of the client to find balance and restore the natural function of the body. The *sobada* can be done through all stages of life, from infancy to the elderly; it can be done to women and men equally during all stages of life, and it will focus on the ailment of the person to restore the balance of the body and the spirit.

One example of *sobada* for kids is to cure something that we called in Mexican culture *empacho*. This sickness of the body comes after an abuse of eating something to the level of overwhelming the digestive system. Sometimes it depends on the severity of the case on if the patient will be prescribed to use herbal remedies along with the *sobada* to help a faster recovery.

In women, the most common *sobadas* are done to help them with menstrual periods problems like amenorrhea, irregular and heavy periods; fertility problems from miscarriages to the inability to get pregnant; pregnancy to aim the optimal position of the baby in the womb avoiding physical discomfort due to pregnancy; during postpartum to help the body recovering and find balance after pregnancy; painful sex; and trauma.

There are two types of *sobadas* well known in the Mesoamerican territory; one is commonly known as Mexican *Sobada*, and the other one is the Mayan *Sobada* (aka Mayan Massage). Both are very similar and work almost the same way, but they have differences in the technique and the part of the country they were developed. In the case of the Mayan Massage, it was developed and practiced in what is known as the Mayan territory that goes from the south of Mexico to Belize and Guatemala. In the center and southeast of Mexico, healers practice Mexican *Sobada*, and it's known by this name.

Most of the time, when people in the United States think about womb massage will make a direct link with Mayan Abdominal Therapy created by Rosita Arvigo. This technique broadly spread in the USA by Arvigo is only her interpretation of the healing. She learned this technique from a traditional healer from Belize and capitalized this knowledge. Although her popular trademark opened the door to one of the oldest traditions of healing of Mesoamerican people in the United States, this is only her version of the healing. The Mayan abdominal massage is a common knowledge among indigenous Mayan people in their territory.

The Mexican *Sobadas* and Mayan Massage are techniques broadly use by people in the cities and the countryside in Mesoamerican territory, mostly among indigenous groups. Traditional healers practice it, and they teach it.

Most traditional healers of Mesoamerica learned their skills through a family member that is also a healer and taught them their knowledge. This way, the tradition continues generation over generation, and they continue to master and polish the techniques. It is common to see midwives and healers of all kinds being a third or fourth generation in the field.

Many indigenous healers had their calling to become healers through dreams. Among indigenous people of Mesoamerica and all the Americas, dreams are an important component of daily lives. Through dreams, we can receive messages about what our path is in life but also about our immediate future. In this case, we can find among healers and midwives people that started their path into healing through dreams. Maybe it was the vision of a Saint, Virgin, God, or even an ancestor who visited them during a dream and gave them the message that they have to become a healer. Through consecutive dreams, they got information about how they are going to heal and what they need to do in specific cases, for example, the use of some herbs, specific prayers, food, etc.

The third way to learn these skills is based on pure interest in learning and continuing with these traditions. This means the healer or midwife will take an apprenticeship. This scenario is more common when no one in the healer's family wants to learn and continue with the tradition. Unfortunately, now there is less interest from the younger generation to learn and carry with this knowledge. In this case, the future apprentice will talk directly with the healer or midwife, expressing his/her interest, and they will start working together. The person who is learning will support the healer/ midwife for many years and won't get any pay for it. The first step is observing and helping with simple tasks, and after a few months, he or she will start practicing on the clients under the supervision of the mentor. This always creates a strong bond between both that will continue in mutual support for the rest of their lives. This was the way I learned.

Conclusions

Sobadas are a type of traditional massage born in Mesoamerica. There are two types of *sobadas*: Mexican *Sobada* and Mayan *Sobada*. Both are practiced and taught by traditional healers (men and women) since before the colonization and are still very alive nowadays in Mexico. This service is provided in the United States by *sobadoras* like myself.

There is a specific *sobada* for woman that is centered in the womb. And this *sobada* changes base on the age and health problems of the woman (person with uterus). Women with fertility problems often seek the help of midwives or *sobadoras* to get this specific "massage" to conceive. This is a non-invasive treatment aimed at fertility problems. During the appointment, the client will receive tips on diet and herbs to help her get pregnant along with the bodywork, *sobada*. There is no "magic recipe". It all depends on each person, and sometimes it can be fast, and sometimes it can take years. The client who receives the womb massage will get always benefits from it.

Sobadas go beyond the physical aspect of health. It is centered on the idea of the spirit of the person. Thus the physical and spiritual parts of the client are both under treatment. Mesoamerican medicine is aligned to the realm of nature, and a healer will intervene in the spiritual world to speak for the client to get the healing the person needs in order to accomplish pregnancy. That's the reason why a sobada session will look like a ceremony taking into account the body and spirit of the client.

The main task of the person receiving this type of treatment is to carefully following the instructions of physical, emotional, and spiritual care provided by the *sobadora*. The healing is within the client's body and the role of the *sobadora* is as an interpreter and guide to understand the messages of the body.

I have learned *sobadas* for over ten years. I have been studying Traditional Mexican Medicine and Indigenous Medicine of Mesoamerica for almost 20 years. I have received and provided *sobadas*, and I can see the benefits of it. This knowledge was passed to me with a lot of respect following the traditions. I'm a keeper of this knowledge, and I have profound respect for it.

By continuing with these types of healing modalities, we are connecting with our roots –in the case we have a lineage with Mesoamerican people- and allowing us to continue millenarian traditions in a world that tends to forget that we are part of nature and the spiritual world. Today this type of care is open to everybody that is looking to connect with the body and the spiritual world. By receiving this care, we are making a true connection with nature and the fertility within us.

METZTLI LOPEZ TORRES, MA

Metztli Lopez Torres was born in Xalapa, Veracruz, Mexico in 1984. She got her Bachelor's Degree in Social Anthropology from the Universidad Veracruzana in 2006 and her Master's Degree by CIESAS-Golfo in 2010 with cum laude for her research about pregnancy and violence among underserved populations. Since 2004 Metztli has been working professionally in topics related to pregnancy, childbirth, and postpartum with an emphasis in Traditional Mexican Medicine, Traditional Midwifery of Mexico, and Feminism.

Metztli became a mother to her first child in 2001. During this experience, she started working in everything related to pregnancy from a spiritual and indigenous-traditional perspective. She moved to the United States in the summer of 2014 with her family, and in 2017 she had her second son in San Diego, CA.

In 2020 Metztli achieved a VBA2C during the delivery of her daughter. Currently, she lives in San Diego with her family and provides in person and online consultations about fertility, menstrual periods, pregnancy, postpartum, and lactation, as well as workshops, pláticas, and ceremonies. All her services are based on Traditional Mexican Medicine and Sobadas.

Website: www.lunamama.net
Email: metztli.loto@gmail.com
Facebook: https://www.facebook.com/lunamamaservices

Instagram: https://www.instagram.com/lunamama_services/

LinkedIn: https://www.linkedin.com/in/metztli-lopez-torres-82358047/

Youtube: https://www.youtube.com/channel/UCyUxowOn7r_TiE65YGekdnw

20

SURRENDER

MICHELLE STROUD

Everyone knows someone who eventually gave up on trying to have a baby and then got pregnant. It maybe the most triggering and yet mysterious aspect of my work as a Holistic Reproductive Practitioner.

The reflexology sessions I offer my clients helps them balance hormones, regulate their cycles and put their nervous system into a parasympathetic state so their body can heal and conceive. Reiki sessions allow me to support the healing of their mother wounds, inherited traumas, grief and other blocks that can prevent conception. I am still in awe of how effective these simple holistic practices have been for so many clients.

The conception block that has challenged me most as a practitioner is surrender. Sharing in the experience of so many families who struggle to conceive, it is the piece that I have invested the most energy into understanding and unlike some of the other ways I have offered support, surrender usually requires a unique approach with each client. No two people can let go and surrender the same way. It has called for me to be creative and incredibly thoughtful as I tune into each client and how to help them surrender so that their baby will come.

We live in a culture that teaches us that if we work hard, if we follow societies rules, we can achieve anything. We can be what we want if we just work hard enough. Surrender and letting go seems to be most difficult for those people who have been very successful in other areas of their lives. The ways that we have achieved other goals in our education, careers, relationships and material things are not working to get the baby and the feelings of frustration, being out of control, grief, longing and envy cause suffering that is incomparable to almost any other situation.

The feeling of not being able to make it happen almost replaces the longing for the baby itself. To not be in control on a deep level makes us feel unsafe. On an energetic level it is our unconscious feeling of not being safe that is actually contributing to us feeling like we need to be in control. What is not realized is that those that struggle the most with this have a life long pattern of being in control or trying to be in control of their own circumstances and life due to an imbalance in the root chakra, the energetic vortex at the base of the spine. There is an excess in the exchange of energy in this particular chakra that can show up in other ways such as an abundance of material flow in life. A person may make or receive lots of money, food or material things but it may flow out as quickly as it flows in. This pattern stems back to infancy, birth and even one's own time in the womb. Or material energy may flow in but be held or hoarded such as the example of food and constipation or money in but not spending or money in but buying all of the things and acquiring a lot of stuff.

The root chakra is about feeling safe in the world, trusting others, knowing that we can depend on others to meet our needs and it's also very connected to the crown chakra at the top of the head. When the root and crown chakras are balanced, we have a healthy flow of material energy, receiving in balance with our needs, not hoarding or holding, not excessively wasting but we also have a connection with a source energy, higher self, God, the divine or universe. There is a trust in this higher source that even if we don't understand what our destiny is, that we trust the journey. It is much easier to go with the flow and we become co-creators with the universe. Rather than feel like we depend on ourselves alone, that we have to figure it out on our own, that if we don't make things happen in our life we won't have them, we have a spiritual relationship or a faith that we are guided and manifestation or the feminine way of creation happens in a mysterious or magic seeming way.

"Just quit trying and it will happen." The words hold so much charge and mere mention of them is excruciating for people who have been trying to get pregnant for a long time. The fear of not being in control is overwhelming. The fear of not doing it right, of quitting and not getting the baby is paralyzing. It doesn't make sense on a logical level and logic seems to have always served us well in the past. And practically speaking, how does one even quit trying in the first place? Are we expecting some kind of immaculate conception? What if medical intervention is needed? How can someone surrender if they need surgery, medications or assisted reproductive technology to conceive?

There are as many ways to surrender as I have had clients to support with surrendering. Each has had their own unique experience with letting go. Some get there much easier than others and I have learned through each of their experiences. It has taken me years of offering this support and being witness to the conception journeys of many to even understand surrender to the depth I do now. There are ways to make surrender easier and these techniques can benefit anyone whether they are manifesting a baby or anything else in their life.

The Root Chakra

The root chakra is about safety, trust, control, material world and security. It is my experience that almost every person at this time in history has some root chakra imbalance. This likely stems from our birth and early parenting practices. Anxiety, depression, money problems, issues with trust, body weight, scoliosis and other structural problems are associated with root chakra deficiency and excess. Energy healing that addresses the root of our imbalance is beneficial, however, due to our distance from the natural world we all seem to need continuous root chakra nurturing almost daily to keep us in balance.

If you identify with needing to be in control and struggling to let go of control, you are likely to find that simply trying not to is not enough. When we address our control challenges from the level of the root chakra, it takes care of itself. Energy healing is all about going to the root of an issue. Rather than try to change a behaviour, understand why the behaviour exists and heal that so the behaviour resolves itself.

As long as the root chakra is in excess we will unconsciously try to control our circumstances. The kinds of practices that we can practice daily or as often as possible to support root chakra balance include being outside in nature, grounding visualizations, walking outside barefoot, yoga, dance, physical touch like massage, reflexology is especially grounding because it is done on the feet and eating root vegetables. When the root chakra is balanced we feel safe in the world, our relationship with material energy like food and money is more balanced and we trust. Yoga and meditation are especially beneficial because they also open the crown chakra in a healthy way. The crown connects us to divinity, higher consciousness or God energy. Being grounded to the feminine earth energy connects us to the physical world, the feminine Goddess and nature. Meditation or prayer opens us up to the flow of universal energy so we can be co-creators with the universe. After all, without a faith in something outside of ourselves, what are we surrendering to? If there is no faith, no spiritual connection, of course we feel we have to do it ourselves and make it happen.

Surrender and letting go is the process of doing what we need to do while also having faith and trust in a universal force that is beyond our logical understanding.

The Masculine and the Feminine

Each of us has our own unique balance of masculine and feminine energy. Biological sex does not dictate whether one is masculine or feminine dominant. Biological females can be more feminine or more masculine in their own healthy balance. To be more masculine energetically is not unhealthy unless there is a block in feminine energy. Blocked feminine energy is very common in my clients who are trying to conceive and can manifest as irregular cycles, absence of menstruation, unexplained infertility and even polycystic ovaries and higher levels of androgens.

The origin of blocked feminine energy is often generational. Many of my clients who have suppressed their feminine energy are strong, confident, independent women who are very successful in their careers, they are often the breadwinners in their family, they wear the pants and are the "big spoon". Interestingly they are often paired with partners who are much more passive, nurturing and emotional than they are. A lot of the biological males I have supported in these relationships enjoy doing some of the more traditional feminine roles like cooking, they may be more soft spoken and passive, maybe even considered lazy. These partnerships work for them in every other aspect of life except for conception. In my experience it's not uncommon for PCO or similar symptoms to occur simultaneously with male factor infertility, low sperm count or other sperm quality issues.

Most of my clients who are the capable, successful, independent women come from a line of similar women. Just as science tells us there is often a genetic link with PCO, the stories get passed down with the hormonal pattern.

When I inquire with my clients about their mothers and grandmothers the stories always make sense. An example of the original wound is something like great grandpa was an abusive alcoholic. My grandma watched her mother live a life of abuse that she could not leave because she had no means to survive on her own. Grandma worked hard and became an engineer and she taught my mom to make sure she could always support herself and have an exit strategy, to never be too dependent on any man that she could not leave. This is a trauma response. It is a shift in the energy and our epigenetics for survival. The traits get passed down with the beliefs.

Blocked feminine energy can also be a result of a trauma experience or other significant energetic imprint about it not being safe or desirable to be female. Sexual assault and shame about sensuality can impact our balance. Our relationship with or the way we perceive our mother has a definite relationship with our feminine. If we did not respect our mother because she lived a passive existence, living only for her children and spouse, not seeming to have a purpose outside of her motherly duties may leave one longing for a different experience. Cultural beliefs may impact our relationship with our feminine energy.

I Never Wanted to be a Girl

One of my clients grew up on the island of St. Vincent with four brothers. In her family and culture as the only daughter it was her responsibility to do everything for her brothers and father. If they were hungry she had to feed them. She did the cleaning. She hated being a girl. She admitted this in our first session. In her adult life she excelled at work and climbed the corporate ladder. She was very successful and made a lot of money. However, significant PCOS prevented her from being able to conceive a baby.

In the major arcana of the tarot the magician shows us how to manifest in the masculine way. He is standing and ready for action. He has all of the tools and he stands before a beautiful wooden table that he built with his own hands, sweat and efforts. He creates in a practical, logical and physical way. The next cards in the deck is the high priestess. Unlike the magician, she sits in stillness. In her stillness she is connected to divinity, universal wisdom, her higher self. He was the master of logic. She is all knowing. She is fertile as symbolized by the many pomegranates (full of seeds) on the curtain behind her. What is behind the curtain or hidden under her cloak? The mysteries of the universe. She manifests by receiving. What she needs comes to her.

From a biological perspective, the masculine makes the baby. The feminine receives the baby. It is in this balance that we can be co-creators with the universe and manifest anything. It is a balance of taking action and surrendering to receive.

How do we heal the roots of blocked feminine (or masculine) energy? Awareness is the first step in most of the healing work that I do. What is the original story or original wound? By understanding what the beliefs are about being still, intuitive, sensual, nurturing and feminine we can better understand the perspective of reality or the lens through which we look and potentially shift it or let it go. Reiki can be very effective for healing because energy is not limited to time and space. Using distance Reiki we can send healing energy up the ancestral line to the original trauma when it was occurring. Prayer or visualization are alternatives that anyone can use to heal the root of the imbalance.

Once the awareness has shifted, a couple can make intentional choices to practice living with a different balance of masculine and feminine energy. It may be very challenging for her to be still if she is a workaholic or a busy body. Yin or restorative yoga, meditation, colouring and other non productive practices may be especially uncomfortable but powerful practices in stillness and connecting to source energy. He can practice being the big spoon in bed and the protector. It is amazing how aware of the feminine and masculine my clients have become through these suggestions. So many of my female clients have always spooned their partners in bed!

A Petition to God

One of my early fertility clients was on a three year journey to conceiving their first baby when I started working with them. They were diagnosed with unexplained infertility and after no success conceiving naturally or using IUI they felt no choice but to resort to IVF and it worked. Prior to that IVF cycle this client experienced what I describe as the surrender breakdown. She described to me how she felt when Snookie on the show Jersey Shore became pregnant. Snookie was drunk every day and her life was a mess and as is so often the case, it was the fact that this person seemed so undeserving of baby or maybe they didn't really want a baby and that was enough to trigger the breakdown as so many of my clients can relate to.

Months later I was invited to attend her baby shower where she shared with everyone the following petition to God. She wrote this petition and signed my name along with any other friends and family who she knew would support it on our behalf. She read this to us at her baby shower. Before I go on, I want to add that I was their doula for all of her following conceptions, pregnancies and births. Natural and easy conceptions followed this experience. This is her surrender story, shared with permission.

"Going through our three year journey of trying to create a family we learned many life lessons. One being to have faith within your faith and there comes a time when you need to give up control, surrender and just believe. Writing our little petition was my way of making my plea and then letting go. I am not sure and will never really know the connection of letting go and our conceiving of baby Jack, but things did work out on our next treatment.

Ryan and I have been so blessed to be surrounded by such amazing family and friends who we will be forever grateful for. Your support and never ending love truly is what got us through a very difficult journey.

We can't wait for you to meet sweet baby Jack! He is such a blessed little boy, who will be surrounded by so much love as he walks through life.

Lots of Love Ryan, Allyson and Jack

A Petition to God

God please grant Allyson and Ryan with the miracle they have been praying for the last three years. A family they can call their own.

Allyson and Ryan vow to raise their children in a Christian home with the following:

- Unconditional Love
- Kindness
- Strong set of morals and values
- Self-respect and Respect for others
- A sense of self-worth
- Empathy towards others
- Tolerance for difference
- Responsibility to the community
- Understanding of consequences

They promise to provide tender love when needed and firm boundaries during times of trial. The children will be nurtured physically and emotionally. They will ensure any child they are blessed to have will make the community a better place for them being granted the gift of life. As a family they promise to give back through service in one form or another.

Ryan and Allyson have done all they can for the past three years in their journey of infertility. There have been many blessings on this journey and they appreciate every one of them. They know that this miracle is in God's hands and that it needs to remain there, they pray daily that their prayers will be answered.

If you have faith they will cherish, love and raise their family as stated above and feel the time has come to grant them their miracle. Please say a small prayer and sign your name below."

How to Balance Trying With Not Trying

Sometimes surrender is about not trying or giving up. One of my clients was so in control of her conception journey that she even modified her own medication doses because she was a nurse. I could sense her very strong need for control and knew that my role in her journey was to allow the surrender breakdown to happen on its own without interfering. IUI wasn't working and she was devastated. Like my previous client, the wrong person in her life got pregnant and said the wrong thing that triggered an emotional breakdown. She described to me at one of our sessions how she self medicated for sleep because the pain was so intolerable. I could have provided comfort or optimism but I maintained my position of holding space and bearing witness to this necessary unraveling at her bi-weekly reflexology sessions. She was going to miss her next appointment because they had a wedding to travel to so I wouldn't be seeing her for a month. It was their month off before they would go for IVF and she told me passionately that if this one cycle of IVF didn't work, they were done and she wasn't going to have a baby. She was at the end of what she could handle mentally, emotionally and financially. I didn't try to convince her otherwise.

When she returned a month later she was depressed and resigned. I let my hands offer her grounding and comfort through reflexology. I asked her if they "tried" that month and she rolled her eyes and said we had sex once at the wedding but I don't even know when or if I ovulated. I was secretly very optimistic for her but didn't let on. When she came back two weeks later she was mad. I held space again as she expressed her frustration with her body. She was several days late and how could she even do IVF now. Everything would be delayed because something else was wrong with her body and now she'd have to go and get blood work for that. I contained my excitement. Her disbelief that conception could happen naturally, having only had sex once without timing, temping, medicating or monitoring was so far from what she believed was possible for her, pregnancy wasn't even a thought. I said nothing and only listened.

Of course two weeks later when she returned for her regular reflexology session, she shared her news that the bloodwork came back positive for pregnancy.

Having intercourse, timing intercourse, choosing positions for intercourse, taking temperatures, checking cervical fluid or position, going for reflexology or acupuncture, blood work, scans, and medical appointments. These are some of the ways people take action to conceive. Some of these things are essential. Only one female has ever been documented to conceive without doing any of the above that we have heard of and that's described as a miracle. It's normal for people who are not getting pregnant or having problems maintaining a pregnancy to easily get obsessed with the above. Feeling out of control of our situation leads to us trying to regain control and now it's all we think about and we lose other aspects of who we are and any other purpose in our life.

Letting go feels more difficult now than ever. Fear of a future with no baby feels not only unbearable but very real. Well intended friends or family members may even be bold enough to suggest we "stop trying and it will happen". No other words could be more offensive. Why are these six words enough to push us over the edge? It feels impossible to stop trying, to stop intentionally doing everything that can be done to maximize fertility, to stop timing intercourse, to stop monitoring cycles. How could not doing these things possibly make someone pregnant when doing everything right does not? It's not logical, but yet, everyone has heard at least one story about someone who signed the adoption papers and then found themselves unexpectedly pregnant a few months later.

We can try too hard to manifest anything. The reason it's so easy to fall into the trap of being too attached to the outcome of conceiving and birthing a baby is because it's one of life's greatest desires. It's our primal and unconscious struggle with our own mortality that creates a longing to recreate ourselves and the person we love most so that we will continue to exist. Our ability to conceive and carry a baby is unconsciously integrated into our perception of self worth, our role as woman or man, our responsibility to our partner. Will they still love us if we cannot get pregnant? We feel a responsibility to our families to expand the family. We long to see ourselves in little people and fulfill a desire to love, nurture, provide for and protect. To not be able to create new life when we want it feels unfair and it messes with our purpose or reason for being here. For most, life feels unliveable without this.

We think of surrender or letting go as giving up or quitting. Sometimes it is. Sometimes it is looking at where we have resistance and going there. For example we may be attached to conceiving naturally, opposed to IVF, adoption or surrogacy. Surrender is about asking for a destination but not knowing how we will get there. Letting go may not be letting go of what we want but of how we get there. I'll sometimes ask my clients who have very strong opposition to how they get their baby how they would feel about those methods five years from now if they had a preschooler on their hip, and their attachments dissolve. We don't get to know what the journey will be like or what we will learn along the way. Transformations happen and wisdom is gained through our most challenging experiences. When the resistance is strong, there's usually something for us there.

A Sneaky Way to Surrender

Another client I was working with rarely experienced menstruation. If she menstruated four times in a year, that was normal. She was wanting to get pregnant but had been waiting months for a period when I saw her for the first time. I offered her vigorous reflexology sessions and suggested tinctures and high doses of vitamin C but her bleed never came. As I got to know her I became aware of her pattern in life of being a high achiever who found much success by working hard and following the rules. There was a tension in her legs that I'd never experienced with other clients. A rigidity in her being that was accustomed to holding and managing everything herself. I knew I had to help this client surrender for all of the biological support to be effective but that my efforts would have to bypass her usual tendency of being in control. I suggested a plan. I knew it would be difficult for her to hear but I took the chance. I suggested that the next three months of summer our focus would be on healing her body and preparing for conception, but not actually trying to conceive. I suggested she plan to try to conceive in the fall and take a break from trying now. She looked sad but I could sense her trust in me and she agreed to the plan. When she went home, she told her husband and she cried. This client wasn't typically emotional. When I saw her a few weeks later she was pregnant even though she still hadn't had a period.

So how can we let go? If we don't have a practitioner to trick our minds into giving up, how can we do this for ourselves? There is power in exploring our fears about the future, of allowing ourselves to imagine "what if we don't..." If there is no baby, what would life look like? Imagine a future without a baby. I've had clients who flat out refuse to go there, and I don't force it, but I know that resistance is what keeps us stuck.

Find the Fear and Release It

A fertility client turned doula client found out at the end of pregnancy that her baby was breech and she was devastated. I asked her to tell me what her fear was. She was completely opposed to a surgical birth. I asked her to tell me what that was about for her and she painted a picture of her in a cold, bright and sterile operating room surrounded by masked faces with her arms tied down. I challenged her to research caesarean birth plans and surgical birth options and to make a caesarean birth plan for herself. She hated the idea but she trusted me. When her baby flipped into a head down position she admitted she shockingly became attached to her new vision of her birth where she knew when her baby was coming and how and getting her head wrapped around a spontaneous vaginal birth again was hard.

What are the blessings in the future you cannot accept? What would life look like without a baby? What are your greatest fears? What would the blessings be? Just thinking about these things is not enough in my experience. Writing them out moves the energy. Talking about it with a space holder or talking it out to a plant or rock in nature is even more powerful. Crying and emotional release is a sign that the energy is releasing. Use your imagination to make a plan B. Consider alternatives that you were previously opposed to. Explore what this is about for you. Ask yourself why your conception has to be natural or has to happen in your body or why the baby you love has to be genetically yours. Yes, you are entitled to all of these desires and no it isn't fair that some people can get babies when and how they want with ease and others cannot. In my experience as a Holistic Reproductive Practitioner who has walked beside many clients through all kind of conceptions, pregnancies, losses, births and postpartum, there is awe in every experience and it is the hardest journeys that have the most potential for growth and transformation. These experiences don't have to break you. They may break you down, but especially with healing support, what we can harvest from these experiences can be the greatest gifts in our life's journey.

MICHELLE STROUD

Michelle Stroud is a Holistic Reproductive Practitioner in Belleville, Ontario, Canada. She has been offering holistic health support to clients who are trying to conceive, pregnant, giving birth and postpartum since 2001. She now teaches Holistic Reproductive Practitioner students internationally through her school By the Moon. It has been Michelle's experience that holding space for the emotional aspects of infertility while supporting healing on a physical and biological level is what is needed. To go deeper by investigating the energetic, ancestral and spiritual pieces helps more clients get pregnant while also having healing, positive, transformative experiences. This approach is so unique and powerful that Holistic Reproductive Practitioners from all over the world are now trained by Michelle.

Website: https://www.bythemoon.ca
Email: michelle@bythemoon.ca
Facebook: https://www.facebook.com/bythemoonquinte
Instagram: https://www.instagram.com/bythemoon/
Youtube: https://www.youtube.com/
channel/UCv__w8R6itNUUS9ckqENzIg

21

FERTILE FAITH

OCTAVIA STEEN, FERTILITY AND HEALTH COACH

As a nurse, I never thought I'd be in this situation, which I think about now was a really stupid thought. 1. because infertility can happen to anyone, and 2. I didn't even realize how much I didn't know (more so retain) about the reproductive system in college. As an insurance nurse, I really didn't think too hard about the process of getting pregnant as something I'd have difficulty with, but here I was, newly married and constantly being asked when we were going to have children. How annoying.

My husband and I had a 'girl meets a guy, guy proposes, and the girl gets married in 14 months" kind of love story. So we, of course, KNEW that this perfect, in our eyes, love story had to produce a child right away, right? Wrong. Initially, I was actually on the pill, which probably didn't help my already imbalanced, bloat-producing hormones for this journey. My husband and I had waited to have sex with each other until marriage. I have to throw the "each other" clause in there because we were by no means virgins. Just a born-again, Jesus-loving couple, looking to do right by each other.

I was on the pill because, as newlyweds, we wanted to "enjoy" ourselves. Insert immediate baby-fever and family nagging. Needless to say, six months later, after seeing multiple babies on our grocery runs and jokingly, but not really joking, telling my husband to "give me one of those," we were ready to start trying. If only the gift of children were that easy. We soon learned that it was a difficult road ahead for us.

Like any other newlywed couple, infertility never crossed our minds as we began to try to get pregnant. We ditched the pill and amped up the intimacy. Even more so than two people who had just got married. We thought that it would happen just like our love life, quick and easy. We were mistaken. The imbalance of my hormones mixed with my digestion issues, we later learned, were probably a hindrance in the early stages of our journey. I was ovulating regularly on day 14 of my 28-day cycle but was holding onto a lot of toxins and inflammation in my body. Just to get a little TMI here, I was pooping once a week. Now looking back, no wonder my body didn't want to cooperate with my goals and aspirations. Unfortunately, none of these issues crossed my mind as we were trying to get pregnant, so the unhealthy cycle (pun intended) continued.

Six months passed, and nothing. We were clueless as to what was going on. I reached out to Aunt Google and also put my nursing brain to work. It was clear as soon as I began my research that I didn't know what TTC[1] even meant. Yes, it meant that when a man and woman love each other, they come together to have babies, but it's so much deeper than that. The science behind it really got my nursing brain spinning, and I dived in. From all of the hormone fluctuations to the two week wait, I studied the ins and outs of TTC. I soon discovered this massive community for women like me who didn't get pregnant on the first try. I fell in love with the journey, but I soon started to hate it as well.

Because somehow I still felt alone. I still have the feeling that because I wasn't pregnant yet that it would never happen. I would search for forums about 3 DPO (days past ovulation) symptoms and find results from 10 years ago and feel defeated. Like pregnancy, symptoms somehow drastically change in the midst of 10 years. For some reason, I needed current. I needed to know that someone at this very moment was going through what I was. Yes, Google and fertility books taught me a lot about TTC, ovulation, and cervical mucus. You know, all the things they failed to bring light to or barely glanced over in nursing school, but somehow I wanted more.

I WASN'T READY

So in my research, I found comfort in reading and watching other women's experiences through their own personal fertility journeys. Because of that, I decided to share my own as well in hopes to help, encourage, and inspire. My husband and I had recently started a YouTube channel on faith and fitness shortly before starting our journey to baby. He's a personal trainer, and I was just trying to get better with my health at the time. We shared a variety of things in regards to our Christian faith and tips for living a healthier lifestyle. We started to love sharing our life there, but in my heart, I know we needed to share more. It's great to see people doing great on YouTube or in movies, right? But we had a story. An infertility story.

We, more so I, began to share our TTC journey, and it was transformational! Not only for myself but for the women that subscribed to our channel. I desired to be transparent with my entire journey there, even if it meant weird looks from family or odd questions from subscribers. I desired the community atmosphere and discovered soon enough other women who did too. Thousands of them! I was blown away by the support and community of women that I discovered then. Now, some I even call friends who have went on to conceive their own babies and now still follow my videos about motherhood.

Just to back it up a bit, I wasn't initially so enthused to share this part of me. I don't think anyone would be. It's a very private and special part of someone's life. I wasn't quite ready to expose that side 1. because my mother was already asking when her future grandbabies were 2. friends kept asking when we were going to have kids, which was not the best feeling when you have been TRYING and 3. I wasn't ready to bare my soul to the world.

I wasn't ready for the vulnerability. I wasn't ready for crying on video. I wasn't ready. But God knew my story would help multiple women in their own journeys to their first babies. So even though I didn't feel like it, God knew I was ready, and so I moved forward in my vulnerability and stepped out on faith. I'm so glad I did.

In December 2017, I posted my first video. It was a declaration to trust God with my trying to conceive journey, and it rippled into more videos sharing my entire story. I absolutely fell in love with sharing my experience and, in turn, helping other women who were in the trenches with me. We formed a little community on my channel of encouragement, information, and prayer. The support was unbelievable, and I no longer felt disabled by the lack of updated forums but took to other YouTuber's channels to encourage and be encouraged.

As my channel and journey evolved, I began to share TTC updates where I would discuss my weekly symptoms and what I was experiencing. I started to share what I was learning in my studies to balance my hormones and optimize my nutrition for fertility, including the smoothies I was trying that particular cycle, and showing ovulation test progressions. It was a literal channel, an outlet, to share my feelings, so I didn't keep them bottled inside. It was a place, although I was talking to myself to a camera every day, where I didn't feel alone. It seems odd, but somehow it worked for this once introverted loner. Who would have thought?

Continuing with the faith-based inspiration on our channel, I would share scriptures about fertility from the Bible. I knew if it was helpful for me, then it had to be for someone else too. I talked about Hannah, who prayed for a son. I talked about inspiring scriptures that helped me in my own personal journey. I turned to the Bible when I was in my two-week waits for additional encouragement and shared that as well. Then it happened.

GOD OPENED MY WOMB

I was driving in my car on the way to church for a midweek service. I was about 2 minutes away from the building when one of my favorite worship songs came on. I began to praise God and sing at the top of my lungs as I often do in my car concerts. But this time was different. I felt a deep butterfly effect in my stomach and a warmth in my heart as I was singing. The word "open" dropped in my spirit, and I automatically knew what that meant because I was currently in my fertile window approaching ovulation and the two-week wait.

Two weeks later, I got my very first positive pregnancy test!! I was so excited I immediately shared it with my husband in the form of a gift with a test inside of a box. But for some reason, I felt like I needed to keep confirming and testing, so I took a Clearblue test where it actually says "pregnant or not pregnant." It said not pregnant, and a day later, another negative test. I started spotting the day after that.

The day that I started spotting, I received a call from my mom. I could hear the grief in her voice as she asked me if I was sitting down, and I was. I can remember the exact moment and the exact place (my couch) where I was when she told me that my 16- year-old cousin had committed suicide.

That night I started to bleed, and double grief hit—the grief and loss of my teenaged cousin and the loss of my unborn child. I took my worry and my grief to God, and he gave me peace. That cycle made me realize that God has a promise and a purpose over my life. He gave me a glimpse of what could have been. I had been battling negative thoughts during my entire journey that I was just incapable of becoming pregnant. My miscarriage opened up my eyes to show that I was capable and God was able.

WHAT DO YOU MEAN I'M NOT PREGNANT?

I experienced an unexplainable mental peace afterward, so I was ready to start trying again. We chose not to wait for a complete cycle, and I ovulated two weeks after my miscarriage. So we went for it. We were able to get pregnant again that next month. We didn't waste any time telling everyone, including YouTube, because we were putting all of our faith in this. I even found a really cute way to tell my husband on camera and post to YouTube, and we were beyond excited! Since we found out so early and had a miscarriage previously, my doctor scheduled an early ultrasound. We made it to my first ultrasound at five weeks pregnant with a pregnancy hormone lab result of 9,000, which was good. They saw a yolk sac but no fetus yet. They assured us that it was too early, so I was scheduled for another ultrasound two weeks later.

Two weeks went by, and we showed up for our next appointment and once again saw only a yolk sac. The gestational sac had increased, but no baby had developed. I was told by the tech the doctor was not available to evaluate the ultrasound, so I would have to wait for a call. A few hours later, I received a call, and the doctor wanted me to come in to recheck my labs. Because I had recently miscarried, she thought still that it might be too early, especially because I did not have a cycle after my miscarriage. Even though I told her my ovulation day, it didn't seem like she was listening. I didn't feel heard.

The next afternoon my lab results were in, and at that point, my pregnancy hormone had increased to 40,000. I remember to this day my doctor telling me that I was not really pregnant. I had what they called a blighted ovum. A blighted ovum is when a fertilized egg implants, but it doesn't grow and develop. I immediately thought: what do you mean I'm not pregnant?

THE WAIT I NEEDED

My second reaction was to burst into tears because I knew what they would say the next steps were, a miscarriage. I decided to forego surgery to terminate the pregnancy. Instead, I prayed and waited. Three weeks went by, and I started to miscarry and bleed at ten weeks pregnant. It lasted a total of 45 days. I know this may sound odd, but that was the wait I needed. It was the mental, spiritual and physical healing that I never knew I needed. It was 45 days of spotting, bleeding, tears, and joy! Yes, I bled for 45 days, but more than that, I learned so much about myself. I found joy in the process of the miscarriage and in the experience of sharing it with women who were going through the same things. It was very emotionally draining, but fortunately, it was not necessarily physically draining. I didn't have intense cramping like most women describe in their miscarriages that are further along. It went in circles of a light period for a week and then huge clots, light again, and then more clots. I think because it did take so long is why it was not as intense. Would I have rather had intense cramping and a shorter miscarriage? Honestly, I'm not sure because that's not my story. Eventually, my pregnancy hormone started to decrease really slowly until it was finally over almost a month and a half later.

While going through my miscarriage, I started a new health journey. During this entire process, from my first BFP[2] (big fat positive) until the moment I decided to turn the health switch back on, I had lost myself. I had become consumed by the journey to pregnancy that I had lost sight of my health. I started a 21-day workout plan because I needed an outlet to physically and mentally improve myself. I started journaling in my prayer journal, working out, and eating healthier every day. I truly believe that improving my physical health helped me for my future fertility and finally balancing my hormones from digestive issues.

I was also still sharing my experience on Youtube with weekly videos on updates of my miscarriage, which was hard, but honestly, the best decision because it helped so many women. I started to receive comments every day about other women who had gone through blighted ovums or long miscarriages as well. Once again, my community was there for me, and I for them. To this day, I am still receiving comments on my videos from my TTC journey about how encouraging my story was and the inspiration other women feel from what I shared years ago. It truly has been a blessing to share that experience with literally anyone willing to watch and listen.

After my miscarriage, we decided to wait for my menstrual cycle to come before we would start trying again. We started trying again one cycle after our miscarriage ended. I shared what I was doing to heal after a miscarriage. From adopting a healthier lifestyle to healing spiritually and mentally, I shared everything I was doing. The first month we tried after our miscarriage, we got pregnant with our rainbow baby, Ava. At the time of writing this, she's two years old. But our journey did not end there. Eight months after Ava was born, we conceived another baby girl, Sinai.

WHAT WORKED FOR ME

Alright, so what worked for me? I think, first of all, we have to start at faith. I kept my faith strong, and maybe you don't believe in God, and you read my story thinking I was a bit crazy but keeping a positive attitude about my journey helped me so much. It gave me the mental strength I needed during a journey that can be so emotionally depleting. I always aimed to turn a negative into a positive and tried not to dwell too long in that negative space. I prayed and spoke affirmations over my life, my future family, and my womb. Those prayers that were written in my prayer journal were the changing point in my TTC journey.

Next, I re-evaluated the food that I was putting into my body. I know for a fact that I have an intolerance to multiple foods, including dairy. I adopted an anti-inflammatory diet and increased healthy fats. I was pretty sure my baby would come out like an avocado. Changing my diet to decrease the inflammation in my body is something I did before conceiving both of my children. I incorporated spinach into my daily smoothies before ovulation and after ovulation focused on eating warm comfort foods. Also, drinking plenty of water to help flush out any toxins, a natural detoxification process, is what I incorporated into my conception month.

What else worked for us is having sex every other day. It wasn't a strategy more so than just a way for us not to stress about the process. We didn't want to have to worry about "scheduling" around ovulation day and just focus on each other. Ultimately, what worked for us is not letting the TTC process mentally bring us down. Yes, at times, it was hard, but it was much easier when we looked at our journey with a more positive perspective.

Because of my journey and the encouragement I received from God on my journey, I became a health coach while pregnant with my first girl. At almost five months pregnant, I started to bring women along with me onto a journey to live healthier lifestyles by leading faith and fitness accountability groups. I now, through my groups, continue to help other women find spiritual peace while creating healthy bodies while on their own fertility journeys. Starting in 2018, I've had the pleasure of crossing paths through my business with hundreds of women who have conceived and now have beautiful babies of their own. It has been such a blessing.

I currently still share on YouTube as well with fertility tips, healthy living, and my motherhood experience. Our community of women continues to grow and thrive into women who are ready to start healthy families and become spiritually and physically fit.

---

1. TTC - Trying to conceive
2. BFP-Big fat positive pregnancy test.

OCTAVIA STEEN

Octavia Steen is a fertility doula, health coach, and owner of Mother Mindset. She is originally from Michigan and now resides with her husband, Carl, and their two girls in Indiana. Her certificate in nursing as well as degrees in Women Studies, B.A., and Health Care Management, M.B.A. have led her into her current passion of inspiring future and current young mothers. She helps them increase their faith in God while creating healthy bodies to prepare for their first babies. Octavia has been featured in Black Enterprise, has worked with fertility brands like Mira Fertility, and is rooted and driven by her faith.

Website: https://mothermindset.com/
Email: hello@mothermindset.com
Instagram: https://www.instagram.com/coach.avi/
Youtube: https://www.youtube.com/octaviasteen
Clubhouse: @octaviasteen

22

LOW-COMPLEXITY IVF

INTERVIEW WITH PETER FUZESI: CHIEF OPERATING OFFICER AT HANABUSA IVF

Interview with Peter Fuzesi: Chief Operating Officer at Hanabusa IVF. Interviewed by Dr. Deb Davies, DACM, L.Ac. and Colleen Reagan Noon
www.hanabusaivf.com

INTERVIEW WITH PETER FUZESI: Chief Operating Officer at Hanabusa IVF

Deb: Thank you for taking the time to speak with us, Peter. Will you tell me what your position is?

Peter: I'm the Chief Operating Officer of Hanabusa IVF. I have a clinical embryology background, as I used to be a laboratory manager, so I'm coming from a science background. I always ended up on the management side of the laboratory and in the IVF practice. After a while, I just decided that I would move forward only with the management part.

Deb: You must be a very busy man! What kind of person is a good candidate for IUI/IVF?

Peter: That's a very broad question, but I think the sooner the patient realizes they are struggling to get pregnant, the sooner they should look for help. I think it's very important nowadays. Lots of patients are delaying family building, and it doesn't help their situation. Many patients realize way too late that they have fertility issues. Once they get out of college, they want to get a job, and they realize they want to get an advanced degree and go back to study again, so there is always an excuse to delay getting married or to have a baby. I think it's very important that they seek help as early as they realize they are having difficulty. It will really be up to the physician to decide about the treatment.

Deb: Can you tell me about the different treatment options?

Peter: Most patients are recommended to try IUI, Inter-uterine Insemination, first. Sometimes even before that, they try a timed intercourse cycle. If the timed intercourse cycle doesn't work out, the next step would be to do an IUI where patients go through a very similar process. They may or may not take medication, and after they come to the office, the male patient collects the specimen that is processed in the lab, then we are injecting this directly into the uterus. The process gets the semen one step closer to the fertilization site, and we hope that this helps. Unfortunately, there is still a very low success rate overall with IUI, and we may repeat this several times. Sometimes way too many times because some insurance companies require patients to complete this 6, 8, or 12 times before they are eligible for IVF coverage. That is not really fair because, for many patients, time is wasted on this process.

However, starting out with the IUI is not always the case. Some patients are deciding earlier to start IVF treatments based on their own desire or from discussing with their physician. There is a big jump in here because the current IVF treatment that most of the IVF centers are offering will involve advanced laboratory add-on services right from the start. Many IVF practices are already doing ICSI,

Intra-Cytoplasmic Sperm Injection, by default on all patients. It doesn't even have to be a male factor case, where due to the male patient's infertility problem, they are utilizing micromanipulation techniques.

Many of the clinics will offer patient embryo chromosome screening procedures. With this procedure, they are doing embryo hatching, and they are doing biopsies and chromosome screening, so-called PGTA – Pre-implantation Genetic Testing for Aneuploidy on the embryo. Each of these adds additional costs to the patient's treatment. Additionally, there are many other sperm selection techniques that these IVF clinics are charging patients for. There is a device called Zymot that is used to select the sperm. Or they have a PICSI dish, before they do the ICSI, to select the right sperm. There is also an Embryoglue media, and now each of these are added to the patient's treatment plan. There are many IVF clinics that are encouraging patients to utilize all of these advanced techniques. There are already studies out there proving that all of these add-on procedures will not significantly increase the patient's chances of succeeding in their particular IVF case. What we see is that from the IUI procedure, patients are getting into these IVF treatments that have all of these add-on costs, which are significantly increasing the burden on the patient financially, with no significant increase in their chances of success.

The gap we are trying to fill in here is to offer a new treatment approach to patients. We call it a low-complexity IVF. We coined this term, it's not mainstream, but that's how we try to differentiate. Whereas these current IVF treatments offer all of these add-ons, let's say high-complexity treatments, without really justifying it. We offer patients an intermediate option between IUI and IVF, which is called low-complexity IVF.

What is low-complexity IVF? It is just the basic IVF approach stripped down to the minimal services that the patient would need to get pregnant. This should be the bridge between IUI and a high-complexity IVF procedure. The goal is to make this affordable to patients and give them a chance to succeed with less financial investment. Not all patients qualify for this, but most patients who would go through all of the traditional timed intercourse and IUI process would be a good candidate. Any patient that is less than 38 years old is probably a good candidate to approach with low-complexity IVF.

Deb: Could you tell us a bit more about the low complexity IVF?

Peter: Basically, low-complexity IVF involves a less aggressive medical treatment, less injections, more oral medicine, and completing the egg retrieval under local anesthesia. There

will be only a few follicles, so there is no need to go for IV sedation. After inseminating the egg, it is cultured for a few days and then transferred as a fresh day-three embryo. Basically, this way, we avoid any of the ICSI. There is no hatching, no blastocyst culture, no freezing involved, and no Pre-implantation Genetic Testing for Aneuploidy (PGT-a). This would give a chance for the patient to experiment with IVF without all the added costs. Literally, we can offer this for half the price of what other centers are charging because there is no need for advanced laboratory procedures. Even just the medications would significantly lower the cost. Again, this is not going to be applicable to all patients. Meanwhile, we would encourage all patients who go through this route to try a low-complexity IVF approach maybe once or twice, and after, if it didn't work, of course, they would be a good candidate to move forward with high-complexity IVF.

Again, a consultation and advanced testing would help the physician decide if a patient is a good candidate for low-complexity IVF. There will be conditions where we can justify that the patient indeed needs ICSI, especially if it's male factor infertility. Or, the patient would need to do PGTA because she's already 42, 43 years old, and there is a high chance of aneuploidy. There are cases where patients should go to high-complexity IVF right away, but it isn't universal. That's why we try to promote low IVF treatment at our center. It's an alternative option. We have been doing this for over a year, and we have seen some successful cases.

Deb: I have seen some of your successful cases too!

Colleen: So, are other places doing this? Is this something that someone can hear about, go to their IVF center, and it even be an option?

Peter: I think it would be an option at many IVF centers, and that's how IVF started. We were doing day-three transfers before. We were utilizing Clomid. The first IVF baby was born through a Clomid IVF treatment. All of these techniques were available, but somehow, as IVF and reproductive medicine evolved, it got to be way too much medicine and way too much add-on technology. We are using way too much technology when you can succeed with less. That's what we are trying to bring back - a more natural approach.

It is something that clinics might offer to patients, but there would only be a few who offer this as a regular program in their center. There are studies out there, especially studies where they are trying to serve underserved communities and patients with less financial backing, that this would be the right approach for them. When we started to promote this, we found studies where they proved the validity of this program. Very few IVF programs picked it up because of financial motivation. They can always make more money if they sell more services.

Deb: Right. So, can you clarify something? You keep saying ICSI, and I'm not familiar with that.

Peter: So, it stands for Intra-Cytoplasmic Sperm Injection (ICSI). This is a micromanipulation technique that was developed in the 1990s. When IVF become available for patient treatment in the early

'80s and '90s, they consistently failed in male factor cases. This is where there are very few sperm cells or very poor-quality sperm that is produced by the male patients. Mixing together one single sperm in a dish with an egg would never result in a pregnancy. Naturally, there are thousands of very good quality sperm surrounding the egg, and eventually, one will penetrate and fertilize it. This is how it happens naturally, and that's what we need to do in the laboratory as well. We're not mixing just one single sperm with an egg. Thousands of healthy sperm need to surround the egg so that fertilization happens. When we don't have this many good sperm because the male partner produces very few or very low-quality sperm, in that case, fertilization won't happen in a petri dish.

That's how why they developed this micromanipulation technique. Basically, think about an inverted microscope with two joysticks that manipulate two arms. One microneedle would hold on to the egg, and the other microneedle would puncture the egg and inject one single sperm cell inside. This is called Intra-cytoplasmic, so inside of the egg, sperm injection. That's where the terminology ICSI is coming from. It was developed in the '90s, and it got popularized in the early 2000s. Now, this is readily available at all IVF centers. But, not all of them are utilizing it only for male infertility cases. You want to maximize fertilization, so you're just injecting all of the eggs to make sure fertilization happens and not just leaving it in the dish.

Deb: So, can you tell me a little bit about day-three embryos versus day-five embryos?

Peter: Early culture systems were not proficient enough to culture embryos all the way to the blastocyst stage. With a natural pregnancy, once the egg is fertilized in the fallopian tube, it descends into the uterus over 5-6 days. It reaches an advanced stage that we call the blastocyst embryo. That is the embryo that we will implant on day 5, 6, or 7 and establish a pregnancy. In early IVF laboratories where conditions were not perfect, and they were still experimenting with air quality, incubators, and culture media, they couldn't culture embryos all the way to the blastocyst stage. They cultured it just for a few days. On day three, they're still in cleavage mode, so there is still a countable number of cells in the embryo. That's when they transfer the embryo to the uterus.

Nowadays, with our advanced technology, we are culturing embryos all the way to the blastocyst stage. Sometimes, though, patients who are consistently failing to produce a blastocyst embryo in culture are told to experiment and implant it on day three. Perhaps their uterine environment may be a better culture condition for this day-three embryo to develop internally. Some patients succeed with this approach. So, we can still transfer day-three embryos, even though these days, more and more practices tend to opt for blastocyst culture because there is an additional selection process. Out of all the embryos, those that make it to blastocyst should have a greater chance for pregnancy and live birth.

Colleen: When someone is getting IVF, how is the blastocyst inserted?

Peter: That happens in the embryo transfer process, and it's a very simple procedure. It doesn't require any anesthesia. However, it's still done in the procedure room because it has to be close to the IVF laboratory. Basically, we use a thin, very soft catheter to go through the cervix and reach to the back of the uterus where the physician, with the help of an embryologist, would insert the embryo into the uterus. There is a small air bubble at the tip of the catheter. Then, with the help of an ultrasound that is there to help us to guide, we go all the way to the back of the uterus. That's where we're injecting, with a very small amount of media, into the uterus. We let the patient rest a little bit. Implantation will happen in the upcoming hours or days. That's the embryo transfer process. It is very similar- whether it's a day-three embryo or day-five blastocyst.

Deb: What makes your clinic special?

Peter: What I'd like to highlight is that being here in San Diego, when we established this program, we didn't mean to give competition to well-established IVF centers. We wanted to fill in the gap for patients who did not qualify for IVF treatment at those centers or felt they had no other options. Our patients come to see us because they may have very high follicle stimulating hormone levels, or they are suffering from premature ovarian insufficiency, diminished ovarian reserve, or they are at an advanced maternal age. These patient's IVF cycles may be canceled in the middle of the treatment because their treating physician didn't see enough follicles. These patients either not welcomed, or they failed with a traditional IVF approach, are the cases where we can see our approach, a minimal stimulation approach, an oral pill minimal stimulation approach, or a natural cycle IVF, give an opportunity for them to succeed.

Again, this isn't taking away the validity of the other IVF center's approaches where the treatment is with multiple hormone injections —many younger patients will be perfectly fine with this approach and succeed very quickly. But many other patients are failing with this approach, and it is not properly recognized. It looks like the whole mini-IVF stimulation, which is actually how IVF was born, was somehow just forgotten. Very few IVF clinics take the time to specialize in this because it is more time-consuming for the patient and the physician as well. And they yield lower success rates because these patients are already struggling, which may not benefit the other IVF clinics' success rate, who are very careful about that. That's why we wanted to give an opportunity to these other patients and specialize in these cases that are the most challenging in the field.

We tried to create a more boutique IVF approach. We're taking on fewer patients and just trying to concentrate on these cases. We have an assigned case nurse coordinator who helps the patient to walk through the process. They become a part of our family a little bit. The patients participate in this treatment for several months, and we give a chance to each and every follicle they have to see if we can succeed. This is the approach we took six years ago when we opened here in San Diego, and we got quite busy, but we still want to maintain a somewhat boutique experience and not become a huge center where patients feel intimidated. That's our specialty: to succeed in the most challenging cases with mini-IVF, natural cycle IVF; we just try to be the best at it.

Colleen: What would you say to someone who's scared of IVF?

Peter: If the patient is coming in for the first time and haven't had previous IVF treatments, I highly recommend them to get educated. There are so many videos online as support material to understand the process, so they don't get overwhelmed. Once they get a consultation and start treatment, the patients easily get overwhelmed and stressed out about the process. They don't understand the time commitment, what's coming up, when to come for monitoring, or when to come for egg retrieval. Everything is happening in a short amount of time, and it adds more and more to the patient's anxiety. So, if the patient already knows that they get easily overwhelmed, I think it's always better to get as much information ahead of time. Many clinics also have an intake process to educate patients about the steps ahead of them, to make sure that they don't stress over them.

In addition to that, I recommend patients to be part of a support group or find another couple or patient that they can share their experience with. We provide a regular monthly support group free-of-charge, and there are others as well in San Diego and everywhere in the country. To be part of it, and hear from other patients and share the experience, I think it helps a lot, psychologically, to go through the process. Sometimes they are scared of a certain aspect; I know some of the patients have a needle phobia, and they are afraid of getting injections. At traditional IVF centers, there are a lot of injections involved, and patients are afraid of that. In addition to that, they have to go through multiple blood drawings for hormone tests throughout this process. These patients should look for alternative IVF centers where they can get treated with less needles. Our program utilizes more oral medicine, very few injections. And there are programs that are just pure oral-based, and they can even minimize the blood drawing, which will help them to minimize the needle anxiety. Programs utilizing the mini-IVF approach perform egg retrieval under local anesthesia. Patients don't have to go through IV sedation with all of the side effects and take a day off for every single procedure. We can reduce all of this with a local anesthesia IVF with a significantly smaller needle and reduce complications like pain and bleeding after the procedure. There are a handful of IVF centers doing this as a standard. Some other IVF centers may not be able to offer this. If the IVF physicians aren't used to doing this on patients, they will be less likely to offer this, but the patient has options. I think all of this is an option for patients to reduce the fear of the whole IVF process.

Colleen: We would love to hear what the experience of someone in the LGBTQIA community would be like.

Peter: Ever since we opened our practice, we have had several lesbian couples find us because they knew they are not infertile; they just need help to get pregnant. They realized that they need a center that has a natural approach to reduce needles, injections that are not necessary. Our program had many LGBTQ couples – many of them lesbian couples, because we were able to treat them with just a little bit of help. When we developed our low-complexity IVF, we realized that this is a perfect approach to reducing costs: they don't have to take that much injectable medication. Later we developed our reciprocal low-complexity IVF, which takes it one step further. Utilizing this technology, both partners can contribute to the pregnancy and to the child, one of the mothers can be the egg provider, and the other can carry the baby. This would help both parents to feel closer to the child. We also call this a co-maternity experience. This is available at other IVF centers, but they would use a lot more drugs, which again brings back all of the concerns that they are not infertile.

We also offer egg donation and surrogacy options for our gay couples. Our surrogacy program already generated a large part of our revenue which was driven by overseas patients seeking surrogacy treatment in California. We also have an egg bank that specializes in Asian egg donation. We are trying to capture egg donation and surrogacy for gay couples because we know that we are one of the best options for them. We have one of the largest selections of eggs of Asian ancestry. And we are proud to say that we have several LGBTQ team members who are open about it and who are also parents. I am one of them. So, we absolutely welcome them at our center.

Deb: Do you support any supplementary therapies to help improve the IUI or IVF outcomes? Do you make recommendations for acupuncture or other holistic services?

Peter: It's so important that the patient's basic nutritional needs are met to begin with. That's why we hear of pre-natal vitamins for any IVF procedure or pregnancy. If a patient is healthy and exercises regularly and gets proper nutrition through their diet, they can get many of the nutrients that they need, but it is very important that the patient is advised on this and prepared. Unfortunately, looking into this at the last minute, just a few days or weeks before any treatment, will not significantly improve their chances. I think it's essential that a healthy lifestyle is part of their daily routine already, over the course of several months at least, before they move forward with IVF. But, if they need any specific nutritional supplement, I would like to leave that between the patient and the physician to discuss.

Beyond the nutritional needs, the whole holistic approach is helpful for helping with anxiety and stress that comes with IVF. Meditation, yoga, acupuncture can all be very important. With any of these approaches—I think it's essential for the patient to have the right mental state and for them to have proper techniques to use. There are many studies that show stress and anxiety will negatively impact the patient's chances of succeeding with the treatment, either producing good eggs, embryos, getting pregnant, or carrying the pregnancy. So, it's very important that the patient spends time in support groups and utilizing additional therapies. The patient should look for these complimentary services that are very important for preparing for this journey and help maximize their chances throughout this process.

We don't endorse one single provider for this type of help; we work with many. So I wouldn't highlight one single medication or the other or nutritional supplement, but rather just take a holistic approach to the whole treatment.

Deb: Who is your ideal client?

Peter: Our ideal clients are patients who've already been through IVF, and they most likely failed. Either because they are not comfortable at bigger IVF programs, where no matter how much they try to prioritize personalized care, it's just overwhelming to sit in a waiting area with 20-30 other patients and be just one patient out of 100 treated in a single day. I believe this is where we can make a difference. Our ideal patient would be someone who is looking for a more personalized setting, a more private setting to go through this process, somebody who failed with IVF. They have specific conditions, as I said before, diminished ovarian reserve, premature ovarian insufficiency, advanced maternal age, dealing with high FSH – these are the challenging cases for other IVF centers. We are the ones who deal with most of these difficult cases, and we are good at it because that's what we do every single day. We understand their day-to-day needs, and our physicians and practice are geared towards making a day-to-day adjustment to their treatment, and not just to have a flat treatment plan. We are the clinic that is not afraid to make day-to-day changes to the patient's treatment plan. And even if it's on a weekend or a holiday, we would be available to go through their procedure and to provide for the most challenging cases.

Deb: How much male infertility are you seeing? Is there a percentage, male infertility versus female infertility in the clinic?

Peter: Many times, we cannot pinpoint if it's a male or female infertility issue, one or the other, and sometimes both. I think our patient population is similar to all the other centers. We don't have higher or lower percentages of patients with male fertility issues. We're also able to help patients where they need to utilize testicular sperm and advanced fertilization techniques such as ICSI processing. We have specialists on board where we can refer patients if they have male factor fertility.

Deb: Okay. I thought I heard something from one of my patients, that the doctor didn't even put her on anything. He just gave her some hormones or something and helped her get pregnant. One of my 42-year-old patients is ready to give birth next month. Is that the mini-IVF?

Peter: I think that may be a patient who may have had a high FSH, and there are already techniques to suppress that. There are some supplements and medication that would help to suppress the patient's FSH level. Once we get to that point, the patient has a better chance of, even naturally, getting pregnant. And that might be the case, without really knowing it, I think that might be a case that fits in here, where we were successfully able to suppress the patient's FSH, and then the patient just went through her natural cycle on her own and was able to produce an egg, a healthy embryo, that led to a pregnancy. I'm not sure if there was any type of instruction for timed intercourse or if she was even monitored. That might be another case, though, and I think she was one of our success stories.

Deb: We had somebody who had ovarian cancer, so I think one of her ovaries was removed, and she's 42, so there were all sorts of problems, but she was so happy—this is what I feel like I get with you guys, especially when people have failed IVF, that you are such a great option because they are then more likely to get pregnant.

Peter: I would like to share some other success stories:

Success Story 1:

This patient came to us with a low AMH (0.36) and a high FSH (39.8). Her periods were irregular, and she was told that she would not become pregnant on her own and would need to use donor eggs.

Good thing she came to Hanabusa IVF. When someone told her that it is impossible to conceive on her own, Dr. Chang found a window of opportunity.

This patient was 38 years old and was never pregnant before seeing us. Before coming to us, she failed multiple IUIs and two IVF cycles at two other fertility centers.

We designed a personalized approach and attempted a few medicated timed intercourse cycles before proceeding with IVF. Since she has Premature Ovarian Insufficiency, we used minimal stimulation and steered clear of oral medications since she suffered from severe migraines. We used injection only, a Mini-Antagonist protocol.

We performed egg retrieval under local anesthesia. This resulted in five eggs retrieved. All the eggs were mature, successfully fertilized, and resulted in one blastocyst which was tested and found to be PGT-A normal!

Although Dr. Chang prefers a natural ovulation cycle for transfers, because of her irregular cycle, we proceeded with an artificial (programmed) cycle.

We performed the transfer using transvaginal ultrasound guidance with an empty bladder so the patient would feel comfortable during the embryo transfer.

We confirmed positive pregnancy one week after the transfer!

Today, the patient is about 20 weeks into her pregnancy journey, and the pregnancy is progressing very well!

Success Story 2:

We recently tele-graduated a patient from our clinic! She came to us three years ago in her mid-30's after two years of trying.

When she first came to us, her gynecologist found that her FSH was 43, and AMH was <0.03. She researched her options and then realized that traditional fertility treatments would not work for her. After discovering we offer different treatment protocols, she traveled to our clinic.

Because of her high FSH, we started a "suppression" stimulation. It took us four months to see any signs of egg follicles.

Eventually, we could perform a single egg retrieval, which resulted in a Day 5 blastocyst. PGT had been performed, but, unfortunately, the biopsied cells degenerated, and we could not provide a diagnosis. We did not dare to repeat the biopsy and risk damaging the embryo.

For the next 14 months, we tried various treatments, but our efforts were to no avail. We did one last egg retrieval, and now she is in complete menopause. Because we only had one opportunity for transfer, she had never been pregnant, and surrogacy was not an option, we had to take everything but the kitchen sink approach to transfer.

To eliminate any uterine lining issues which could come about from not having regular periods, we cleaned out the uterus and artificially brought back her menstrual cycle for 3 months.

Although ERA testing is unnecessary for most patients, we only had one chance. We performed this test to confirm our protocol.

Although the likelihood of embryo rejection resulting in miscarriage is <1% because we only had one chance and embryo rejection testing is fraught with false positives and negatives, we took the risk and treated with blood thinners and steroids.

Fortunately, she is pregnant and started seeing her Ob for obstetrical care. We still have a long way to go, but the pregnancy has been progressing perfectly.

Success Story 3:

The Hanabusa IVF team is happy report a patient success story. Prior to coming to Hanabusa IVF, a 37-year old patient had been trying to conceive for three years without success. She had never been pregnant before. She was diagnosed with Diminished Ovarian Reserve (DOR) and Primary Ovarian Insufficiency (POI). Her AMH was < 0.10 and had a peak FSH of 51.17, with an AFC of 2-3. Unfortunately, numerous IUI cycles were failures and her two IVF cycles, while resulting in two retrieved eggs, never reached fertilization. After little success with the conventional IVF route, she came to Hanabusa IVF in mid-September. Based on her history, we developed a curtailed approach for her particular infertility issues. We significantly reduced stimulation by lowering her fertility drug use and opting for only five injections. We monitored her through weekly blood tests and performed one ultra sound. After one month, we were able to stimulate one follicle and retrieve one egg under local anesthesia. The egg was mature and fertilized with success. It then reached blastocyst stage and we were able to freeze it. The PGS was normal and she can now use this embryo whenever she is ready for embryo transfer.

Success Story 4:

It thrills us to share the exciting pregnancy journey of one of our patients with the baseline follicle-stimulating hormone (FSH) of 46.6 mIU/ml which is commonly considered menopause.

This is an important story for us because it highlights our focus and expertise. This patient started treatment with us over five years ago, and she was told by another IVF center that conception with her eggs was not possible, and her best option would be egg donation. Today she is about 12 weeks pregnant and her non-invasive chromosome testing came back negative/normal.

We used the **patient's egg,** not a donor egg. Because of her extremely high FSH, the egg was stimulated using a "Suppression Stimulation," which is a protocol involving only non-traditional oral medication such as birth control pills for "stimulation." The egg was retrieved under local anesthesia, cultured, and frozen as a Day 3 embryo.

It is important to remember that we do have a long way to go until a healthy baby, but the heartbeat on the ultrasound showed that we are over 95 percent out of the woods.

This patient officially graduated from our clinic and shared the news with family last week!

We wanted to share this incredible story with all of you, to remind you that during these challenging times to not lose hope. We are here for you always.

23

ABOUT THE PUBLISHER

COLLEEN REAGAN NOON

COLLEEN REAGAN NOON is a best-selling author, educator and the founder of Wise Women Book Collective. Throughout her career, Colleen has held space for women and families: first, as an educator working with children, later supporting parents experiencing substance abuse and trauma recovery through her practice, The Respected Child. Today, she provides publishing services for women and continues to guide parents through several of her own titles, including the Amazon #1 bestseller *Baby Got VBAC: An Inspiring Collection of Wisdom for Better Births After a Cesarean.*

Through the Wise Women Book Collective, Colleen empowers women authors, aspiring authors and female-owned publishers to launch their books, providing them with resources, industry knowledge and individualized support. Colleen is respected for her expertise in both single-author titles and multi-author books, which are released under her own publishing name. To date, she has helped more than 35 individuals become best selling authors.

Colleen earned her B.A. at Rollins College in Winter Park, FL, and her Master's in Education at Lesley University in Cambridge, MA.

She is a mother of two and considers Florida, Massachusetts and New York all home.

HAVE you ever thought of writing a book?

Are you a holistic practitioner? Would you like to participate in the next Wise Women Book Collective multi-author book? Mom Bod: The Holistic Approach to Physical, Mental, & Spiritual Health for Women in their 30s, 40s, & 50s is looking for holistic practitioners that are the best of the best in their field and offer unique perspectives on women's health. Check out the application to see if you could be a good fit.

https://forms.gle/mfLPdg57vZeZDG3d7

FACEBOOK GROUP INFORMATION

If you would like to connect more with the others and other parents going through similar struggles, please join us on Facebook in our private group: (In)Fertility Book Community.

Made in the USA
Middletown, DE
10 May 2023

30324620R10189